Discrete Structures

Harriet Fell   Javed A. Aslam

cognella | ACADEMIC PUBLISHING

Bassim Hamadeh, CEO and Publisher
Kassie Graves, Director of Acquisitions
Jamie Giganti, Senior Managing Editor
Miguel Macias, Senior Graphic Designer
Seidy Cruz, Senior Acquisitions Editor
Monika Dziamka, Project Editor
Brian Fahey, Licensing Specialist
Abbey Hastings, Associate Production Editor

Cover Image: Copyright 2017 by Depositphotos / dpenn.

Printed in the United States of America

ISBN: 978-1-63487-646-9 (pbk) / 978-1-63487-645-2 (br)

Discrete Structures

First Edition

Harriet Fell   Javed A. Aslam

College of Computer and Information Science

Northeastern University

Boston, Massachusetts

On the front page: *Pascal's triangle*, mod 2. The figure represents 256 rows of Pascal's triangle: each odd entry is denoted by a dot, and each even entry is left blank. The resulting self-similar pattern of dots is closely related to the *Sierpinski triangle fractal*.

Table of Contents

VII   Appendices   251

A   Variables and Expressions   253

B   Composite Expressions   255

C   Exponentials and Logarithms   259

D   Special Functions   263

Solutions to Selected Exercises   267

Preface

Course Goals

This course introduces the mathematical structures and methods that form the foundation of computer science. It includes many techniques that students are likely to use throughout their careers in computer and information science. These techniques are motivated by applications from computer science and supported by mathematical theory. Students will learn:

- **specific skills**, e.g., binary and modular arithmetic, set notation, and methods of counting, evaluating sums, solving recurrences, ...

- **general knowledge**, e.g., basics of probability, proof by induction, growth of functions, and analysis techniques

- **general problem solving techniques** with many applications to real problems.

Topics

The course material is divided into five modules. Each module starts with a motivating application then goes into techniques related to that application and the theory behind those techniques. Each module ends with one or more fairly deep applications based on the material.

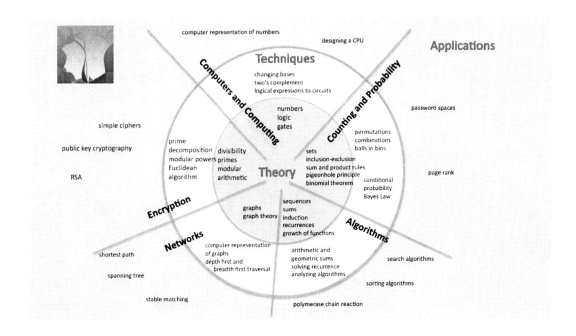

Computers and Computing: Numbers, Circuits, and Logic

We start by discussing how we can represent things on a computer using only 0s and 1s and how this can be implemented with transistors and switches. This leads naturally into a study of gates (e.g. AND, OR, NOT gates), the mathematics (*Boolean Algebra* or *Symbolic Logic*) underlying logic gates and how to design circuits based on truth tables. The module ends with the construction of a ripple-carry adder and even a simple, programmable CPU.

Cryptography: Integers and Modular Arithmetic

We use the *Caesar Cipher* and other simple shift ciphers as a link to modular arithmetic. We then encipher messages with linear functions and see the need to learn more about the algebra of modular arithmetic. In particular, we need modular multiplicative inverses to decipher messages and this leads us to primes, prime factorization, the Euclidean Algorithm for efficiently computing the GCD (greatest common divisor) of two positive integers, and the Extended

Euclidean Algorithm to efficiently compute multiplicative inverses $\bmod n$ when they exist. Finally, we talk about public-key cryptography and apply all of this math to understanding the RSA (Rivest-Shamir-Adleman) public-key cryptosystem.

Combinatorics: Sets, Counting, and Probability

We start by evaluating password criteria by counting how many passwords satisfy the given conditions. Before we can count how many items there are in a set, we find that we need some of the mathematics of sets e.g, set-builder notation, Venn diagrams, set operations, power sets, and Cartesian products. Then we really get down to counting. That sounds simple but, for most students, it is the hardest part of the course. We introduce the sum and product rules, the inclusion-exclusion principle, the pigeonhole principle, permutations and combinations, the Binomial theorem, and balls-in-bins alone and together to solve complex problems.

We first introduce probability in spaces where all outcomes are equally likely so that finding the probability of an event comes down to counting the number of successful occurrences and dividing by the total number of possible occurrences. This helps reinforce the counting methods. We go on to conditional probability and Bayes' theorem and its application to hypothesis testing. We end with an introduction to Markov chains and their applications.

Algorithmic Analysis: Searching and Sorting

We begin by describing three algorithms for searching an ordered list of length n that run in time proportional to n, $\sqrt{n}$, and $\lg(n)$, respectively, in order to introduce the ideas of algorithmic analysis. In order to analyze the performance of even for these simple algorithms, we see the need for some mathematical formalization and tools for sequences and sums. We put these tools to work for sorting algorithms but also delve into recurrence equations to model and analyze binary search and merge sort. We introduce mathematical induction to support working with and solving recurrence equations.

Growth of functions comes up as we discuss what all our analysis of algorithms means on real computers. We demonstrate that a good algorithm is probably more important than a faster machine. We also demonstrate that some algorithms are wholly impractical in the real world because they take too long to run on any conceivable machine.

Networks: Graphs and Trees

Networks are ubiquitous these days: the internet, phone networks, the local area network at your work or school, the subway system in your city are all networks. We use mathematical graphs to model networks and work with the data structures that are used to represent them on computers. We investigate some graph theory problems that are important in computing, e.g., finding the shortest or cheapest path between two nodes and finding a minimal sub network that connects all the nodes. When you complete this module, you should be able to give the adjacency list of a graph, use traversal algorithms to visit all the nodes of a graph, and follow algorithms to find shortest paths and minimal spanning trees.

Acknowledgments

Several people have contributed to this book, and we would like to thank them here. Rajmohan Rajaraman wrote the chapter on building a CPU. This chapter is based on material from the course "Great Theoretical Ideas in Computer Science" taught by Steven Rudich at Carnegie Mellon University. Eric Ropiak added the section on programming the CPU. He also contributed many of the solutions to exercises. Chris Burrows wrote the chapter on mathematical induction, and Ravi Sundaram wrote the chapter on PCR (polymerase chain reaction). We would also like to thank the many instructors who have taught *Discrete Structures* in the College of Computer and Information Science at Northeastern University, as well as the students who have taken this course. Their collective feedback has been invaluable.

Part I

Computers and Computing: Numbers, Circuits, and Logic

CHAPTER 1

Number Representations

Everything on computers is represented using 0s and 1s: positive integers, negative integers, real numbers, text, all sorts of symbols, images, music, even videos and games. To understand how we can do everything with just 0s and 1s, we'll start by seeing how nonnegative integers (0, 1, 2, and so on) can be represented this way.

We usually use ten *digits* (0, 1, 2, 3, 4, 5, 6, 7, 8, 9) to represent numbers. If we do not allow leading zeros, every nonnegative integer has a unique representation as a finite sequence of digits. This way of representing numbers is called the *decimal* or *base 10* system. This system seems natural to us, partly because we have grown up with it and partly because we have ten fingers. The word "digits" comes from the Latin word for finger, *digitus*. Computers don't usually have fingers; they have *bits* (0, 1) from the words "Binary" and "digIT." Numbers on computers are represented with just 0 and 1, using the *binary* or *base 2* system. Before we look at the binary system let's remember and formalize how the decimal system works.

Let's look at the number 35032 in decimal or base 10 notation. We don't think of this number as just the digits that make it up. We know that the position of the digits matters. At a glance, we know this number as "thirty-five thousand thirty-two" Each of the digits represents some number of ones or tens or hundreds or thousands or ten thousands depending on its position. There are two 3s in 35032. The leftmost 3 represents three 10-thousands or $3 \cdot 10^4$ and the other 3 represents 3 tens or $3 \cdot 10^1$. The zero means there are no hundreds and we write it to make sure that the digits to the left of it land in the right place.

$$
\begin{aligned}
35032_{10} &= 3 \cdot 10^4 + 5 \cdot 10^3 + 0 \cdot 10^2 + 3 \cdot 10^1 + 2 \cdot 10^0 \text{ (remember that } 10^0 \text{ is just 1)} \\
&= 30000 + 5000 + 00 + 30 + 2
\end{aligned}
$$

We only need the digits 0, 1, ... ,9 to represent all nonnegative integers base 10, and there is only one way to write each of these integers base 10.

Formally, if $d_0, d_1, \cdots, d_{n-1}, d_n$ are digits, then

$$
\begin{aligned}
d_n d_{n-1} \cdots d_2 d_1 d_0 &= d_n \cdot 10^n + d_{n-1} \cdot 10^{n-1} + \cdots + d_1 \cdot 10^1 + d_0 \cdot 10^0 \\
&= \sum_{k=0}^{n} d_k \cdot 10^k.
\end{aligned}
$$

The following theorem tells us that we can use any integer **b** as a base for a number representation system.

Theorem 1 *Let b be an integer greater than 1. Then if n is a positive integer, n can be expressed uniquely in the form*

$$
n = a_k \cdot b^k + a_{k-1} \cdot b^{k-1} + \cdots + a_1 \cdot b^1 + a_0 \cdot b^0
$$

where k is a nonnegative integer, $a_0, a_1, \cdots, a_k$ are nonnegative integers less than b and $a_k \neq 0$.

We say b is the *base of expansion* of n and we write $n = (a_k a_{k-1} \cdots a_1 a_0)_b$. For "short" numbers, typically those with three digits or less, we often eliminate the parentheses (e.g., 101_2). When the base is understood, we do not write it as a subscript.

Example 1.1

$$
\begin{aligned}
201_3 &= 2 \cdot 3^2 + 0 \cdot 3^1 + 1 \cdot 3^0 \\
&= 2 \cdot 9 + 0 \cdot 3 + 1 \cdot 1 \\
&= 19_{10}
\end{aligned}
$$

$$
\begin{aligned}
201_5 &= 2 \cdot 5^2 + 0 \cdot 5^1 + 1 \cdot 5^0 \\
&= 2 \cdot 25 + 0 \cdot 5 + 1 \cdot 1 \\
&= 51_{10}
\end{aligned}
$$

We use the decimal (base 10) representation of integers in our everyday lives but as computer scientists, we will also use binary (base 2) and hexadecimal (base 16) representations. The octal (base 8) representation is rarely used these days but is included below for historical reasons.

1.1   Binary Representation

In the binary representation, the base is 2 and the integers, $a_k, a_{k-1}, \ldots, a_1, a_0$ must be nonnegative and less than 2. The only choices are 0 and 1 but we are still able to express any positive integer as indicated in the theorem.

Example 1.2

$$
\begin{aligned}
(100101)_2 &= 1 \cdot 2^5 + 0 \cdot 2^4 + 0 \cdot 2^3 + 1 \cdot 2^2 + 0 \cdot 2^1 + 1 \cdot 2^0 \\
&= 1 \cdot 32 + 0 \cdot 16 + 0 \cdot 8 + 1 \cdot 4 + 0 \cdot 2 + 1 \cdot 1 \\
&= 37_{10}
\end{aligned}
$$

$$
\begin{aligned}
(11010111)_2 &= 1 \cdot 2^7 + 1 \cdot 2^6 + 0 \cdot 2^5 + 1 \cdot 2^4 + 0 \cdot 2^3 + 1 \cdot 2^2 + 1 \cdot 2^1 + 1 \cdot 2^0 \\
&= 1 \cdot 128 + 1 \cdot 64 + 0 \cdot 32 + 1 \cdot 16 + 0 \cdot 8 + 1 \cdot 4 + 1 \cdot 2 + 1 \cdot 1 \\
&= 215_{10}
\end{aligned}
$$

The decimal numbers 0 through 15 written in their binary or base 2 representation are:

$$0, 1, 10, 11, 100, 101, 110, 111, 1000, 1001, 1010, 1011, 1100, 1101, 1110, 1111.$$

1.1.1   Simple Binary Arithmetic

Binary Addition

When you add two positive decimal integers by hand, you probably use the addition algorithm you learned in elementary school. You write the numbers one under the other, right adjusted, then, starting on the right-hand side, you add the two digits in the ones column. If the sum is 9 or less, i.e. a single digit, you write the digit and go on to the tens place. If the sum is 10 or greater, you write the ones place digit and carry the tens place digit by writing it above the tens column. You then add the digits in the tens column as you did with the ones column, carrying to the hundreds column and so one, until you have no digits left to add.

Example 1.3

```
  1       1       1
  3   8   0   8   5   3
+         5   4   3   2   9
―――――――――――――――――――――――――
  4   3   5   1   8   2
```

The same algorithm applies to adding binary integers but when you add the bits in a column, you either get a sum less than two and you write the single bit, 0 or 1, in that place, or you get a sum of 2 or 3 and you write the ones bit of the sum in that place and carry the twos bit to the next place.

Example 1.4

```
  1   1       1   1   1
      1   1   0   1   0   1                      5   3
+         1   0   1   1   1        ⟺         +   2   3
―――――――――――――――――――――――――                    ―――――――――
  1   0   0   1   1   0   0                      7   6
```

Binary Subtraction

The subtraction algorithm you learned in elementary school can also be applied to subtracting binary numbers. Let's first look at the following example of decimal (base 10) subtraction. We start on the right-hand side, in the ones place. Since 3 is less than 9, we borrow 1 from the tens place to make 13. To do this, we replace the 5 in the tens place with a 4. We than subtract 9 from 13 and write down the resulting 4 in the answer's ones place. We subtract 2 from 4 in the tens place to get 2. In the hundreds place, we have to borrow again but this time we have to do a double borrow as there is a 0 in the top number's thousands place. We borrowed 1 from the 8 in the ten-thousands place to make 10 in the thousands place and then borrowed 1 from that ten to make 12 in the hundreds place.

Example 1.5

```
          7   9       4
  3   8  ¹0  ¹2   5  ¹3
−         5   4   3   2   9
―――――――――――――――――――――――――
  3   2   5   9   2   4
```

The following example shows a subtraction of one binary number from another. In the ones place, 1 take-away 1 results in 0. In the twos place, we have to borrow 1 from the fours place. Then $10_2 = 2_{10}$ take-away 1 results in 1. We now have to subtract 1 from 0 in the fours place so we have to borrow again and this time it is a double borrow similar to the situation in the decimal example above.

Example 1.6

$$
\begin{array}{ccccccc}
 & {}^{1}0 & 1 & {}^{1}0 & & & \\
1 & 1 & {}^{1}0 & 1 & {}^{1}0 & 1 & \\
- & & 1 & 0 & 1 & 1 & 1 \\
\hline
 & 1 & 1 & 1 & 1 & 0 &
\end{array}
\qquad \Longleftrightarrow \qquad
\begin{array}{ccc}
 & 5 & 3 \\
- & 2 & 3 \\
\hline
 & 3 & 0
\end{array}
$$

Binary Multiplication

Once again, let's start by looking at an example of the multiplication algorithm in standard decimal (base 10) notation. Below, we compute the product 312×2013. We multiply 312 by each of the digits of 2013, starting at the right and writing the results below the line. Each successive product is placed one space to the left of the previous product to account for the extra power of 10 implicit in the computation. When a digit of the multiplier is 0, we usually just write a single 0 for the product and then place the next product on the same line, as shown below. Finally, we add the results of our multiplies by one digit to get the desired result.

Example 1.7

$$
\begin{array}{cccccc}
 & & & 3 & 1 & 2 \\
\times & & 2 & 0 & 1 & 3 \\
\hline
 & & & 9 & 3 & 6 \\
 & & 3 & 1 & 2 & \\
 & 6 & 2 & 4 & 0 & \\
\hline
 & 6 & 2 & 8 & 0 & 5 & 6
\end{array}
$$

Binary multiplication works the same way but it is much easier to do since there are only 0s and 1s to work with. Each little computation is a multiply by 1 where you just copy the multiplicand or a multiply by 0 where you just write 0 and go on to the next bit. With binary arithmetic, you are writing each little result one place further to the left to account for an extra power of 2. Here is an example of binary multiplication.

Example 1.8

$$
\begin{array}{ccccccc}
 & & & & 1 & 1 & 0 \\
\times & & & 1 & 0 & 1 & 1 \\
\hline
 & & & & 1 & 1 & 0 \\
 & & & 1 & 1 & 0 & \\
 & & 1 & 1 & 0 & 0 & \\
\hline
 & 1 & 0 & 0 & 0 & 1 & 0 \\
\end{array}
$$

Multiplication and Division by 2

When we multiply an integer by ten all we have to do is add a zero to the right side of the integer's decimal representation.

$$10 \times 3257 = 32570$$

This follows from the meaning of the decimal representation.

$$3257 = 3 \cdot 10^3 + 2 \cdot 10^2 + 5 \cdot 10^1 + 7 \cdot 10^0$$

$$10 \times 3257 = 3 \cdot 10^4 + 2 \cdot 10^3 + 5 \cdot 10^2 + 7 \cdot 10^1 = 32570$$

Inversely, if a decimal integer ends in a zero, we can easily divide the integer by ten by simply removing the zero. If the integer does not end in a zero then removing the rightmost digit gives the integer part of the result of dividing by ten.

Similarly, in binary, we can multiply an integer by two by adding a zero to the right hand side of its binary representation.

$$2_{10} \times 110101 = 10_2 \times 110101_2 = 1101010_2$$

This follows from the meaning of the binary representation.

$$110101_2 = 1 \cdot 2^5 + 1 \cdot 2^4 + 0 \cdot 2^3 + 1 \cdot 2^2 + 0 \cdot 2^1 + 1 \cdot 2^0$$

$$2_{10} \times 110101_2 = 1 \cdot 2^6 + 1 \cdot 2^5 + 0 \cdot 2^4 + 1 \cdot 2^3 + 0 \cdot 2^2 + 1 \cdot 2^1 = 1101010_2$$

Division by two in binary works just like division by 10 in decimal. If the binary representation ends in a zero, just remove the zero to divide by two. If the binary representation ends in one, the integer is odd and removing the one on the right, give the integer part of the result of dividing by two.

1.2 Bytes

Essentially all digital data is stored in binary. A *byte* is an 8-bit binary number with leading zeros allowed. There are 256 different bytes and they represent the integers from 0 (00000000) to 255 (11111111). A *word* is a basic unit of storage whose size depends on the particular computer. Words are commonly composed of four or eight bytes, 32 or 64 bits respectively.

Bytes are commonly used to represent characters. *ASCII* uses the lower 7-bits of a byte, 0 to 127, to represent letters and special characters; *ISO Latin-1* and *Mac-Roman* (now obsolete) use values above 127 for accented letters and additional special characters. *Unicode* is an international standard intended to encode all characters in all languages as well as mathematical and other specialized characters. *UTF-32*, also called *UCS-4*, uses four bytes to encode Unicode characters.

1.3 Hexadecimal Representation

The word *hexadecimal* combines the Greek *hexa* for six with the English word decimal [fr. L. *decimus* tenth]. "Hexadecimal" is too long to say all the time so we usually just say *hex*. We need 16 *hex-digits* to represent integers in base 16. We use the ordinary decimal digits $0, \ldots, 9$ and the letters A, B, C, D, E, and F (or a, b, c, d, e, and f) to represent 10, 11, 12, 13, 14, and 15 respectively.

Example 1.9

$$
\begin{aligned}
A2_{16} &= 10 \cdot 16^1 + 2 \cdot 16^0 \\
&= 162_{10}
\end{aligned}
$$

$$
\begin{aligned}
(30AC92)_{16} &= 3 \cdot 16^5 + 0 \cdot 16^4 + 10 \cdot 16^3 + 12 \cdot 16^2 + 9 \cdot 16^1 + 2 \cdot 16^0 \\
&= 3 \cdot 1048576 + 0 \cdot 65536 + 10 \cdot 4096 + 12 \cdot 256 + 9 \cdot 16 + 2 \cdot 1 = (3189906)_{10}
\end{aligned}
$$

The binary representations of numbers can be quite long and difficult for humans to read. Hexadecimal numbers are particularly useful for representing patterns of binary values (bit-masks), machine addresses, or any particular bytes or words. Each hex-digit corresponds to four bits which is half a byte or a *nibble*.

0	1	2	3	4	5	6	7	8	9	A	B	C	D	E	F
0000	0001	0010	0011	0100	0101	0110	0111	1000	1001	1010	1011	1100	1101	1110	1111

A byte can be represented by two hex-digits instead of 8 bits, and a 32-bit word can be written with only 8 hex-digits. It is easier for a human to correctly copy 8 hex-digits than 32 bits. To convert a binary integer to hex, each four-bit cluster corresponds to a single hex-digit. If the number of bits in the binary integer is not a multiple of four, add zeros to the left, e.g., $11011 = 00011011$.

Example 1.10

There are spaces between the nibbles in the numbers below so you can see the correspondence with the hex-digits.

$(1101\ 0011)_2 = D3_{16}$

$(0101\ 1110\ 1001\ 1111)_2 = (5E9F)_{16}$

$(1100\ 0001\ 0000\ 1010\ 0111\ 1110\ 1011\ 0101)_2 = (C10A7EB5)_{16}$

Example 1.11

The pattern 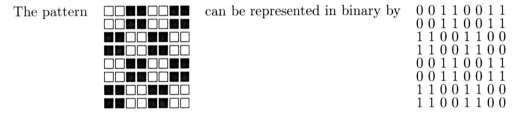 can be represented in binary by

$$
\begin{array}{cccccccc}
0&0&1&1&0&0&1&1\\
0&0&1&1&0&0&1&1\\
1&1&0&0&1&1&0&0\\
1&1&0&0&1&1&0&0\\
0&0&1&1&0&0&1&1\\
0&0&1&1&0&0&1&1\\
1&1&0&0&1&1&0&0\\
1&1&0&0&1&1&0&0
\end{array}
$$

or by 33, 33, CC, CC, 33, 33, CC, CC in hex.

1.4 Octal Representation

"The Octal system used to be widespread back when many computers used 6-bit bytes, as a 6-bit byte can be conveniently written as a two-digit octal number. Since nowadays a byte is almost always 8-bits long the octal system lost most of its appeal to the hexadecimal system."

The Free On-line Dictionary of Computing (2003-OCT-10)

Octal represents numbers in base 8.

Example 1.12

$$
\begin{aligned}
723_8 &= 7 \cdot 8^2 + 2 \cdot 8^1 + 3 \cdot 8^0 \\
&= 7 \cdot 64 + 2 \cdot 8 + 3 = 448 + 16 + 3 \\
&= 467_{10}
\end{aligned}
$$

$$
\begin{aligned}
(2045)_8 &= 2 \cdot 8^3 + 0 \cdot 8^2 + 4 \cdot 8^1 + 5 \cdot 8^0 = 2 \cdot 512 + 0 \cdot 64 + 4 \cdot 8 + 5 \\
&= 1024 + 0 + 32 + 5 \\
&= (1061)_{10}
\end{aligned}
$$

To convert a binary integer to octal, each three-bit cluster corresponds to a single octal-digit. If the number of bits in the binary integer is not a multiple of three, add zeros to the left, e.g., $11011 = 011011$. There are spaces between to separate the three-bit clusters in the numbers below so you can see the correspondence with the octal-digits.

Example 1.13

$$
(010\ 011)_2 = 23_8
$$
$$
(111\ 010\ 011\ 111)_2 = (7237)_8
$$
$$
(100\ 000\ 100\ 001\ 010\ 111\ 111\ 010\ 110\ 101)_2 = (4041277265)_8
$$

1.5   Converting Between Decimal and Binary

In the examples above, we converted numbers given in binary, hex, and octal representations to their decimal equivalents by multiplying each bit, digit, hex-digit, or octal-digit by the appropriate power of the base, using base-10 arithmetic, and adding up the pieces. We were really just evaluating a polynomial at the base 2, 16, or 8. Recall that:

$$
\begin{aligned}
n &= (a_k a_{k-1} \cdots a_1 a_0)_b \\
&= a_k \cdot b^k + a_{k-1} \cdot b^{k-1} + \cdots + a_1 \cdot b^1 + a_0 \cdot b^0
\end{aligned}
$$

$$
\begin{aligned}
(1101)_2 &= 1 \cdot 2^3 + 1 \cdot 2^2 + 0 \cdot 2^1 + 1 \cdot 2^0 \\
&= 8 + 4 + 0 + 1 \\
&= 13_{10}
\end{aligned}
$$

$$
\begin{aligned}
(1101)_8 &= 1 \cdot 8^3 + 1 \cdot 8^2 + 0 \cdot 8^1 + 1 \cdot 8^0 \\
&= 512 + 64 + 0 + 1 \\
&= 577_{10}
\end{aligned}
$$

$$
\begin{aligned}
(1101)_{16} &= 1 \cdot 16^3 + 1 \cdot 16^2 + 0 \cdot 16^1 + 1 \cdot 16^0 \\
&= 4096 + 256 + 0 + 1 \\
&= (4353)_{10}
\end{aligned}
$$

How do you convert a decimal integer to its binary equivalent? For small integers N, you can easily do this by finding the largest power of 2 less than or equal to N, say 2^k, and then finding the binary representation of $N - 2^k$. Just remember to use "place-keeper" zeros for missing powers of 2. For example, $39 = 32 + 7$ so we need a 1 in the $2^5 = 32$ place. The remaining 7 is too small for any 16s or 8s so we put a 0 in each of those places and then 1s in the 4, 2, and 1 places.

$$
39_{10} = (100111)_2
$$

The *division algorithm* provides a way to convert an integer to any base by simple division.

Theorem 2 *The Division Algorithm*

If b and n are integers with $b > 0$, there are unique integers q and r such that

$$
n = q \cdot b + r \qquad\qquad 0 \le r < b
$$

The integers q and r are called the **quotient** *and* **remainder** *of the division of n by b.*

The remainder r is the base-b digit that goes in the 1s place, the rightmost digit. Now divide q by b. We have $q = q_1 \cdot b + r_1$ where $0 \le r_1 < b$. The remainder r_1 is the base-b digit that is second from the right, and so on.

$$
\begin{aligned}
39 &= 19 \cdot 2 + 1 \\
19 &= 9 \cdot 2 + 1 \\
9 &= 4 \cdot 2 + 1 \\
4 &= 2 \cdot 2 + 0 \\
2 &= 1 \cdot 2 + 0 \\
1 &= 0 \cdot 2 + 1
\end{aligned}
$$

Therefore, once again, we see that $39_{10} = (100111)_2$.

Though we mostly use this method to convert from base 10 to base 2, we can use it to convert to other bases too. In this example, we convert 143_{10} to base 8.

$$
\begin{aligned}
143 &= 17 \cdot 8 + 7 \\
17 &= 2 \cdot 8 + 1 \\
2 &= 0 \cdot 8 + 2
\end{aligned}
$$

So $143_{10} = 217_8$.

1.6   Representing Negative Numbers: Two's Complement

We have discussed binary representations of the nonnegative integers $\{0, 1, 2, \ldots\}$. However, one must often deal with negative numbers; how can they be represented as well? One obvious solution would be to use a single bit to represent the *sign* of the number ($+$ or $-$) and the remaining bits to represent the *magnitude* of the number (how positive or negative it is). In such a *signed magnitude* representation, a most significant bit of 0 represents "$+$" while a most-significant bit of 1 represents "$-$"; the remaining bits give the magnitude of the number. For example, an 8-bit signed magnitude representation of 13 is 00001101 while -13 is 10001101. Note that using 8-bit signed magnitude, one can represent integers in the range -127 (11111111) to 127 (01111111). This is a fairly natural way to represent positive and negative integers and it was used in some early computers like the **IBM 7090** (1959-1961). Signed magnitude has one peculiarity—the integer 0 can be represented in two ways: 00000000 $= +0$ and 10000000 $= -0$.

Some other machines of the 60's like the **Dec PDP-1** used the *ones' complement* representation of signed integers. That's the machine the first computer game, **Spacewar!** ran on. The 8-bit ones complement representation of positive integers less than 128 is the same as their signed magnitude representation. For negative integers from -127 to -1, just subtract the magnitude from $11111111 = 2^8 1 = 255$.

Example 1.14

The 8-bit binary representation of 55 is 00110111

$$
\begin{array}{cccccccc}
  & 1 & 1 & 1 & 1 & 1 & 1 & 1 & 1 \\
- & 0 & 0 & 1 & 1 & 0 & 1 & 1 & 1 \\
\hline
  & 1 & 1 & 0 & 0 & 1 & 0 & 0 & 0
\end{array}
$$

The 8-bit ones complement representation of -55 is 11001000.

Each bit b is replaced by its ones complement, $1 - b$. All you have to do is flip the bits. Again the leftmost bit tells sign of the number, 0 for $+$ and 1 for $-$. And again there are two ways to write 0, 00000000 and 11111111.

By far, the most common representation of positive and negative integers is *two's complement*. In two's complement, positive integers are represented in standard binary, as in the signed magnitude and ones' complement representations. However, the representation of a negative number is determined as follows:

1. Compute a binary representation of the magnitude of the number.

2. Flip all the bits.

3. Add 1.

In general, the two's complement of an $N-$bit number is defined as the complement with respect to 2^N, that is, the result of subtracting the number from 2^N.

Since the ones complement of a positive binary number B is $(2^N - 1) - B$ and we got this by flipping the bits of B, all we have to do to get the two's complement B' of B is

$$
\begin{array}{ll}
\text{Flip the bits} & (2^N - 1) - B \\
\text{Add 1} & 2^N - B = B'.
\end{array}
$$

To go back, do the same thing to B'

$$
\begin{array}{ll}
\text{Flip the bits} & (2^N - 1) - B' = (2^N - 1) - (2^N - B) = B - 1 \\
\text{Add 1} & (B - 1) + 1 = B.
\end{array}
$$

For example, the 8-bit two's complement representation of 13 is 00001101 (as before) while -13 is represented as follows (using the steps given above):

$$
-13 \overset{(1)}{\Longrightarrow} 00001101 \overset{(2)}{\Longrightarrow} 11110010 \overset{(3)}{\Longrightarrow} 11110011.
$$

Note that a most significant bit of 1 again signifies a negative number, but the remaining bits do not encode the magnitude in the usual way. Here are a few more examples of converting integers to 8-bit two's complement form (remember that nonnegative integers are represented in standard binary).

Example 1.15

$$15 \implies 00001111$$

$$-15 \stackrel{(1)}{\implies} 00001111 \stackrel{(2)}{\implies} 11110000 \stackrel{(3)}{\implies} 11110001$$

$$28 \implies 00011100$$

$$-28 \stackrel{(1)}{\implies} 00011100 \stackrel{(2)}{\implies} 11100011 \stackrel{(3)}{\implies} 11100100$$

To convert a negative two's complement number back to decimal, follow these steps:

1. Flip all the bits.

2. Add 1.

3. Interpret the result as a binary representation of the magnitude and add a negative sign.

For example,
$$11110011 \stackrel{(1)}{\implies} 00001100 \stackrel{(2)}{\implies} 00001101 \stackrel{(3)}{\implies} -13.$$

Here are a few more examples of converting 8-bit two's complement back to decimal (remember that if the number begins with a 0, it's a nonnegative integer represented in standard binary).

Example 1.16

$$00010110 \implies 22$$

$$10010110 \stackrel{(1)}{\implies} 01101001 \stackrel{(2)}{\implies} 01101010 \stackrel{(3)}{\implies} -106$$

$$01001001 \implies 73$$

$$11001001 \stackrel{(1)}{\implies} 00110110 \stackrel{(2)}{\implies} 00110111 \stackrel{(3)}{\implies} -55$$

Using 8-bit two's complement, one can represent integers in the range -128 (10000000) to 127 (01111111), and 0 is represented in only one way (00000000). Finally, the real utility and power of two's complement is that one can add pairs of two's complement numbers (whether positive *or* negative) in the usual way, and the result will be the correct answer in two's complement! In the following examples, superscripts in the binary addition represent carries.

Example 1.17

$$
\begin{array}{rcccccccccc}
 & 13 & & & 0 & 0 & 0 & 0^1 & 1^1 & 1^1 & 0^1 & 1 \\
+ & 15 & \Longleftrightarrow & + & 0 & 0 & 0 & 0 & 1 & 1 & 1 & 1 \\
\hline
 & 28 & & & 0 & 0 & 0 & 1 & 1 & 1 & 0 & 0
\end{array}
$$

Note that this is just standard binary addition. Now, however, let's consider subtracting 15 from 28; this is equivalent to adding -15 to 28.

$$
\begin{array}{rcrcrcccccccc}
 & 28 & & & 28 & & & 0^1 & 0^1 & 0^1 & 1 & 1 & 1 & 0 & 0 \\
- & 15 & \Longleftrightarrow & + & -15 & \Longleftrightarrow & + & 1 & 1 & 1 & 1 & 0 & 0 & 0 & 1 \\
\hline
 & 13 & & & 13 & & & 0 & 0 & 0 & 0 & 1 & 1 & 0 & 1
\end{array}
$$

Note that we ignore the carry out of the last column. In general, carries into or out of the most significant bit must be carefully considered as this may result from an overflow condition, i.e., obtaining a result which is too large (> 127) or too small (< -128) to be represented in 8-bit two's complement.

If the resulting magnitude of a sum is too large to fit in 7 bits, we get an *overflow* and the result is invalid. To check whether an addition gives a valid result, keep track of the carry bits, 0 or 1, as you do the addition. If the last two carry bits on the left are different, the result is invalid. If they are the same, the result is valid. We leave the proof this as an exercise.

Example 1.18

$$
\begin{array}{rcccccccclll}
\mathbf{0} & \mathbf{1} & 0 & 0 & 1 & 0 & 0 & 0 \\
 & 0 & 1 & 0 & 0 & 1 & 0 & 0 & 0 & & 72 \\
+ & 0 & 1 & 0 & 0 & 1 & 0 & 0 & 0 & & 72 \\
\hline
 & 1 & 0 & 0 & 1 & 0 & 0 & 0 & 0 & & \text{This is not valid.}
\end{array}
$$

$$
\begin{array}{rcccccccclll}
\mathbf{0} & \mathbf{0} & 0 & 0 & 0 & 0 & 0 & 0 \\
 & 0 & 1 & 0 & 0 & 1 & 0 & 0 & 0 & & 72 \\
+ & 1 & 0 & 1 & 0 & 0 & 1 & 1 & 0 & & \text{-90} \\
\hline
 & 1 & 1 & 1 & 0 & 1 & 1 & 1 & 0 & & \text{This is valid.}
\end{array}
$$

Now consider subtracting 28 from 15.

$$
\begin{array}{r}
15 \\
-\quad 28 \\
\hline
-13
\end{array}
\iff
\begin{array}{r}
15 \\
+\ -28 \\
\hline
-13
\end{array}
\iff
\begin{array}{r}
0\ \ 0\ \ 0\ \ 0^1\ 1^1\ 1\ \ 1\ \ 1 \\
+\ 1\ \ 1\ \ 1\ \ 0\ \ 0\ \ 1\ \ 0\ \ 0 \\
\hline
1\ \ 1\ \ 1\ \ 1\ \ 0\ \ 0\ \ 1\ \ 1
\end{array}
$$

Note that the answer obtained is the proper two's complement representation of -13. Finally, consider adding -13 and -15.

$$
\begin{array}{r}
-13 \\
+\ -15 \\
\hline
-28
\end{array}
\iff
\begin{array}{r}
1^1\ 1^1\ 1^1\ 1\ \ 0\ \ 0^1\ 1^1\ 1 \\
+\ 1\ \ 1\ \ 1\ \ 1\ \ 0\ \ 0\ \ 0\ \ 1 \\
\hline
1\ \ 1\ \ 1\ \ 0\ \ 0\ \ 1\ \ 0\ \ 0
\end{array}
$$

Note that we again ignore the carry out of the last column, and we obtain the proper two's complement representation of -28.

More examples of two's complement may be found at:

http://en.wikipedia.org/wiki/Two's_complement

1.7   Summary

Everything on computers is represented using 0s and 1s. The binary representation and the two's complement representation use only 0s and 1s to represent nonnegative integers and all integers, respectively. The two's complement representation allows for efficient arithmetic operations. We can use one hex-digit to represent four binary bits so hexadecimal notation makes for shorter strings that are easier for humans to read and enter. In this chapter, we saw methods to convert between decimal, binary, hex, and octal representations and between decimal and two's complement representations. We saw how to perform addition and multiplication with binary and two's complements integers.

Exercises

Changing Bases: 2, 8, 10, 16

Exercise 1.1

Convert the following binary numbers (base 2) to their decimal (base 10) equivalents. You should not need a calculator.

a.	1010	**b.**	10100	**c.**	10101	**d.**	10110
e.	11101110	**f.**	10101011	**g.**	11111	**h.**	10000
i.	11100111	**j.**	11111111	**k.**	10000001	**l.**	10111111

Exercise 1.2

Convert the following decimal numbers (base 10) to their binary (base 2) equivalents. You should not need a calculator.

a.	17	**b.**	19	**c.**	24	**d.**	29
e.	35	**f.**	42	**g.**	56	**h.**	61
i.	73	**j.**	99	**k.**	115	**l.**	143

Exercise 1.3

Use the Division Algorithm method 1.5 to convert these decimal number to binary.

a. 34092

b. 4997

c. 20507

Exercise 1.4

Convert each of the binary numbers in Exercise 1.1 to

a. their octal equivalents.

b. their hexadecimal equivalents.

Exercise 1.5

Convert each of the following hexadecimal numbers to their binary equivalents.

a.	17	**b.**	19	**c.**	24	**d.**	29
e.	3A	**f.**	B2	**g.**	CF	**h.**	60
i.	F3	**j.**	99	**k.**	DD	**l.**	A3

Multiplication

Exercise 1.6

Perform the following multiplications in binary. For each problem part, you must (1) convert each decimal number to binary, (2) perform the multiplication in binary, and (3) convert the binary result back to decimal. You must show your work.

Note: For consistency, place the binary representation of the left multiplicand in the top row of your multiplication and place the binary representation of the right multiplicand on the bottom row of your multiplication. Thus, "4 × 7" would be

$$
\begin{array}{r}
1\ 0\ 0 \\
\times\ 1\ 1\ 1 \\
\hline
\end{array}
$$

while "7 × 4" would be

$$1 \quad 1 \quad 1$$
$$\times \quad 1 \quad 0 \quad 0$$

by this convention.

    a. 27×6

    b. 23×11

    c. 11×23

    d. 46×7

Patterns

Exercise 1.7

Patterns, like the ones below, are available in most drawing programs for filling regions. A pattern is defined by an 8×8 array of bits. In each of the following two examples, the 8×8 array of bits on the left corresponds to the pattern on the right.

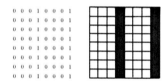
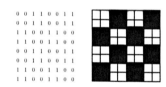

The 0s represent white, and the 1s represent black. Each row is an 8-bit binary number. As we know, a 4-bit binary number can be expressed as a single hex-digit, so an 8-bit binary number can be expressed with two hex-digits. Designers specify a pattern by giving eight 2-hex-digit numbers, one 2-hex-digit number per row. The two patterns given above are encoded as "11, 11, 11, 11, 11, 11, 11, 11" and "33, 33, CC, CC, 33, 33, CC, CC."

    a. For each of the following patterns, give the eight 2-hex-digit encoding.

    b. Use graph paper to show the pattern described by each of the following sequences of eight 2-hex-digit numbers. (See written Homework 01 for a link to printable graph paper.)

        39, 7B, 42, 88, 88, 24, B7, 93   BD, A3, DB, 3A, BD, A3, DB, 3A

Two's Complement

Exercise 1.8

Negative numbers and two's complement. You *must* show your work to obtain full credit.

  a. Give the 8-bit two's complement representations of the following integers: 34, 66, −71, −27.

  b. Give the integer (in standard base-10 notation) represented by each of the following 8-bit two's complement numbers: 01100110, 10011001, 01010101, 11011101.

  c. Compute the following sums and differences using 8-bit two's complement representations: $66 − 27$, $−71 − 27$. Verify that your answers are correct by converting the results back to standard base-10 notation.

  Note: Use the two's complement representations from part **a** above.

CHAPTER 2

Circuits

Chapter 1 describes how numbers are represented and manipulated by computers, but how are these representations physically realized, and how are these manipulations actually effected? At a high level, computer components (such as *central processing units* or *CPUs*) are constructed from *digital circuits* which are constructed from *logic gates* which are in turn ultimately constructed from *transistors*. In this chapter, we examine digital circuits and how they are constructed from logic gates (and ultimately transistors), and in the next chapter we will examine the mathematics that underpins these components at a logical level, *Boolean algebra*.

2.1 Transistors and Switches

A transistor is effectively a digital switch that is used to either establish or break an electrical connection in much the same way that a light switch can either connect or disconnect a light bulb to or from household current. Diagrammatically, switches are shown below. Note that the

Figure 2.1: Diagrammatic representation of digital switches. The left switch is "normally open" while the right switch is "normally closed."

left switch is "normally open" and "pushing" the switch establishes the electrical connection, while the right switch is "normally closed" and "pushing" the switch breaks the electrical connection.

2.2   Basic Logic Gates: AND, OR, NOT

Switches can be wired together to form basic *logic gates* which are used to construct circuits which can manipulate numbers. The basic logic gates are the AND, OR, and NOT gates.

2.2.1   AND Gate

An AND gate takes two inputs (switches) and is "on" (switched) so long as *both* switches have been "pushed." In terms of switches, an AND gate is represented diagrammatically as follows. In this diagram, A and B represent the two input switches, and a connection is established

Figure 2.2: Switch diagram of an AND gate.

only if both switches are "pushed." Logic gates arise so frequently that they have their own diagrammatic representations; the diagram corresponding to an AND gate is given below. Actual CPUs constructed from circuits, logic gates, and ultimately transistors do not function

Figure 2.3: Logic diagram of an AND gate.

physically like switches in that no transistor is actually ever "pushed." Instead, a "high" voltage (typically +5V) given as input to a transistor causes it to "close" and supply a "high" voltage to its output; similarly, a "low" voltage (typically 0V) given as input to a transistor causes it to remain "open" and supply no voltage (i.e., 0V) to its output. Physically and logically, binary 1s and 0s are represented by these "high" and "low" voltages, respectively. Given this representation, we can describe the action of an AND gate using a *truth table*. For example, the truth table corresponding to the possible actions of an AND gate are given below. Given two inputs (A and B) that can each take on two values (0 or 1), there are four possible input pairs to the AND gate. Each row in the truth table corresponds to one such input pair, and

A	B	A AND B
0	0	0
0	1	0
1	0	0
1	1	1

Figure 2.4: Truth table corresponding to an AND gate.

the corresponding output of the AND gate is also given. Note that the "A AND B" is 1 if and only if both A and B are 1; this corresponds to the logical idea that for a connection to be established, both switches must be "pushed."

2.2.2   OR Gate

An OR gate takes two inputs and is "on" so long as at least one of the inputs is "on." The switch diagram, logic gate representation, and truth table for an OR gate is given below. Note

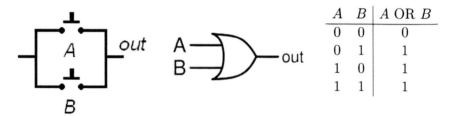

A	B	A OR B
0	0	0
0	1	1
1	0	1
1	1	1

Figure 2.5: OR: switch diagram, logic gate, and truth table.

that an OR gate is 1 ("on") if and only if at least one of its inputs is 1, and note how this is realized physically with switches.

2.2.3   NOT Gate

The final basic logic gate is the NOT gate. Unlike the AND and OR gates, the NOT gate has only one input, and its output is simply the opposite of its input. The switch diagram, logic gate representation, and truth table for a NOT gate is given below. Note that in the

A	NOT A
0	1
1	0

Figure 2.6: NOT: switch diagram, logic gate, and truth table.

switch diagram, the switch is of the "normally closed" variety; pushing the switch breaks the connection in this case.

2.3   Other Logic Gates: NAND, NOR, XOR, XNOR

As we shall learn in the next chapter, every conceivable truth table and its corresponding logic gate can be realized using combinations of AND, OR, and NOT gates. However, some truth tables are so common that they have their own dedicated logic gate representations; four such logic gates are described below.

2.3.1   NAND Gate

The NAND gate is the opposite of an AND gate: it is 1 (on) if and only if it is *not* the case that both of its inputs are 1. A NAND gate can be constructed from an AND gate whose output is attached to a NOT gate. The switch diagram, logic gate representation, and truth table for a NAND gate is given below. The NAND gate has two interesting properties: (1) It is

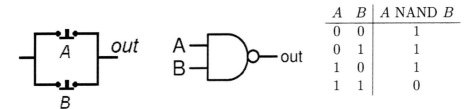

A	B	A NAND B
0	0	1
0	1	1
1	0	1
1	1	0

Figure 2.7: NAND: switch diagram, logic gate, and truth table. Note the use of normally closed switches.

the simplest logic gate to construct from common electrical components (transistors, resistors, wires, etc.) or to fabricate as part of an integrated circuit. (2) The NAND gate is "logically complete" in that every conceivable truth table, logic gate, or circuit can be constructed solely from NAND gates.

2.3.2   NOR Gate

The NOR gate is the opposite of an OR gate: it is 1 (on) if and only if it is *not* the case that at least one of its inputs 1. A NOR gate can be constructed from an OR gate whose output is attached to a NOT gate. The switch diagram, logic gate representation, and truth table for a NOR gate is given below.

	A	B	A NOR B
	0	0	1
out	0	1	0
	1	0	0
	1	1	0

Figure 2.8: NOR: switch diagram, logic gate, and truth table. Note the use of normally closed switches.

2.3.3 XOR Gate

The XOR gate is the "exclusive OR" gate; it is 1 (on) if and only if one input is 1, but not both. The logic gate representation and truth table for a XOR gate is given below. The XOR gate

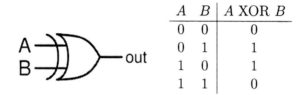

A	B	A XOR B
0	0	0
0	1	1
1	0	1
1	1	0

Figure 2.9: XOR: logic gate and truth table.

is very useful in implementing binary arithmetic. Consider adding two binary digits: if both bits are 0, the sum is 0; if one of the bits is 0 and the other bit is 1, the sum is 1; and if both bits are 1, the sum is 2, or in binary, 10. Note that the XOR gate gives the proper output of the *least significant bit* in adding two bits, and further note that an AND gate gives the proper output of the *most significant bit* (or carry) in adding two bits. Such a simple circuit is called a *half adder*; see the figure below. In later sections, we will see how logic gates can be used to

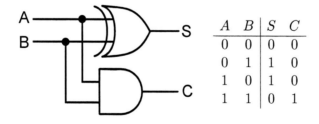

A	B	S	C
0	0	0	0
0	1	1	0
1	0	1	0
1	1	0	1

Figure 2.10: Half adder circuit and truth table.

perform arithmetic on arbitrarily long binary numbers.

2.3.4   XNOR Gate

The XNOR gate is the "exclusive NOR" gate; it is the opposite of the XOR gate and can be constructed by an XOR gate whose output is attached to a NOT gate. The XNOR gate is 1 (on) if and only if both of its inputs are identical (i.e., both 1 or both 0). The XNOR gate is used to test if its inputs are identical, and as a consequence, it is often referred to as the "equivalence gate."

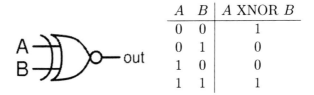

A	B	A XNOR B
0	0	1
0	1	0
1	0	0
1	1	1

Figure 2.11: XNOR: logic gate and truth table.

2.4   Binary Arithmetic: Ripple-carry Adders

As we saw in the previous chapter, in order to perform the addition of two binary numbers, one must in each column sum the corresponding bits from each input number together with any input carry bit, producing an output bit and possibly a carry bit. Letting A, B, and C_i denote the first and second input bits and the input carry bit, and letting S and C_o denote the output sum and carry bit, the following truth table shown in Figure 2.12 represents the required action for a circuit dealing with one column of binary addition; a circuit implementing this truth table is shown in Figure 2.13

Stringing together a series of full adders, one for each column binary addition, yields a *ripple-carry adder* as shown in Figure 2.14.

A	B	C_i	S	C_o
0	0	0	0	0
0	0	1	1	0
0	1	0	1	0
0	1	1	0	1
1	0	0	1	0
1	0	1	0	1
1	1	0	0	1
1	1	1	1	1

Figure 2.12: Full truth table.

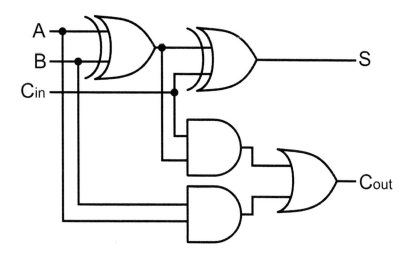

Figure 2.13: Circuit implementing a full adder

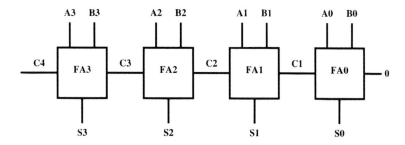

Figure 2.14: Ripple-carry adder for four-bit addition. Here, FA_i represents a full adder for column i, and note the use of a 0 for the initial "carry in" to column 0.

2.5   Summary

We have seen in this chapter how computer components such as a ripple-carry adder are constructed from *digital circuits* which are constructed from *logic gates* which are in turn ultimately constructed from *transistors* that act like digital switches. In a subsequent chapter, we will take a more in-depth look at how one can create a simple CPU from digital circuits such as those described in this chapter, but in the next chapter, we will first examine the mathematics that underpins these digital circuits at a logical level, *Boolean algebra*.

Credits

Exercises

Exercise 2.1

Converting circuits to truth tables.

   a. Convert the following circuit to its equivalent truth table.

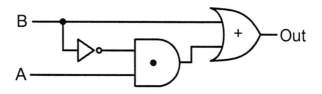

   b. What logical operation does this circuit compute?

Exercise 2.2

Convert the following truth table to an equivalent circuit.

A	B	C	Out
0	0	0	0
0	0	1	0
0	1	0	0
0	1	1	1
1	0	0	0
1	0	1	1
1	1	0	0
1	1	1	1

Logic

In the previous chapter, we saw how digital switches (typically implemented with transistors in integrated circuits) can be used to construct logic gates and that these logic gates can be used to construct circuits such as ripple-carry adders. The mathematics underlying such constructs is variously referred to as *Boolean algebra*[1], *symbolic logic*, or simply *logic* for short. In this chapter, we shall overview the basic principles of logic.

3.1 Truth Values

As we have seen, switches may be "on" or "off," a terminal in an integrated circuit may read "+5 Volts" or "0 Volts," and a bit may be 1 or 0. Since switches, voltages in integrated circuits, and bits each represent two distinct states (on vs. off, +5V vs. 0V, and 1 vs. 0), each may represent the other. In logic, the mathematics that underlies switching, circuits, and implementations of binary arithmetic, these two states correspond to *truth values* which may be *true* or *false*, denoted by T and F, respectively. The truth value "true" typically corresponds to "on," "+5V," and "1," while the truth value "false" typically corresponds to "off," "0V," and "0" as shown in Table 3.1. By far, the most common representations of these two states used in computer science are the logical T and F and the corresponding bits 1 and 0; these representations will be used somewhat interchangeably throughout this text.

---

[1]Boolean algebra was largely invented by the mathematician George Boole in the 19th century, and hence the term "Boolean" is always capitalized.

Logic	Switching	Integrated Circuits	Bits
T	on	+5V	1
F	off	0V	0

Table 3.1: Equivalent representations of truth values.

3.2   Basic Operators

The basic operators of Boolean algebra correspond to the basic logic gates (AND, OR, NOT) that we saw in the last chapter. They are defined in Table 3.2.

Operation	Representations		Definition
AND (conjunction)	$x \wedge y$	x AND y	$x \wedge y = 1$ if $x = y = 1$ and $x \wedge y = 0$ otherwise.
OR (disjunction)	$x \vee y$	x OR y	$x \vee y = 1$ if $x = 1$ or $y = 1$ and $x \vee y = 0$ otherwise.
NOT (negation)	$\neg x$	NOT x	$\neg x = 0$ if $x = 1$ and $\neg x = 1$ if $x = 0$.

Table 3.2: Boolean Algebra: Basic Operations

The *formulae* or *propositions* of Boolean algebra are expressions such as $(A \vee (B \wedge C))$ or $(x \wedge y) \vee \neg(y \vee z)$. To create formulae, you start with a set V of *propositional variables*, e.g. $V = \{A, B, C\}$ or $V = \{u, v, x, y, z\}$. You use these variables along with the basic operators and parentheses "(" and ")" to form *well-formed formulae* or WFFs.

The well-formed formulae or WFFs are defined inductively as follows:

Each propositional variable is a formula, e.g. A or B.

If ϕ is a formula, then $\neg\phi$ is a formula, e.g. $\neg A$

If ϕ and ψ are formulae then $\phi \wedge \psi$ and $\phi \vee \psi$ are formulae, e.g. $A \vee B$ or $A \wedge B$.

If ϕ is a formula, then (ϕ) is a formula, e.g $(A \wedge B)$.

We can build long formulae by applying these rules repeatedly, e.g.

$(A \vee B \wedge (C \vee B)) \wedge \neg((C \wedge B) \vee (A \vee C))$.

There is an order of precedence on these operations $\neg$, then $\wedge$, then $\vee$. This corresponds to that of unary minus, times, and plus in arithmetic and algebra. So $\neg A \wedge B \vee C \wedge \neg A$ is the same as $((\neg A) \wedge B) \vee (C \wedge (\neg A))$.

Sometimes, two formulae are the same for all values of their variables. The following sections are about ways to tell when two formulae are really the same.

3.3 Truth Tables

In logic, variables may take on one of two truth values (T or F), and these variables are manipulated and combined by various *logical operators*. The actions of these logical operators are typically defined using *truth tables*, in a manner identical to the use of these truth tables in defining the actions of logic gates in the previous chapter. The basic circuits AND, OR, and NOT correspond to the basic logical operators *conjunction*, *disjunction*, and *negation*, typically represented by the symbols $\wedge$, $\vee$, and $\neg$, respectively. The truth tables for these operators are shown in Figure 3.1—compare these to the corresponding logic gate truth tables given in the previous chapter.

p	q	$p \wedge q$
F	F	F
F	T	F
T	F	F
T	T	T

p	q	$p \vee q$
F	F	F
F	T	T
T	F	T
T	T	T

p	$\neg p$
F	T
T	F

Figure 3.1: Truth tables for the basic logical operators.

While logic is defined with respect to the basic operators $\wedge$, $\vee$, and $\neg$ (corresponding to conjunction, disjunction, and negation), other logical operators exist, including exclusive-OR (represented by the $\oplus$ symbol) and equivalence (represented by the $\equiv$ symbol) which correspond to the XOR and XNOR logic gates discussed in the previous chapter.

Truth tables can be used to represent much more than just the actions of primitive logical operators. Truth tables can represent the arbitrary input/output behavior of Boolean (logical) formulae or circuits. One goal of *logic design* is to find efficient implementations of truth tables and their corresponding Boolean formulae using logic gates. For example, Figure 2.10 gives the truth table for a two-input, two-output half adder together with an implementation using logic gates. Table 3.3 shows the truth table for the Boolean formula $\neg p \wedge (q \vee \neg r)$ which is true if and only if p is false *and* either q is true or r is false (or both).

3.4 Logical Equivalence

Two Boolean formulae are said to be *logically equivalent* if they have the same truth table, i.e., they perform the same actions on their inputs. For example, $\neg(\neg p)$ is logically equivalent to p, and this is typically written $\neg(\neg p) \equiv p$. This is shown in Figure 3.2 as well as the equivalence of $\neg(p \vee q)$ and $\neg p \wedge \neg q$.

As mentioned above, one of the goals of logic design is to find the simplest circuit that

p	q	r	$\neg p \wedge (q \vee \neg r)$
F	F	F	T
F	F	T	F
F	T	F	T
F	T	T	T
T	F	F	F
T	F	T	F
T	T	F	F
T	T	T	F

Table 3.3: Truth table for the Boolean formula $\neg p \wedge (q \vee \neg r)$.

p	$\neg p$	$\neg\neg p$
0	1	0
1	0	1

p	q	$\neg(p \vee q)$	$\neg p \wedge \neg q$
F	F	T	T
F	T	F	F
T	F	F	F
T	T	F	F

Figure 3.2: Equivalent formulae: $\neg(\neg p) \equiv p$ and $\neg(p \vee q) \equiv \neg p \wedge \neg q$

is logically equivalent to any given Boolean formula. Two Boolean formulae can be proven logically equivalent by constructing their truth tables or through the repeated application of various laws of logic. Repeated application of these laws can also lead to a simpler formula or to a formula in a special form, e.g. the normal forms, discussed below 3.5.

The laws of Boolean algebra (Table 3.4) we give here are identities that say two WFFs are equivalent, such as $(p \wedge q) \wedge r \equiv p \wedge (q \wedge r)$. We'll see in Chapter 8 that with somewhat different notation, the same laws apply to sets.

In general, a *Boolean algebra* is a set $\mathcal{A}$ of elements, with two binary operations defined on them $\wedge$ (AND), $\vee$ (OR), and a unary operation $\neg$ (NOT) (The $\wedge$ (AND) of any two elements in $\mathcal{A}$ is in $\mathcal{A}$, the $\vee$ (OR) of any two elements in $\mathcal{A}$ is in $\mathcal{A}$, and the $\neg$ (NOT) of any element in $\mathcal{A}$ is in $\mathcal{A}$.) and such that the laws in Table 3.4 hold. Given an alphabet like $\mathcal{A} = \{A, B, C\}$ or $\mathcal{A} = \{u, v, w, x, y, z\}$, the set of WWFs over that alphabet forms a Boolean algebra with $\wedge$, $\vee$, and $\neg$ as defined in Figure 3.1.

Some of these laws, e.g. the *commutative*, *associative*, and *distributive* correspond to laws of arithmetic or algebra if we replace $\vee$ by $+$, $\wedge$ by $\times$, T by 1 and F by 0. *De Morgan's* laws, as shown in Table 3.4 is quite useful when reasoning about sets, as we shall discover in Chapter 8. Not all of these laws are necessary as some of them can be proved form the others.

Commutative laws	$p \wedge q \equiv q \wedge p$
	$p \vee q \equiv q \vee p$
Associative laws	$(p \wedge q) \wedge r \equiv p \wedge (q \wedge r)$
	$(p \vee q) \vee r \equiv p \vee (q \vee r)$
Distributive laws	$p \wedge (q \vee r) \equiv (p \wedge q) \vee (p \wedge r)$
	$p \vee (q \wedge r) = (p \vee q) \wedge (p \vee r)$
Identity laws	$p \wedge T \equiv p$
	$p \vee F \equiv p$
Complement laws	$p \wedge \neg p \equiv F$
	$p \vee \neg p \equiv T$
Annihilator laws	$p \wedge F \equiv F$
	$p \vee T \equiv T$
Idempotence laws	$p \wedge p \equiv p$
	$p \vee p \equiv p$
Absorption laws	$p \wedge (p \vee q) \equiv p$
	$p \vee (p \wedge q) \equiv p$
Double negation law	$\neg(\neg p) \equiv p$
De Morgan's laws	$\neg(p \wedge q) \equiv \neg p \vee \neg q$
	$\neg(p \vee q) \equiv \neg p \wedge \neg q$

Table 3.4: Laws of Boolean Algebra for WFFs

Example 3.1

Prove $(\neg a \wedge \neg b) \vee (\neg a \wedge b) \vee (a \wedge b) \equiv \neg a \vee b$ **using the laws in Table 3.4.**

$\quad (\neg a \wedge \neg b) \vee (\neg a \wedge b) \vee (a \wedge b)$

$\equiv (\neg a \wedge \neg b) \vee [(\neg a \wedge b) \vee (a \wedge b)]$ _associative_

$\equiv (\neg a \wedge \neg b) \vee [(\neg a \vee a) \wedge b]$ _distributive and commutative_

$\equiv (\neg a \wedge \neg b) \vee [T \wedge b]$ _complement_

$\equiv (\neg a \wedge \neg b) \vee b$ _identity_

$\equiv (\neg a \vee b) \wedge (\neg b \vee b)$ _distributive_

$\equiv (\neg a \vee b) \wedge T$ _complement_

$\equiv \neg a \vee b$ _identity_

3.5   Normal Forms

When we try to analyze Boolean formulae, it often helps to write the formulae in a standard or **normal form**. These forms are particularly useful for counting-based arguments, automatic theorem proving and for showing that certain problems are NP-hard [8].

3.5.1 Conjunctive Normal Form

A Boolean formula is in **conjunctive normal form (CNF)** if it is a conjunction ($\land$) of clauses, where each clause is a disjunction ($\lor$) of variables, e.g. A or **NOT**s of variables, $\neg B$. Every Boolean formula can be converted into an equivalent formula that is in CNF by using the rules about logical equivalences above [7].

These formulae are in **conjunctive normal form (CNF)**.

formula	clauses
$A \land \neg B \land (B \lor C)$	$A, \neg B, B \lor C$
$(A \lor B \lor \neg C) \land (\neg B \lor A \lor D) \land (F \lor \neg E)$	$A \lor B \lor \neg C, \neg B \lor A \lor D, F \lor \neg E$
$A \land B$	A, B
$A \lor B$	$A \lor B$

These formula are not in **conjunctive normal form (CNF)**.

formula	reason
$A \land \neg B \land \neg(B \lor C)$	$\neg$ outside $(B \lor C)$
$(A \land B) \lor \neg C$	This is a disjunction and one clause, $A \land B$ is a conjunction

3.5.2 Disjunctive Normal Form

A Boolean formula is in **disjunctive normal form (DNF)** if it is a disjunction ($\lor$) of clauses, where each clause is a conjunction ($\land$) of variables, e.g. A or **NOT**s of variables, $\neg B$. The disjunctive normal form is dual to the conjunctive normal form (ORs of ANDs instead of ANDs of ORs) and every Boolean formula can be converted into an equivalent formula that is in DNF by using the rules about logical equivalences above.

These formulae are in **disjunctive normal form (DNF)**.

formula	clauses
$\neg B \lor (A \land C)$	$\neg B, A \land C$
$(A \land B \land \neg C) \lor (\neg B \land A \land D) \lor (F \land \neg E)$	$A \land B \land \neg C, \neg B \land A \land D, F \land \neg E$
$A \land B$	$A \land B$
$A \lor B$	A, B

These formula are not in **disjunctive normal form (DNF)**.

formula	reason
$A \land \neg B \land (B \lor C)$	This is in conjunctive normal form and $(B \lor C)$ is a disjunction
$(A \land B \lor C) \lor \neg C$	$(A \land B \lor C)$ is not a proper clause

3.5.3   Truth Tables, Formulae, and Circuits

Let's return to our goal of finding the simplest circuit that is logically equivalent to a given Boolean formula. We have seen that it may be possible to simplify a complex Boolean formula using the laws of logic but this may be difficult.

We have seen that we can check whether two Boolean formulae are equivalent by computing their truth tables. We can also use truth tables to construct the CNF or DNF normal form of a formula from which we can construct a circuit (though perhaps not the simplest circuit). In fact, if there are N variables in a formula, the truth tables will have 2^N rows so the conversion will take exponential time in the number of variables. We'll see in Chapter 15, Growth of Functions, that this is a serious problem.

First, we'll take a small table with just two inputs. We usually use 0s and 1s instead of Fs and Ts when we have circuits in mind.

A	B	out
0	0	1
0	1	0
1	0	1
1	1	0

The output out is 1 on the first and third lines, i.e. when A and B are both 0 ($\neg A \wedge \neg B$ is true or 1) or when A is 1 and B is 0 ($A \wedge \neg B$ is true or 1). So out is equivalent to $(\neg A \wedge \neg B) \vee (A \wedge \neg B)$. You may have noticed that out for this little table is equivalent to $\neg B$ but what we have just done gives us a method that works in general. We call it the *DBF Construction by 1s.*

Given a truth table with one output:

- for each row where the output is 1, write a conjunction clause (AND or $\wedge$) of all the variables with $\neg$ (NOT) preceding each variable with a 0 in that row.

  $\neg A \wedge \neg B$

  $A \wedge \neg B$

- take the disjunction (OR or $\vee$) of all those clauses.

  $(\neg A \wedge \neg B) \vee (A \wedge \neg B)$

Going from a Boolean formula to circuit is pretty straightforward – just use AND, OR, and NOT gates for $\wedge$, $\vee$, and $\neg$—but it is likely to result in a pretty messy circuit if the formula is not simplified; see Figure 3.3 below.

This process works with any number of variables. Here is an example with 3 variables.

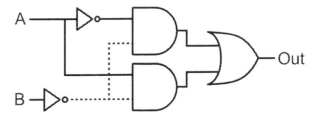

Figure 3.3: This circuit comes directly from the truth table without any simplification.

Example 3.2

p	q	r	out
0	0	0	0
0	0	1	0
0	**1**	**0**	**1**
0	**1**	**1**	**1**
1	0	0	0
1	0	1	0
1	1	0	0
1	**1**	**1**	**1**

The three boldface rows have output 1: We create a conjunction clause for each of those rows.

$\neg p \wedge q \wedge \neg r$

$\neg p \wedge q \wedge r$

$p \wedge q \wedge r$

and take the disjunction of the three clauses to get a formula equivalent to *out*.

$(\neg p \wedge q \wedge \neg r) \vee (\neg p \wedge q \wedge r) \vee (p \wedge q \wedge r)$

Example 3.3

If there are a lot of rows with output 1, the resulting DNF formula will be long. We can work instead with the rows with output 0.

p	q	r	out
0	0	0	1
0	0	1	0
0	1	0	1
0	1	1	1
1	0	0	0
1	0	1	1
1	1	0	1
1	1	1	1

The output out is 1 if and only if it is not the case that $p = 0$ and $q = 0$ and $r = 1$ (row 2) or $p = 1$ and $q = 0$ and $r = 0$ (row 5). So

$$out = \neg[(\neg p \wedge \neg q \wedge r) \vee (p \wedge \neg q \wedge \neg r)]$$

If out is 1 on four rows and 0 on four rows, it's messy either way.

Though we can construct circuits from all Boolean formulae with just two-input AND, OR and NOT gates, our circuit drawing can be made much simpler if we allow three-input AND and OR gates. You can use these in your work for this course unless instructions say otherwise.

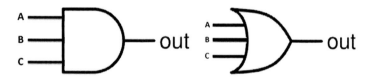

Figure 3.4: Three-input AND and OR gates

3.6   Summary

In this chapter we have studied *logic*, the mathematics underlying digital circuits. We have seen how logic can be used to help construct digital circuits, prove the equivalence of two digital ciruits, and potentially simplify the design of a digital circuit. In the next chapter, we will employ logic to construct circuits implementing some of the basic building blocks of a modern CPU, culminating in the design of a simple processor.

Exercises

Logical Completeness

Exercise 3.1

Every truth table, Boolean formula, and circuit can be implemented using just AND, OR, and NOT gates; hence, the collection {AND, OR, NOT} is *logically complete*. In this problem, you will show that the NAND gate, by itself, is logically complete. To do so, you will show how to construct the AND, OR, and NOT gates from NAND gates.

i. Fill in the following truth table:

X	X NAND X
0	?
1	?

What logical operation does X NAND X correspond to?

ii. Fill in the following truth table:

X	Y	$\neg X$ NAND $\neg Y$
0	0	?
0	1	?
1	0	?
1	1	?

What logical operation does $\neg X$ NAND $\neg Y$ correspond to?

iii. Using only NAND gates, draw circuit diagrams corresponding to the AND, OR, and NOT gates. *Hint:* The constructions for two of these circuits are essentially given in parts i and ii above, and the construction of the third should be relatively straightforward given what you've learned above.

Truth Tables, Boolean Formulae, and Circuits

Exercise 3.2

Fill in the following table with the missing truth tables, Boolean formulae, and circuits.

Truth Table	Boolean Formula	Circuit
$\begin{array}{cc\|c} A & B & \text{Out} \\ \hline 0 & 0 & 0 \\ 0 & 1 & 1 \\ 1 & 0 & 0 \\ 1 & 1 & 0 \end{array}$		
	$A \vee (\neg A \wedge \neg B)$	

CHAPTER 4

Design of a Simple Processor

4.1 Architecture

The processor we will design will have the following components:

- 8 32-bit registers R_0, R_1, ..., R_7 for holding data.

- 256 16-bit registers P_0, P_1, ..., P_{255} for holding a program.

- A 32-bit adder.

- An 8-bit register PC that will serve as a program counter.

It is useful to have the constant values 0 and 1 available for use. So we set registers R_0 and R_1 to hold the values 0 and 1, respectively, permanently.

The processor will have four types of instructions: *add*, *negate*, *load*, and *jump-if-zero*. A program consists of a sequence of instructions stored in the 256 program registers. Each of these registers holds 16 bits. The 16 bits of an instruction specify the type of instruction and its operands. We need two bits to specify the instruction; the two high bits (positions 14-15) will specify the instruction type. The formats of the 4 instructions are as follows.

4.1.1 Addition

The add instruction adds the contents of two registers R_a and R_b and stores the result in register R_c. The indices a, b, and c are specified in bit positions 11-13, 8-10, and 5-7, respectively. Bit positions 0-4 will be ignored. The add instruction also increments the program counter by 1. The add instruction

$$add \ R_a, R_b \to R_c$$

is encoded as follows.

15	14	13	12	11	10	9	8	7	6	5	4	3	2	1	0
0	0	a	a	a	b	b	b	c	c	c	0	0	0	0	0

4.1.2   Negation

The negate instruction replaces R_a with $-R_a$, using the two's complement representation. The index a is specified by bit positions 11-13. The negate instruction also increments the program counter by 1. The negate instruction

$$neg \ R_a$$

is encoded as follows.

15	14	13	12	11	10	9	8	7	6	5	4	3	2	1	0
0	1	a	a	a	0	0	0	0	0	0	0	0	0	0	0

4.1.3   Loading

The load instruction loads an 8-bit number d into the 8 low-order bit positions of register R_a. The index a is specified by bit positions 11-13. The value d is specified in binary by the 8 low-order positions of the instruction; that is, positions 0-7. The effect of the instruction is to set the value in register R_a to d; note that the 24 high-order bits of R_a are set to 0. Also, the program counter is incremented by 1. The load instruction

$$lod \ d \to R_a$$

is encoded as follows.

15	14	13	12	11	10	9	8	7	6	5	4	3	2	1	0
1	0	a	a	a	0	0	0	d	d	d	d	d	d	d	d

4.1.4   Jump If Zero

The jump-if-zero instruction changes the program counter register to the value specified by an 8-bit number d if register R_a is 0; otherwise the program counter PC is incremented by 1 as usual. The jump-if-zero instruction

$$jiz \ R_a \to d$$

is encoded as follows.

15	14	13	12	11	10	9	8	7	6	5	4	3	2	1	0
1	1	a	a	a	0	0	0	d	d	d	d	d	d	d	d

4.1.5   Programming the CPU

The four instructions *add, negate, load,* and *jump-if-zero* are enough to do complex computation. Here is a small program that computes the sum of the integers between 0 and 10.

PC	Operation	In Binary	Explanation
0	lod 10 to R2	10 010 000 00001010	Load 10 (*ten*) into register 2
1	lod 0 to R3	10 011 000 00000000	Load 0 into register 3 as accumulator
2	lod -1 to R4	10 100 000 11111111	Load -1 into register 4
3	add R2, R3 into R3	00 010 011 01100000	Add number in R2 to accumulator R3
4	add R4, R2 into R2	00 010 100 01000000	Add R4(-1) to R2 and store it in R2s old spot
5	jiz R2 to 7	11 010 000 00000111	If R2 is 0, jump to command 7
6	jiz R0 to 3	11 010 000 00000011	R0 is always 0, so jump back to step 3
7	jiz R0 to 7	11 000 000 00000111	Ends the program

Note: R0 always holds 0, R1 always holds 1.

How does this work? We first load 10 into R2, zero into R3 and -1 into R4.

- R2: 1010 (10)

- R3: 0

- R4: 11111111 (-1)

The first time through, R2(10) is added to R3(0) and stored in R3's spot. Then, R4(-1) is added to R2 and stored in R2's spot. After commands 3 and 4 we are left with:

- R2: 1001 (9)

- R3: 1010 (10)

- R4: 11111111

Command 5 checks is R2 is zero, which it isn't, so it just moves onto the next command. Command 6 checks is R0 is zero, which it always is, so it jumps the counter back to command 3. Commands 3 and 4 repeat the steps above giving us:

- R2: 1000 (8)

- R3: 10011 (19)

- R4: 11111111

The program keeps adding R2 to the existing total in R3 and then decrements R2. Once R2 is decremented to zero and the program reaches command 5, R2 is zero so the program skips to command 7, which terminates the program.

4.2   Multiplexers and Demultiplexers

Digital circuits are designed in a modular fashion—building more and more complex components out of basic building blocks. A key component of almost every digital circuit is a device that selects any one of many inputs and sends that value to a single output, called a *selector*.

Consider a 2-way 1-bit multiplexer that has three inputs X_0, X_1, and Y and a single output Z. If Y (called the *control*) is 0, then the output Z is the same as X_0; if Y is 1, then the output Z is the same as X_1. For example, if X_0 is 0, X_1 is 1, and Y is 1, then Z equals 1. The truth table for the above multiplexer is as follows.

X_0	X_1	Y	Z
0	0	0	0
0	0	1	0
0	1	0	0
0	1	1	1
1	0	0	1
1	0	1	0
1	1	0	1
1	1	1	1

We can now express the output Z as a Boolean formula in terms of the inputs X_0, X_1, and Y. Simplifying the Boolean formula as much as you can by applying the laws of logical equivalence, we obtain the following.

Begin by reading off the disjunctive normal form (DNF) of Z from the truth table:

$$Z = (\neg X_0 \wedge X_1 \wedge Y) \vee (X_0 \wedge \neg X_1 \wedge \neg Y) \vee (X_0 \wedge X_1 \wedge \neg Y) \vee (X_0 \wedge X_1 \wedge Y)$$

Then simplify using commutativity, distributivity, and the fact that $A \vee \neg A = T$:

$$
\begin{aligned}
Z &= (\neg X_0 \wedge X_1 \wedge Y) \ \vee \ (X_0 \wedge \neg X_1 \wedge \neg Y) \ \vee \ (X_0 \wedge X_1 \wedge \neg Y) \ \vee \ (X_0 \wedge X_1 \wedge Y) \\
&= \quad (\neg X_0 \wedge X_1 \wedge Y) \ \vee \ (X_0 \wedge X_1 \wedge Y) \ \vee \ (X_0 \wedge X_1 \wedge \neg Y) \ \vee \ (X_0 \wedge \neg X_1 \wedge \neg Y) \\
&= \quad\quad\quad\quad ((\neg X_0 \vee X_0) \wedge X_1 \wedge Y) \ \vee \ (X_0 \wedge (X_1 \vee \neg X_1) \wedge \neg Y) \\
&= \quad\quad\quad\quad\quad\quad\quad (X_1 \wedge Y) \ \vee \ (X_0 \wedge \neg Y)
\end{aligned}
$$

We are now ready to design a circuit for the multiplexer.

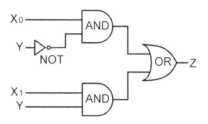

Figure 4.1: Circuit for a 2-way 1-bit multiplexer.

As one can imagine, an equally important device is the *demultiplexer*; it essentially does the opposite of what the multiplexer does: it sends a single input to one of many outputs, depending on a control value. Consider a demultiplexer that has two inputs X and Y and two outputs Z_0 and Z_1. If Y is 0, then Z_0 takes the value of X, and Z_1 is 0. On the other hand, if Y is 1, then Z_1 takes the value of X, and Z_0 is 0.

We now design a circuit for the demultiplexer, proceeding as above. The DNF is particularly simple for this truth table, so we don't need to simplify the Boolean formulae.

X	Y	Z_0	Z_1
0	0	0	0
0	1	0	0
1	0	1	0
1	1	0	1

$$Z_0 = X \wedge \neg Y$$
$$Z_1 = X \wedge Y$$

Figure 4.2: Truth Table, Logical Expressions, and Circuit for a 2-way 1-bit demultiplexer.

4.3   Design of the Processor

We will design the entire processor using the basic gates that we have studied, along with clocks. We have already seen how to build adders from gates. We will next use gates (unclocked and clocked) to build multiplexers, demultiplexers, and registers, and then move on to more complex components. We will present the design in a modular fashion, building more complex components from simpler components that we have already designed. Finally we assume that the registers $P_0, \ldots, P_{255}$ already contain the instructions to run, and their contents do not need to be changed.

Our design will proceed in steps.

1. We lay out the registers (giving names to the input bits, output bits, and registers for convenience).

2. We design the circuits for extracting the next instruction and incrementing the PC.

3. We design the circuits for implementing the add, negate, load, and jump-if-zero operations.

4. We design the circuit that determines the input and the set bits for the data registers and the PC based on the above circuits.

5. In each of the above circuits, we clearly label the inputs and outputs. These circuits can be put together by matching the appropriate labeled inputs and outputs.

4.3.1   Registers

Figure 4.3 shows the layout of the registers. Note that the set bit for PC is always 1 and the set bit of program registers is always 0. So the PC changes at every clock cycle and the program registers never change. The set bits for the data registers will be determined by the instruction.

4.3.2   Extracting the Instruction and Incrementing the PC

Figure 4.4 shows the circuits for extracting the next instruction using the PC and calculating the increment of PC. Note that whether the PC will be actually incremented (or set to something else) will be determined by the instruction, as we will see shortly.

4.3.3   The Add, Negate, Load, and Jump-if-zero Instructions

Figures 4.5, 4.6, 4.7, and 4.8 show the circuits for implementing the add, negate, load, and jump-if-zero instructions, respectively.

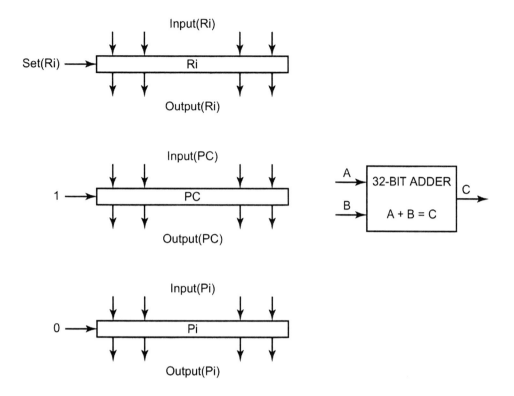

Figure 4.3: Layout for data registers, program counter, program register, and 32-bit adder.

4.3.4   Storing the New Values into the Data Registers and PC

The values computed by the add, negate, load, and jump-if-zero circuits give us potential values that need to be stored in the data registers. Whether the registers need to be updated and what their new values will be determined by the particular instruction type. The circuit shown in Figure 4.9 pushes the correct value into the registers. It also determines the correct value of the PC. The inputs to the program registers are the same as their outputs (since they are not allowed to change).

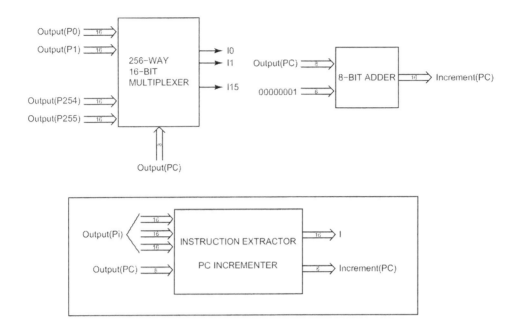

Figure 4.4: Circuits for extracting the next instruction using the PC, and calculating the PC increment.

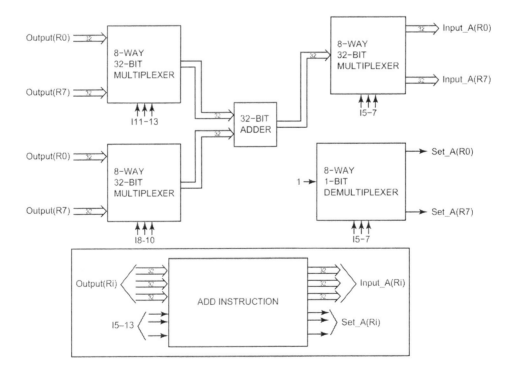

Figure 4.5: Circuit for implementing the add instruction.

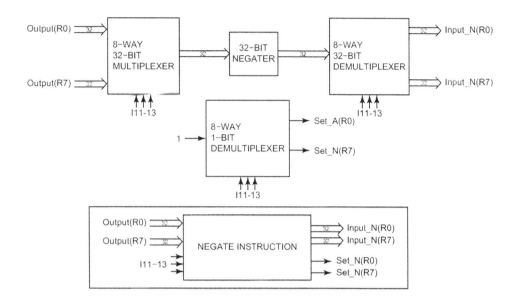

Figure 4.6: Circuit for implementing the negate instruction.

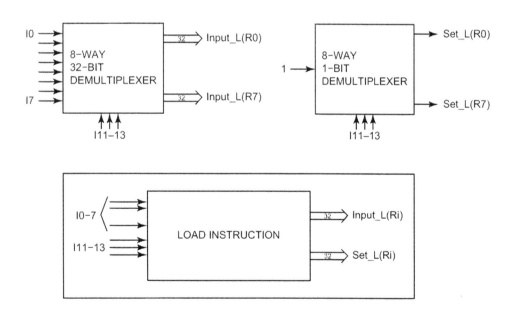

Figure 4.7: Circuit for implementing the load instruction.

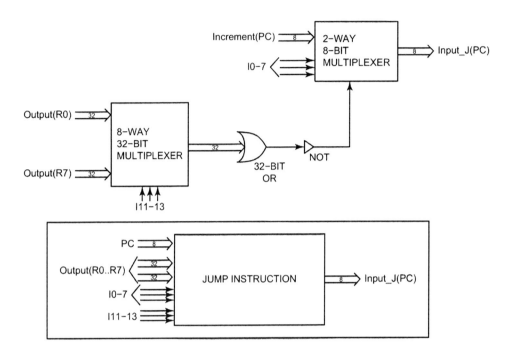

Figure 4.8: Circuit for implementing the jump-if-zero instruction.

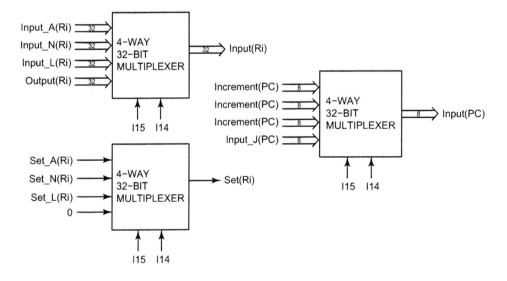

Figure 4.9: Circuit for pushing the correct value into the data registers and PC.

Acknowledgments

This unit is based on material from the course "Great Theoretical Ideas in Computer Science" taught at Carnegie Mellon University. It was written up by Rajmohan Rajaraman with additions by Eric Ropiak.

Exercises

Exercise 4.1

Write a program for the above processor to multiply two numbers, which are stored in registers R_2 and R_3. The final result is to be placed in register R_4. Don't worry about overflows. Since our processor does not have a halt instruction, you can end your program by going into an infinite loop.

The following example program takes two numbers, say x and y, which are stored in registers R_2 and R_3, respectively, computes $x + 15 - y$, stores the result in R_4, and enters into an infinite loop.

$$
\begin{array}{lll}
0 & lod & 15 \rightarrow R_5 \\
1 & add & R_2, R_5 \rightarrow R_6 \\
2 & add & R_3, R_0 \rightarrow R_5 \\
3 & neg & R_5 \\
4 & add & R_6, R_5 \rightarrow R_4 \\
5 & jiz & R_0 \rightarrow 5
\end{array}
$$

Exercise 4.2

Write a program for the above processor to compute F_n, the nth Fibonacci number. Assume that n is stored in register R_2, and that the final answer is stored in R_3. Again, don't worry about overflows; and you can end your program by going into an infinite loop.

Part II

Cryptography: Integers and Modular Arithmetic

CHAPTER 5

Cryptography and Modular Arithmetic

Cryptography has been important through the ages for sending secret military information. It has also been used by secret societies like the Freemasons. Today, computers and the internet have made cryptography a part of all our lives. Critical information like passwords, on-line purchases, and ATM transactions all use cryptography. Many companies protect their industrial secrets by encryptinging their files. Companies and individuals often encrypt their email to protect themselves from third party snooping.

We will introduce some simple methods of encrypting that use algebraic methods, in particular modular arithmetic to encrypt messages. We refer to the original message as the *plaintext* and the encrypted message as the *ciphertext*.

5.1   Simple Shift Ciphers

Julius Caesar was one of the first people known to use cryptography to protect messages of military significance (`http://en.wikipedia.org/wiki/Caesar_cipher`). Suetonius describes Julius Caesar's simple cipher in his *Life of Julius Caesar* 56 (tr. J. C. Rolfe):

> There are also letters of his to Cicero, as well as to his intimates on private affairs, and in the latter, if he had anything confidential to say, he wrote it in cipher, that is, by so changing the order of the letters of the alphabet, that not a word could be made out. If anyone wishes to decipher these, and get at their meaning, he must substitute the fourth letter of the alphabet, namely D, for A, and so with the others.

(http://laudatortemporisacti.blogspot.com/2004/09/secret-writing.html)

We call this the *Caesar Cipher*. Every letter is shifted over by three. Using our modern alphabet, look up a plaintext letter in the top row of this table and replace that letter with the corresponding letter in the bottom row. To decrypt, look up a cipher text letter in the bottom row and replace it with the corresponding letter in the upper row.

A	B	C	D	E	F	G	H	I	J	K	L	M	N	O	P	Q	R	S	T	U	V	W	X	Y	Z
D	E	F	G	H	I	J	K	L	M	N	O	P	Q	R	S	T	U	V	W	X	Y	Z	A	B	C

DISCRETE MATH becomes GLVFUHWH PDWK.

Using this table, a letter is encrypted by replacing it with a letter three places further on in the alphabet or shifting it forward by three places.

The quote from Suetonius tells us that the shift was actually in the other direction—a letter was encrypted by replacing it with a letter three places further back in the alphabet or shifting it back by three places. Decrypting was then done by replacing it with a letter three places further on in the alphabet or shifting it forward by three places.

A	B	C	D	E	F	G	H	I	J	K	L	M	N	O	P	Q	R	S	T	U	V	W	X	Y	Z
X	Y	Z	A	B	C	D	E	F	G	H	I	J	K	L	M	N	O	P	Q	R	S	T	U	V	W

DISCRETE MATH becomes AFPZOBQB JXQE

More generally, we could shift by any number from 1 to 25: for example, if we shift by 7,

DISCRETE MATH becomes KPZJYLAL THAO.

With a general shift cipher, the number you shift by, e.g. 7, is the *key* to the code. The simple shift cipher *rot13* from "rotate alphabet 13 places," is used on many newsgroups for posting things that might offend some readers. One advantage of rot13 over other shifts is that it deciphers itself. If you shift a letter 13 places and then shift the result 13 places, you are back to the original letter. Wikipedia has a good explanation of rot13 and its history, in addition to some nice examples of shift ciphers in general:

http://en.wikipedia.org/wiki/ROT13

Make sure to look at the "Trivia" section.

5.1.1   Simple Shift Cipher Toys

A number of encryption toys are based on the simple shift cipher. In 1934, the radio program *Little Orphan Annie*, sponsored by Ovaltine, had a simple substitution cipher in its handbook. In 1935, the show offered a membership pin that included a cipher disk—enciphering the letters A-Z to numbers 1-26. Captain Midnight Secret Decoder Badges were popular in the mid-1950s. You can view a 1950s commercial for the badge on YouTube. Ovaltine Secret Decoder Rings were a hit in 2000. These toys, however, all replace plaintext letters with ciphertext numbers.

Figure 5.1: Captain Midnight Decoder Badge

5.2   Encoding

Actually, using numbers instead of letters gives us the advantage that we can put math and computers to work to encrypt and decrypt for us. So, the first thing we will do is *encode* our plaintext—that is, replace the letters with numbers by an agreed upon, public method. There are many ways we can do this. Computers often use ASCII (American Standard Code for Information Interchange http://www.lookuptables.com/) to represent characters. We will just use the numbers from 0 to 25 for the letters A to Z (or a to z).

A	B	C	D	E	F	G	H	I	J	K	L	M
00	01	02	03	04	05	06	07	08	09	10	11	12
N	O	P	Q	R	S	T	U	V	W	X	Y	Z
13	14	15	16	17	18	19	20	21	22	23	24	25

We have added leading 0s to the single digit numbers so that all the codes are 2 digits long. If we need punctuation, we will use 26 for a space, 27 for a period and 28 for a comma.

Encoding, going from letters to numbers, and *decoding*, going from numbers back to letters, are different from encrypting (or enciphering) and decrypting (or deciphering). There is nothing secret about encoding and decoding. MATH IS COOL becomes 12001907 0818 02141411 if we leave the spaces or 120019072608182602141411 if we encode the spaces.

What is the original message that encodes to: 1804170413081924 ?

5.3   The mod Function

The *mod* function has many applications in computer science so we will study it in some detail. It is used for simple and complex cryptography, calendars and clocks, random number generators, and hash tables for a start. We will then use the mod function to generate shift ciphers and more general *linear ciphers*.

If n is an integer that is greater than 1 and a is any integer, then

a mod **n** is the integer remainder when a is divided by n.

In fact, $a \bmod n$ is defined when n is negative but we'll restrict our attention to $n > 1$. In this case, $a \bmod n$ is always an integer between 0 and $n - 1$. In Racket (formerly named PLT Scheme), the mod function is given by (`modulo a n`).

Example 5.1

$17 \bmod 5 = 2$	17 divided by 5 is 3; the remainder is 2.
$8 \bmod 5 = 3$	8 divided by 5 is 1; the remainder is 3.
$55 \bmod 5 = 0$	55 divided by 5 is 11; the remainder is 0.
$4 \bmod 5 = 4$	4 divided by 5 is 0; the remainder is 4.
$37 \bmod 17 = 3$	37 divided by 17 is 2; the remainder is 3.

How do we evaluate $a \bmod n$ when a is negative? Remember that as long as $n > 1$, the values of $a \bmod n$ must be between 0 and $n - 1$. In general, $a \bmod n$ is the unique integer between 0 and $n - 1$ that satisfies $a = q \cdot n + a \bmod n$ for some integer q.

Example 5.2

$-17 \bmod 5 = 3$	$-17 = -4 \cdot 5 + 3$
$-8 \bmod 5 = 2$	$-8 = -2 \cdot 5 + 2$
$-55 \bmod 5 = 0$	$-55 = -11 \cdot 5 + 0$
$-4 \bmod 5 = 1$	$-4 = -4 \cdot 1 + 1$
$-37 \bmod 17 = 14$	$-37 = -3 \cdot 17 + 14$

5.3.1   Properties of mod

Let n be an integer greater than 1 and let a and b be any integers: then

1. If $a \bmod n = b \bmod n$ then there is an integer k such that $a - b = k \cdot n$.

2. $(a + b) \bmod n = ((a \bmod n) + (b \bmod n)) \bmod n$.

3. $(a \cdot b) \bmod n = ((a \bmod n) \cdot (b \bmod n)) \bmod n$.

4. $(-a) \bmod n = n - (a \bmod n)$.

We need the final mod n in properties 2) and 4) because the sum $(a \bmod n) + (b \bmod n)$ or product $(a \bmod n) \cdot (b \bmod n)$ might be larger than n.

Example 5.3

$19 \bmod 8 = 3$ and $51 \bmod 8 = 3$ $\qquad$ $51 - 19 \bmod 8 = 32 \bmod 8 = 0 = 3 - 3 \bmod 8$

$19 \bmod 5 = 4$ and $7 \bmod 5 = 2$ $\qquad$ $(19 + 7) \bmod 5 = 26 \bmod 5 = 1 = (4 + 2) \bmod 5$

$\qquad\qquad\qquad\qquad\qquad\qquad\qquad$ $(19 \cdot 7) \bmod 5 = 133 \bmod 5 = 3 = (4 \cdot 2) \bmod 5$

$37 \bmod 17 = 3$ and $-37 \bmod 17 = 14$ $\quad$ $3 + 14 = 17,\ 17 \bmod 17 = 0$

5.4   Simple Substitution Ciphers

A *simple substitution cipher* is a cryptographic system in which letters (or their codes) are arbitrarily transposed or replaced with other letters (or their codes). The Caesar cipher and general shift cipher are both simple substitution ciphers. Cryptograms that sometimes appear as newspaper puzzles are also simple substitution ciphers. Each letter is replaced by another letter. We will study some simple substitution ciphers that can be generated by using the mod or modulo function.

5.4.1   Shift Cipher

Once we have encoded the letters A, ..., Z, a general shift cipher with shift k can be described by

$$n \rightarrow (n + k) \bmod 26$$

or by

$$n \rightarrow (n + k) \bmod 29$$

if we encode and encipher space, period, and comma as well as the letters A $\cdots$ Z. If we want our encrypted message to look like letters, possibly with punctuation, we decode the shifted codes to get our ciphertext. Here's an example.

MATH IS COOL becomes 12001907 0818 02141411 if we just encode the letters. If we shift by 15 and decode, we get 'BPIWXHRDDA" as shown in this table.

Plaintext	M	A	T	H	I	S	C	O	O	L
Coded	12	00	19	07	08	18	02	14	14	11
Shifted	1	15	8	22	23	7	17	3	3	00
Ciphertext	B	P	I	W	X	H	R	D	D	A

If we receive the message "BPIWXHRDDA" and we know that the shift key is 15, we just reverse the procedure above to decrypt our message, code the letters, shift by -15 which is the same as $+11 \mod 26$, decode the result.

Ciphertext	B	P	I	W	X	H	R	D	D	A
Coded	01	15	08	22	23	07	17	3	03	00
Shifted	12	00	19	07	08	18	02	14	14	11
Plaintext	M	A	T	H	I	S	C	O	O	L

5.4.2   Linear Ciphers

We can create somewhat more complex simple substitution ciphers by using linear functions along with mod instead of just adding a constant and then using mod. Let's work again with just the 26 letters. In general, we choose two constants m and k then generate a *linear cipher* by

$$a \to (m \cdot a + k) \mod 26.$$

Lets look at an example with $m = 5$ and $k = 11$. In this case, the letter "H" gets encrypted as shown here:

$$H \xrightarrow{encode} 07 \xrightarrow{\times 5} 35 \xrightarrow{+11} 46 \xrightarrow{\mod 26} 20 \xrightarrow{decode} U.$$

The encryption of the rest of the alphabet is shown here.

Plaintext	A	B	C	D	E	F	G	H	I	J	K	L	M
Coded	00	01	02	03	04	05	06	07	08	09	10	11	12
Moved	11	16	21	00	05	10	15	20	25	04	09	14	19
Ciphertext	L	Q	V	A	F	K	P	U	Z	E	J	O	T
Plaintext	N	O	P	Q	R	S	T	U	V	W	X	Y	Z
Coded	13	14	15	16	17	18	19	20	21	22	23	24	25
Moved	24	03	08	13	18	23	02	07	12	17	22	01	06
Ciphertext	Y	D	I	N	S	X	C	H	M	R	W	B	G

This seems to make a pretty good simple substitution cipher. Two different letters always have different cipher letters so an enciphered message should be decipherable. No letter is enciphered to itself so the message won't be trivial to read. Given the table, it is pretty easy to decipher a message. Can you decipher this message? QHKKBXOLBXMLTISFX

There are a few questions we should think about when we make a simple linear cipher.

1. What values of m and k make good linear ciphers if the alphabet has 26 characters?

2. What if the alphabet has 29 characters, e.g. with space, "." and "," included?

3. What if the alphabet has 128 ASCII characters?

4. Can we say anything in general for an alphabet of n characters?

5. Can the person receiving our message decipher it without reconstructing the table, i.e. with just knowing n, m, and k? This will be important if n is large.

To answer these questions, we need to understand more about mod and the arithmetic it induces.

5.5 Modular Arithmetic

Once we fix an integer n greater than 1, the properties of mod we cited above allow us to talk about arithmetic mod n on the set $\mathbb{Z}_n$ of integers from 0 to $n-1$. We define addition and multiplication by these formulae.

$$a + b = (a + b) \bmod n$$

$$a \times b = (a \times b) \bmod n$$

Consider these $+$ and $\times$ tables for arithmetic mod 3.

+	0	1	2
0	0	1	2
1	1	2	0
2	2	0	1

×	0	1	2
0	0	0	0
1	0	1	2
2	0	2	1

Arithmetic mod 3 has some very nice properties. If a, b, and c are in $\mathbb{Z}_3$ (the set $\{0, 1, 2\}$) then these properties hold true:

closure: $a + b$ and $a \times b$ are in $\mathbb{Z}_3$.

commutativity: $a + b = b + a$ and $a \times b = b \times a$.

associativity: $(a + b) + c = a + (b + c)$ and $(a \times b) \times c = a \times (b \times c)$.

identity +:   0 is an *additive identity* $a + 0 = a$ for all $a \in \mathbb{Z}_3$.

identity ×:   1 is a *multiplicative identity* $a \times 1 = a$ for all $a \in \mathbb{Z}_3$.

inverse +:   Every $a \in \mathbb{Z}_3$ has an *additive inverse* $b \in \mathbb{Z}_3$ such that $a + b = 0$.

inverse ×:   Every non-zero $a \in \mathbb{Z}_3$ has an *multiplicative inverse* $b \in \mathbb{Z}_3$ such that $a \times b = 1$.

distributive law: $c \times (a + b) = (c \times a) + (c \times b)$.

Note: The symbol $\in$ means "in" so $a \in \mathbb{Z}_3$ means "a in $\mathbb{Z}_3$."

These properties mean that the set $\mathbb{Z}_3$ with $+$ and $\times$ mod 3 is a mathematical *field*. The real numbers, rational numbers, and complex numbers are also mathematical fields with their regular addition and multiplication.

Now, let's consider these $+$ and $\times$ tables for arithmetic mod 4 on the set $\mathbb{Z}_4 = \{0, 1, 2, 3\}$.

+	0	1	2	3
0	0	1	2	3
1	1	2	3	0
2	2	3	0	1
3	3	0	1	2

×	0	1	2	3
0	0	0	0	0
1	0	1	2	3
2	0	2	0	2
3	0	3	2	1

Addition mod 4 has similar properties to addition mod 3. There is an additive identity, 0, and every $a \in \mathbb{Z}_4$ has an additive identity, $0 + 0 = 1 + 3 = 2 + 2 = 0$. But $\mathbb{Z}_4$ is not a field. It does have a multiplicative identity, $a \times 1 = a$ for all $a \in \mathbb{Z}_4$ but 2 does not have a multiplicative inverse. We cannot solve $2 \times b = 1$ or $2 \times b = 3$ in $\mathbb{Z}_4$. In fact, $2 \times 2 \bmod 4 = 0$. We say *2 is a zero-divisor mod 4*. In general, We say $a \in \mathbb{Z}_n$ is a *zero-divisor* mod n if there is a non-zero $b \in \mathbb{Z}_n$ such that $a \times b \bmod n = 0$.

Can you now say what values of m will be bad for linear ciphers, $a \rightarrow (m \cdot a + b) \bmod 26$?

5.6   Powers mod n

We often have to compute powers of numbers mod n. The RSA Encryption Algorithm, that we will look at in more detail later, is widely used in electronic commerce protocols uses high powers of integers mod n. We can easily compute powers mod n when the exponent is itself a power of 2 by using the property

$$(a \cdot b) \bmod n = ((a \bmod n) \cdot (b \bmod n)) \bmod n$$

and the fact that

$$a^{(2^k)} = a^{(2 \cdot 2^{k-1})} = a^{(2^{k-1}+2^{k-1})} = \left(a^{\left(2^{(k-1)}\right)}\right) \cdot \left(a^{\left(2^{(k-1)}\right)}\right) = \left(a^{\left(2^{(k-1)}\right)}\right)^2.$$

The idea is to alternate evaluating mod n and squaring. This is probably best understood by looking at some examples.

Example 5.4

$$
\begin{aligned}
37^2 \bmod 3 \quad &= (37 \bmod 3)^2 = 1^2 = 1 \\
115^4 \bmod 7 \quad &= (115 \bmod 7)^4 = (3 \bmod 7)^4 = (3^2 \bmod 7)^2 = (9 \bmod 7)^2 \\
&= (2 \bmod 7)^2 = (2^2 \bmod 7) = (4 \bmod 7) = 4 \\
115^{32} \bmod 7 \quad &= (115 \bmod 7)^{32} = ((115 \bmod 7)^4)^8 = (4 \bmod 7)^8 \\
&= (16 \bmod 7)^4 = (2 \bmod 7)^4 = (16 \bmod 7) = 2
\end{aligned}
$$

To compute $a^m \bmod n$ when m is not a power of 2, we use the binary representation of m to express m as a sum of powers of 2 and the rule (see C.1.1) for the product of two powers with the same base. In general, m can be expressed as $m = b_k 2^k + b_{k-1} 2^{k-1} + \cdots + b_1 2 + b_0$ where $b_i = 0$ or 1 for $0 \le i \le k$. Then

$$a^m = a^{b_k 2^k + b_{k-1} 2^{k-1} + \cdots + b_1 2 + b_0} = a^{b_k 2^k} \cdot a^{b_{k-1} 2^{k-1}} \cdots a^{b_1 2} \cdot a^{b_0}.$$

Each factor in this product where $b_i = 0$ evaluates to 1. In the other factors, $b_i = 1$ and the factor is just a raised to a power that is a power of 2. To evaluate $a^m \bmod n$ we apply the repeated squaring and evaluating mod n described above to each of these factors and then multiply the results mod n.

Example 5.5

$$40^{121} \bmod 7 \quad = 40^{1111001_2} = 40^{2^6} 40^{2^5} 40^{2^4} 40^{2^3} 40^{2^0} \bmod 7$$

$$= 40^{64} 40^{32} 40^{16} 40^8 40 \bmod 7$$

$40 \bmod 7 \quad = 5$

$40^2 \bmod 7 \quad = 5^2 \bmod 7 = 25 \bmod 7 = 3$

$40^4 \bmod 7 \quad = 3^2 \bmod 7 = 9 \bmod 7 = 2$

$40^8 \bmod 7 \quad = 2^2 \bmod 7 = 4 \bmod 7 = 4$

$40^{16} \bmod 7 \quad = 4^2 \bmod 7 = 16 \bmod 7 = 2$

$40^{32} \bmod 7 \quad = 2^2 \bmod 7 = 4 \bmod 7 = 4$

$40^{64} \bmod 7 \quad = 4^2 \bmod 7 = 16 \bmod 7 = 2$

$$121_{10} = 64 + 32 + 16 + 8 + 1 = 1111001_2 \text{ so}$$

$40^{121} \bmod 7 \quad = (40^{64})(40^{32})(40^{16})(40^8)(40^1)$

$40^{121} \bmod 7 \quad = 2 \cdot 4 \cdot 2 \cdot 4 \cdot 5 \bmod 7$

$$= ((8 \bmod 7)(8 \bmod 7)(5 \bmod 7)) \bmod 7 = (1 \cdot 1 \cdot 5) \bmod 7 = 5$$

5.7   Summary

Shift ciphers and *linear ciphers* provide simple ways of encrypting messages. We introduced the mod function and *modular arithmetic* to implement these ciphers. We saw that integers mod n can be *zero-divisors* or have *multiplicative inverses*. The integer m must have a multiplicative inverse mod n for $a \to (m \cdot a + b) \bmod n$ to be a valid linear shift. We ended the chapter by seeing how to efficiently find powers of integers mod n. We will apply this later when we learn about the RSA cryptosystem.

Credits

Figure 5.1: Copyright © 2009 by Sobebunny / Wikimedia Commons, (CC BY-SA 3.0) at https://en.wikipedia.org/wiki/Secret_decoder_ring.

Exercises

Caesar Cipher and Encoding

Exercise 5.1

Apply the Caesar Cipher 5.1 to the following messages:

  a. EXIT UNDER STAIRS

b. TEN PACES N BY NE

Encode these messages as in Section 5.2.

c. EXIT UNDER STAIRS

d. TEN PACES N BY NE

The mod Function

Exercise 5.2

Evaluate the following

a. 19 mod 7   **b.** 7 mod 19   **c.** 27 mod 7

d. 27 mod 19   **e.** 14 mod 7   **f.** 52 mod 13

g. 14 mod 24   **h.** 51 mod 11   **i.** 212 mod 3

Exercise 5.3

Evaluate the following

a. −19 mod 7   **b.** −7 mod 19   **c.** −27 mod 7

d. −27 mod 19   **e.** −14 mod 7   **f.** −52 mod 13

g. −14 mod 24   **h.** −51 mod 11   **i.** −212 mod 3

Exercise 5.4

Evaluate the following without using a calculator.

	337 mod 3	9962 mod 3
a.	(9962 + 337) mod 3	(337 × 9962) mod 3
	−337 mod 3	(9962 − 337) mod 3

	337 mod 5	9962 mod 5
b.	(9962 + 337) mod 5	(337 × 9962) mod 5
	−337 mod 5	(9962 − 337) mod 5

Simple Substitution Ciphers

Exercise 5.5

Use the methods of Section 5.4 to encipher the following messages with the indicated shifts.

a. BEHIND BIG CLOCK, shift 11

b. L NINE R SEVEN L FOUR, shift 15

Exercise 5.6

Use the methods of Section 5.4 to decipher the following messages. Each is given with the shift used to encipher it. The spaces have been removed.

a. UBTFURNQGUERRCZBEQREOHGGREORRE, shift 13

b. DRIBKNRZEYFLJVYRIKWFIUTKJLEURP, shift 17

Linear Encryption

Exercise 5.7

A spy has been captured, but all attempts to interrogate him have failed: he speaks a very strange language, unintelligible to any translator. However, this spy was caught with a number of documents. Linguists who have studied these documents believe that they were written in the spy's language, but that they have been encrypted. Decrypting these documents to obtain valid text in the spy's language would be incredibly helpful; your job is to decrypt the spy's documents and hopefully determine where he's from and what language he speaks.

Linguists analyzing the spy's documents have determined that the spy's language consists of 26 linguistic units (analogous to English letters), where each unit consists of one or more case-sensitive English letters or punctuation marks. The units of the spy's language, numbered from 0 to 25, are given below.

0	1	2	3	4	5	6	7	8	9	10	11	12
a	b	ch	D	e	gh	H	I	j	l	m	n	ng
13	14	15	16	17	18	19	20	21	22	23	24	25
o	p	q	Q	r	S	t	tlh	u	v	w	y	'

You suspect that the spy has used a linear encryption scheme with $m = 15$ and $k = 3$ since symbols representing these values were found tattooed on the spy's scalp. Finally, the linguists and interrogators are particularly interested in following phrase, which was written on the top of each document the spy possessed:

$$rebDng \quad wDq \quad lDghjDp$$

a. Parse the phrase above to obtain the individual linguistic units of the spy's language, i.e., "r" followed by "e" followed by "b" and so on. Note the multi-letter combinations that correspond to individual linguistic units.

b. Encode each linguistic unit with its corresponding number from the table given above, e.g., r → 17 and so on.

c. Since you suspect that these values were encrypted using the function

$$a \rightarrow (15 \cdot a + 3) \bmod 26$$

you must subtract 3 and then multiply by the multiplicative inverse of 15 (mod 26) in order to decrypt these values. Start by determining the multiplicative inverse of 15 (mod 26).

d. Decrypt each value by inverting the linear encryption.

e. Decode these values using the table given above to obtain a phrase in the spy's language. (It will *not* be intelligible to most people.)

f. Conduct some research on the Web to see if you can determine what this phrase means. (Try typing the decrypted words or the entire phrase into Google.) What is the English translation of this phrase? Where does our spy come from and what language does he speak?

Modular Arithmetic

Exercise 5.8

Construct the addition and multiplication tables for mod 8 in a manner similar to those for mod 3 and mod 4 given in Section 5.5.

Exercise 5.9

Use the tables you created for Exercise 5.8 to answer the following.

a. Give the additive inverse mod8 for each of 0, 1, 2, 3, 4, 5, 6, 7.

b. Give the multiplicative inverse mod 8 for each of the numbers 0, 1, 2, 3, 4, 5, 6, 7 that has a multiplicative inverse.

c. Which of the numbers 0, 1, 2, 3, 4, 5, 6, 7 are zero-divisors mod 8? For each of these zero-divisors, give a non-zero number you can multiply it by to yield 0 mod 8.

Powers mod n

Exercise 5.10

Compute the following by hand.

a. $48 \bmod 5$ b. $48^2 \bmod 5$ b. $48^4 \bmod 5$
d. $48^8 \bmod 5$ e. $48^{16} \bmod 5$ f. $48^{32} \bmod 5$
g. $48^{64} \bmod 5$ h. $48^{128} \bmod 5$ i. $48^{256} \bmod 5$
j. $48^{79} \bmod 5$ k. $48^{153} \bmod 5$ l. $48^{222} \bmod 5$

Exercise 5.11

Repeat Exercise 5.10 mod 11 instead of mod 5.

CHAPTER 6

Integers and Division

Though you probably learned about integers and division back in fourth grade, we need formal definitions and theorems to describe the algorithms we use and to verify that they are correct, in general. We ended Section 5.5 with the question, "Can you now say what values of m will be bad for linear ciphers, $a \rightarrow (m \cdot a + b) \bmod 26$?" Perhaps you figured out that m must have a multiplicative inverse mod 26 for the decryption to be possible. To actually decrypt, we must be able to find the multiplicative inverse of $m \bmod 26$. In this chapter, we will develop techniques to do that and to work with more complex cryptographic systems.

6.1 Divides

If a and b are integers and $a \neq 0$, we say that a *divides* b (or that a is a *factor* of b) if there is an integer c such that $b = ac$.

$$a \mid b \text{ means } a \text{ divides } b.$$

$$a \nmid b \text{ means } a \text{ does not divide } b.$$

Theorem 3 *Let a, b, and c be integers: then*

1. *if $a \mid b$ and $a \mid c$ then $a \mid (b + c)$*

2. *if $a \mid b$ then $a \mid bc$ for all integers, c*

3. *if $a \mid b$ and $b \mid c$ then $a \mid c$.*

Proof: Here is a proof of (1); try to prove the other parts yourself.

Assume that a, b, and c be integers and that $a \mid b$ and $a \mid c$. From the definition of *divides*, there must be integers m and n such that:

$$b = ma \qquad (6.1)$$

$$c = na \qquad (6.2)$$

Adding the left- and right-hand sides of Equations 6.1 and 6.2, we obtain

$b + c = ma + na.$

By the distributive law and commutativity,

$b + c = (m + n)a.$

By the closure of addition, $m + n$ is an integer, so by the definition of *divides*,

$a \mid (b + c).$ □

Corollary 1 *If a, b, and c are integers such that $a \mid b$ and $a \mid c$ then $a \mid (mb + nc)$ for all integers m and n.*

6.2 Primes

A positive integer $p > 1$ is called *prime* if the only positive factors of p are 1 and p. Extremely large prime numbers are used in RSA and other algorithms for public key cryptography. Primes are also used for hash tables and pseudorandom number generators.

6.2.1 Finding Primes

How can you find prime numbers? The mathematician Eratosthenes (276-194 BC) invented a prime number sieve, the Sieve of Eratosthenes, which, in modified form, is still used in number theory research. Here is how the sieve works if you want to find all the prime numbers less than or equal to N.

1. Make a list-to-check of the numbers from 2 to N.

2. Make a list-of-primes that starts out empty.

3. Repeat the following until the first number in the list-to-check is $> \sqrt{N}$

   (a) Put the first number in the list-to-check in the list-of-primes.

   (b) Remove all multiples of that number from the list-to-check.

4. Put all the numbers still in list-to-check into list-of-primes.

Example 6.1

To find all the primes up to $N = 25$, we start with:

list-to-check = 2 3 4 5 6 7 8 9 10 11 12 13 14 15 16 17 18 19 20 21 22 23 24 25

list-of-primes =

Then we put 2 in the list-of-primes and remove all multiples of 2 from the list-to-check. We now have:

list-to-check = 3 5 7 9 11 13 15 17 19 21 23 25

list-of-primes = 2

Now put 3 in the list-of-primes and remove all multiples of 3 from the list-to-check. We now have:

list-to-check = 5 7 11 13 17 19 23 25

list-of-primes = 2 3

Now put 5 in the list-of-primes and remove all multiples of 5 from the list-to-check. We now have:

list-to-check = 7 11 13 17 19 23

list-of-primes = 2 3 5

Since $\sqrt{25} = 5$, we put all the numbers remaining in the list-to-check into the list-of-primes.

list-of-primes (less than or equal to 25) = 2 3 5 7 11 13 17 19 23.

6.2.2   Prime Number Decomposition

A positive integer $n > 1$ that is not prime is call a *composite*. Composite integers can always be expressed as products of primes.

Theorem 4 (Fundamental Theorem of Arithmetic) *Every positive integer greater than 1 can be written uniquely as a prime or as the product of two or more primes where the prime factors are written in order of non-decreasing size. This is the* **prime number decomposition of the integer.**

Example 6.2

  a. $364 = 2 \cdot 2 \cdot 7 \cdot 13 = 2^2 \cdot 7 \cdot 13$

  b. $7581 = 7 \cdot 19 \cdot 57$

    c. $32768 = 2^{15}$

    d. $31752 = 2^3 \cdot 3^4 \cdot 7^2$

    e. $31 = 31^1$

    f. $6! = 6 \cdot 5 \cdot 4 \cdot 3 \cdot 2 = 2 \cdot 3 \cdot 5 \cdot 2 \cdot 2 \cdot 3 \cdot 2 = 2^4 \cdot 3^2 \cdot 5$

6.2.3   More About Primes

Theorem 5 *There are infinitely many primes.*

Proof: Here is an elementary proof due to Euclid. Suppose, for the sake of contradiction, that there are only a finite number of primes; let $\mathcal{S} = \{p_1, p_2, \ldots, p_n\}$ be the set of **all** prime numbers. Now consider the number

$$P = p_1 \cdot p_2 \cdots p_n + 1.$$

Now P must be either prime or composite. If P is prime, it must be in the list but this cannot happen since it is larger than any number in the list. So P must be composite but then it must be divisible by a prime in $\mathcal{S}$ since, by assumption, all primes are in $\mathcal{S}$. However, the remainder after the division of P by any p_i is 1, by construction so P is not divisible by any p_i in the list. This is a contradiction. Thus, our assumption that there are a finite number of primes must be false. □

Want to listen to some primes? Try the Prime Number Listening Guide at

`http://primes.utm.edu/programs/music/listen/`.

6.3   Division

Back in elementary school, you probably wrote out division problems like this:

$$
\begin{array}{r}
4 \\
7 \,)\, \overline{29} \qquad r = 1
\end{array}
$$

In this equation, 29 is the *dividend*, 7 is the *divisor*, 4 is the *quotient*, and 1 is the *remainder*. The following theorem tells us that we can always find a quotient and remainder in a division problem.

Theorem 6 (The Division "Algorithm") *Let a be an integer and b a positive integer. Then there are unique integers q and r, with $0 \le r < b$, such that $a = b \cdot q + r$.*

6.3.1   Racket (Scheme) Functions Related to Division

These definitions and examples are taken from *The Scheme Programming Language, Second Edition* by R. Kent Dybvig [1]. You can find similar functions and examples in *The Racket Reference* by Matthew Flatt [2].

procedure: (quotient int1 int2)

returns: the integer quotient of int1 and int2

   (quotient 45 6) $\Rightarrow$ 7

   (quotient 6.0 2.0) $\Rightarrow$ 3.0   The function remainder is similar to

   (quotient 3.0 $-$ 2) $\Rightarrow$ -1.0 but not quite the same as modulo.

procedure: (remainder int1 int2)   procedure: (modulo int1 int2)

returns: the integer remainder of int1 and int2   returns: the integer modulus of int1 and int2

The result of remainder has the same sign as int1.   The result of modulo has the same sign as int2.

   (remainder 16 4) $\Rightarrow$ 0   (modulo 16 4) $\Rightarrow$ 0

   (remainder 5 2) $\Rightarrow$ 1   (modulo 5 2) $\Rightarrow$ 0

   (remainder $-$ 45.0 7) $\Rightarrow$ -3.0 (modulo $-$ 45.0 7) $\Rightarrow$ 4.0

   (remainder 10.0 $-$ 3.0) $\Rightarrow$ 1.0   (modulo 10.0 $-$ 3.0) $\Rightarrow$ -2.0

   (remainder $-$ 17 $-$ 9) $\Rightarrow$ -8 (modulo $-$ 17 $-$ 9) $\Rightarrow$ -8

In some computing languages, the functions *quotient* and *modulo* are called *div* and *mod*. Mathematicians usually write "a mod b" instead of "$(modulo\ a\ b)$."

6.4   Greatest Common Divisor and Least Common Multiple

If a and b are integers that are not both 0, the *greatest common divisor* of a and b, $\gcd(a,b)$ is the largest integer d such that $d \mid a$ and $d \mid b$. The *least common multiple* of a and b, $\text{lcm}(a,b)$ is the smallest integer divisible by both a and b.

Example 6.3

   a. $\gcd(75,21) = 3$

   b. $\gcd(52,81) = 1$

c. $\gcd(2^2 \cdot 7 \cdot 13, 2^3 \cdot 3^4 \cdot 7^2) = 2^2 \cdot 3^0 \cdot 7 \cdot 13^0 = 2^2 \cdot 7$ What is the rule?[1]

d. $\gcd(49831, 825579) = ?$ We will soon learn a way to solve this efficiently.

e. $\operatorname{lcm}(75, 21) = 75 \cdot 7 = 25 \cdot 21 = 525$

f. $\operatorname{lcm}(52, 81) = 52 \cdot 81 = 4212$

g. $\operatorname{lcm}(2^2 \cdot 7 \cdot 13, 2^3 \cdot 3^4 \cdot 7^2) = 2^3 \cdot 3^4 \cdot 7^2 \cdot 13$ What is the rule?[2]

Two integers m and n are said to be *relatively prime* or *coprime* if $\gcd(m, n) = 1$. The integers 52 and 81 are relatively prime.

6.4.1   Applications of gcd and lcm

The most common application of the gcd and lcm is in working with fractions. You put them to use whenever you reduce or add fractions and you would use them in the same way if you were implementing a class to represent fractions.

To reduce a fraction to *lowest terms*, we divide the numerator and denominator by their gcd.

$$\frac{84}{36} = \frac{12 \cdot 7}{12 \cdot 3} = \frac{7}{3} \qquad \gcd(84, 36) = 12$$

We use the lcm when we add fractions.

$$\frac{3}{5} + \frac{2}{7} = \frac{21+10}{35} = \frac{31}{35} \qquad \operatorname{lcm}(5, 7) = 35$$

$$\frac{2}{15} + \frac{10}{21} = \frac{14+50}{105} = \frac{64}{105} \qquad \operatorname{lcm}(15, 21) = 105$$

In both these sums of fractions we see that the denominator of the result is given by the lcm of the denominators in the summands but where did the numbers 14 and 50 come from?

$$14 = 2 \cdot \frac{21}{\gcd(15, 21)} \qquad and \qquad 50 = 10 \cdot \frac{15}{\gcd(15, 21)}$$

In general, if a, b, c, and d are positive integers then

---

[1]$\gcd(a, b)$ divides both a and b so the exponent of each prime factor of $\gcd(a, b)$ must be the minimum of that prime's exponent in a and in b.

[2]$\operatorname{lcm}(a, b)$ is a multiple of both a and b so the exponent of each prime factor of $\operatorname{lcm}(a, b)$ must be the maximum of that prime's exponent in a and in b.

$$\frac{a}{b}+\frac{c}{d} = \frac{a \cdot d + c \cdot b}{b \cdot d} = \frac{(a \cdot d)/\gcd(b,d) + (c \cdot b)/\gcd(b,d)}{(b \cdot d)/\gcd(b,d)} = \frac{a \cdot (d/\gcd(b,d)) + c \cdot (b/\gcd(b,d))}{\operatorname{lcm}(b,d)}.$$

Will the resulting fractions always be reduced? The last equality comes from the following theorem.

Theorem 7 *Let a and b be positive integers. Then* $ab = \gcd(a,b) \cdot \operatorname{lcm}(a,b)$.

We also use the gcd in cryptography. For example, to decrypt a linear cipher

$$a \to (m \cdot a + b) \bmod n$$

we need a multiplicative inverse for $m \bmod n$. In fact, a multiplicative inverse for $m \bmod n$ exists if and only if $\gcd(m,n) = 1$. If we are working with a large number of letters or blocks, n, we need an efficient way calculate $\gcd(m,n)$ in order to check whether we are using a good multiplier, m.

6.5   Euclidean Algorithm

How do you find $\gcd(49831, 825579)$ or $\gcd(8094702578291, 7403070229547)$ or the gcd of two hundred-digit numbers? You could factor both numbers but that is a costly operation and will not be feasible if the numbers are too large. The **Euclidean Algorithm** is a method to compute the gcd of two non-zero integers, a and b. The method is based on the Division Algorithm.

Theorem 8 (Euclidean Algorithm) *If r is the remainder when a is divided by b, i.e.* $a = q \cdot b + r$, *with* $0 \le r < b$, *then* $\gcd(a,b) = \gcd(b,r)$.

If $a = q \cdot b + r$, with $0 \le r < b$ then, by definition, $r = a \bmod b$. So another way of stating the Euclidean algorithm is $\gcd(a,b) = \gcd(b, a \bmod b)$. This still sounds like a theorem rather than an algorithm that lays out the steps to find the $\gcd(a,b)$. This is how we use it as an algorithm.

Euclidean Algorithm

Input: Two positive integers, a and b.

Output: $\gcd(a,b)$

- If $a < b$, swap a and b.

- If b divides a, return b.

- else return $gcd(b, a \bmod b)$

The correctness of the Euclidean Algorithm can be proven in many ways. Here, we make use of the following lemma concerning *divides* and *gcd*.

Lemma 1 *If $x \mid y$ and $x \mid z$, then $x \mid \gcd(y, z)$.*

Proof: Since x is a common divisor of both y and z, it must be a factor of the *greatest* common divisor of y and z. □

We can now make use of this lemma to verify the correctness of the Euclidean Algorithm.
Proof: In what follows, we show that $\gcd(a, b) \mid \gcd(b, r)$ and $\gcd(b, r) \mid \gcd(a, b)$. Since $n \mid m$ and $m \mid n$ if and only if $n = m$, we must have that $\gcd(a, b) = \gcd(b, r)$.

$\gcd(a, b) \mid \gcd(b, r)$:

$$
\begin{aligned}
&\quad \gcd(a, b) \mid a \text{ and } \gcd(a, b) \mid b &&\text{by definition}\\
\Rightarrow\ &\quad \gcd(a, b) \mid (a - q \cdot b) &&\text{by algebra and definition of divides}\\
\Rightarrow\ &\quad \gcd(a, b) \mid r &&\text{since } a = q \cdot b + r
\end{aligned}
$$

But if $\gcd(a, b) \mid b$ and $\gcd(a, b) \mid r$, then $\gcd(a, b) \mid \gcd(b, r)$, by the Lemma 1.

Similarly, we have the following:

$\gcd(b, r) \mid \gcd(a, b)$:

$$
\begin{aligned}
&\quad \gcd(b, r) \mid b \text{ and } \gcd(b, r) \mid r &&\text{by definition}\\
\Rightarrow\ &\quad \gcd(b, r) \mid (q \cdot b + r) &&\text{by algebra and definition of divides}\\
\Rightarrow\ &\quad \gcd(b, r) \mid a &&\text{since } a = q \cdot b + r
\end{aligned}
$$

But if $\gcd(b, r) \mid a$ and $\gcd(b, r) \mid b$, then $\gcd(b, r) \mid \gcd(a, b)$, by the Lemma 1. □

6.5.1   Using the Euclidean Algorithm

The following recursive pseudocode for gcd can easily be turned into Racket (or Scheme) code.

```
function gcd(a, b)
    if b = 0
        return a
```

```
    else
        return gcd(b, a mod b)
```

In fact, the functions gcd and lcm are defined in Racket (and Scheme).[3]

```
> (gcd 12 81)
3
> (lcm 12 81)
324
> (gcd 12 81 25)
1
```

Example 6.4

  a. $\gcd(42, 35) = \gcd(35, 7) = \gcd(7, 0) = 7$.

  b. $\gcd(612, 1275) = \gcd(1275, 612) = \gcd(612, 51) = \gcd(51, 0) = 51$.

  c. $\gcd(49831, 825579)$

$$= \gcd(825579, 49831) = \gcd(49831, 28283) = \gcd(28283, 21548)$$

$$= \gcd(21548, 6735) = \gcd(6735, 1343) = \gcd(1343, 20)$$

$$= \gcd(20, 3) = \gcd(3, 2) = \gcd(2, 1) = \gcd(1, 0) = 1$$

   Notice that it took only 10 applications of mod to compute $\gcd(49831, 825579)$.

6.5.2   Euclidean Algorithm Links

For further discussion of the Euclidean Algorithm, see the Prime Pages glossary
   http://primes.utm.edu/glossary.
The *Visible Euclidean Algorithm*
   http://www.math.umn.edu/~garrett/crypto/a01/Euclid.html
is a tool that computes the gcd of two numbers and shows the steps using repeated applications
of the Division Algorithm, i.e., following the proof. (Remember that you are supposed to
understand the Euclidean Algorithm and will have to perform it by hand on exams.)

---

[3]The gcd and lcm in Racket (and Scheme) are actually defined for non-integer values, "for non-integer n(umber)s, the result is the gcd of the numerators divided by the lcm of the denominators." [2]

6.6   Extended Euclidean Algorithm

The Euclidean Algorithm take two positive integers, a and b and returns the $\gcd(a,b)$. It does this efficiently by repeated application of

$$\gcd(a,b) = \gcd(b, a \bmod b).$$

The Extended Euclidean Algorithm is a way to get more information than just the gcd of a and b just by doing some extra bookkeeping in the regular Euclidean Algorithm computation. In particular, it helps us find values for x and y in an important identity found by the French mathematician Étienne Bézout (1730 - 1783)[10].

Theorem 9 (Bézout's Identity) *If a and b are nonzero integers and d is their greatest common divisor. Then there exist integers x and y such that*

$$xa + yb = d = \gcd(a,b)$$

also   *i) d is the smallest positive integer that can be written as $xa + yb$*
          ii)   every integer of the form $xa + yb$ is a multiple of d.

Bézout's Identity may look very abstract but it has an important application that we will use in cryptography. Suppose $gcd(N, a) = 1$. Bézout's Identity tells us there are integers x and y such that $xN + ya = \gcd(N, a) = 1$. Then $ya = 1 - xN$. So $ya \bmod N = 1$ and y is the multiplicative inverse of $a \bmod N$. Here are some examples.

Example 6.5

1. $\gcd(6, 14) = 2 = -2 \cdot 6 + 1 \cdot 14$

2. $\gcd(12, 19) = 1 = -5 \cdot 19 + 8 \cdot 12$ so 8 is the multiplicative inverse of 12 mod 19.

3. $\gcd(6735, 1343) = 1 = -470 \cdot 6735 + 2357 \cdot 1343$ so 2357 is the multiplicative inverse of 1343 mod 6735.

The values of the coefficients x and y in the last example are pretty big and it's not obvious how to find them. For Bézout's Identity to be useful, we need an efficient method to compute the coefficients. If you keep track of the quotients in the Euclidean Algorithm while finding $\gcd(a, b)$, you can reverse the steps to find x and y. This method is called the **Extended Euclidean Algorithm**. It is especially useful when a and b are relatively prime. Then we can solve $ax + by = 1$ and x will be the multiplicative inverse of a mod b and y will be a multiplicative inverse of b mod a. It will be easier to understand how this works by looking at some examples.

Example 6.6

If we use the Division Algorithm repeatedly to compute $\gcd(6735, 1343)$, the steps look like this.

1. $\mathbf{6735} - 5 \cdot \mathbf{1343} = \mathbf{20}$ so $\gcd(6735, 1343) = \gcd(1343, 20)$

2. $\mathbf{1343} - 67 \cdot \mathbf{20} = \mathbf{3}$ so $\gcd(1343, 20) = \gcd(20, 3)$

3. $\mathbf{20} - 6 \cdot \mathbf{3} = \mathbf{2}$ so $\gcd(20, 3) = \gcd(3, 1)$

4. $\mathbf{3} - 1 \cdot \mathbf{2} = \mathbf{1}$ so $\gcd(3, 1) = 1$

We see that $\gcd(6735, 1343) = 1$.

When we are just interested in computing the gcd, we usually just keep track of the successive remainders (gcds) and write:

$$\gcd(6735, 1343) = \gcd(1343, 20) = \gcd(20, 3) = \gcd(3, 1) = 1.$$

To find integers x and y such that $x \cdot a + y \cdot b = 1$, we will also make use of the successive quotients. Here is one way to find x and y such that $x \cdot 6735 + y \cdot 1343 = 1$. Start with line 4 of the calculation above and work backwards:

$\quad \mathbf{3} - 1 \cdot \mathbf{2} = 1$

Use line 3 above to substitute for $\mathbf{2}$ in this expression then rearrange the result so it looks like $u \cdot 20 + v \cdot 3 = 1$ where u and v are integers.

$\quad \mathbf{3} - 1 \cdot (\mathbf{20} - 6 \cdot \mathbf{3}) = 1$

$\quad -1 \cdot \mathbf{20} + 7 \cdot \mathbf{3} = 1$

Now use line 2 above to substitute for $\mathbf{3}$ in this expression then rearrange the result so it looks like $u \cdot 1343 + v \cdot 20 = 1$ where u and v are integers.

$\quad -1 \cdot \mathbf{20} + 7 \cdot (\mathbf{1343} - 67 \cdot \mathbf{20}) = 1$

$\quad 7 \cdot \mathbf{1343} - (1 + 67 \cdot 7) \cdot \mathbf{20} = 1$

$\quad 7 \cdot \mathbf{1343} - 470 \cdot \mathbf{20} = 1$

Finally, use line 1 above to substitute for $\mathbf{20}$ in this expression then rearrange the result so it looks like $u \cdot 6735 + v \cdot 1343 = 1$ where u and v are integers.

$\quad 7 \cdot \mathbf{1343} - 470 \cdot (\mathbf{6735} - 5 \cdot \mathbf{1343} = 1$

$\quad -470 \cdot \mathbf{6735} + 2357 \cdot \mathbf{1343} = 1$

We have found a solution for $x \cdot 6735 + y \cdot 1343 = 1$, $x = -470$ and $y = 2357$.

You can turn this calculation into a general method but you must be very careful after each substitution not to just add everything up. You must keep the successive remainders intact when you substitute and rearrange. It is easy to get lost in the arithmetic.

Here is another method that many students find much easier to work by hand; it's sometimes called the *Table Method*[11]. We show it first on the same example.

$$A = 6735 \text{ and } B = 1343$$

Line	Q	R	X	Y	$X \cdot A + Y \cdot B = R$
1		6735	1	0	$1 \cdot A + 0 \cdot B = 6735 = A$
2		1343	0	1	$0 \cdot A + 1 \cdot B = 1343 = B$
3	5	20	1	-5	$1 \cdot A - 5 \cdot B = 20 = \text{mod}(6735, 1343)$
4	67	3	-67	336	$-67 \cdot A + 336 \cdot B = 3 = \text{mod}(1343, 20)$
5	6	2	403	-2021	$403 \cdot A - 2021 \cdot B = 2 = \text{mod}(20, 3)$
6	1	1	-470	2357	$-470 \cdot A + 2357 \cdot B = 1 = \text{mod}(3, 2) = \gcd(6735, 1343)$
7	1	0			

If you look down the R column of the table, you see that we have just done the same computation we did above. We start with A and B and starting with line 3, the R value is the number two lines above mod the number one line above. In the Q column, we keep track of the successive quotients. So $5 = \lfloor 6735/1343 \rfloor$ and $20 = \text{mod}(6735, 1343)$, the remainder of the division. Continuing, $67 = \lfloor 1343/20 \rfloor$ and $3 = \text{mod}(1343, 20)$, and so on. We stop at line 7 because $R = 0$. By the Division Algorithm, the R in line 6 is $\gcd(A, B)$. The X, Y and R values on each line always satisfy $X \cdot A + Y \cdot B = R$ so the X and Y values in line 6 satisfy $X \cdot A + Y \cdot B = 1$. In general, the *Table Method* works like this.

Start with positive integers A and B, with $A \geq B$. Enter the first two lines of the table as shown below, leaving the Q column empty. It is clear the these two lines satisfy the condition $X \cdot A + Y \cdot B = R$. Once we have two successive lines line k and line $k + 1$ filled in, we fill in the next line $k + 2$ as follows:

- $Q[k + 2] = $ the integer quotient of $R[k]$ divided by $R[k + 1] = \lfloor R[k]/R[k + 1] \rfloor$.

- $R[k + 2] = R[k] - Q[k + 2] \cdot R[k + 1]$ This is the remainder of the division and equals $\text{mod}(R[k], R[k + 1])$.

- $X[k + 2] = X[k] - Q[k + 2] \cdot X[k + 1]$ and $Y[k + 2] = Y[k] - Q[k + 2] \cdot Y[k + 1]$.

- When $R = 0$, STOP. The R on the previous line is $\gcd(A, B)$ and the X and Y on that line satisfy $X \cdot A + Y \cdot B = R = \gcd(A, B)$.

Line	Q	R	X	Y
1		A	1	0
2		B	0	1
$\vdots$	$\vdots$	$\vdots$	$\vdots$	$\vdots$
k	$Q[k]$	$R[k]$	$X[k]$	$Y[k]$
$k+1$	$Q[k+1]$	$R[k+1]$	$X[k+1]$	$Y[k+1]$
$k+2$	$\lfloor R[k]/R[k+1] \rfloor$	$R[k] - Q[k+2] \cdot R[k+1]$	$X[k] - Q[k+2] \cdot X[k+1]$	$Y[k] - Q[k+2] \cdot Y[k+1]$
$\vdots$	$\vdots$	$\vdots$	$\vdots$	$\vdots$
	some Q	$\gcd(A, B)$	x	y
	another Q	0		

The x and y in the next-to-the-last row are just what we were looking for: $x \cdot A + y \cdot B = \gcd(A, B)$. We can prove that this works using induction and we'll get to that later in this course. For now, just observe that if we believe that $X[k] \cdot A + Y[k] \cdot B = R[k]$ and $X[k+1] \cdot A + Y[k+1] \cdot B = R[k+1]$ then

$$X[k+2] \cdot A + Y[k+2] \cdot B$$
$$= (X[k] - Q[k+2] \cdot X[k+1]) \cdot A + (Y[k] - Q[k+2] \cdot Y[k+1]) \cdot B$$
$$= X[k] \cdot A + Y[k] \cdot B - Q[k+2] \cdot (X[k+1] \cdot A + Y[k+1] \cdot B)$$
$$= R[k] - Q[k+2] \cdot R[k+1] = R[k+2].$$

You can see additional discussion and examples at

     http://en.wikipedia.org/wiki/Extended_Euclidean_algorithm

6.7   Inverses mod n

We have already seen that we need to find multiplicative inverses mod n to decipher the cipher text that was created using linear ciphers 5.4.2 on page 62. Multiplicative inverses mod n are important in the decryption process in much more sophisticated encryption systems as we will see in the next chapter, *The RSA (Rivest-Shamir-Adelman) cryptosystem*. We have just seen that we can apply the Extended Euclidean Algorithm to efficiently find multiplicative inverses mod n when they exist.

Above, we used the Extended Euclidean Algorithm to find that $-470 \cdot \mathbf{6735} + 2357 \cdot \mathbf{1343} = 1$. This tells us that 2357 and 1343 are multiplicative inverses mod 6735. This also tells us that $-470 \cdot 6735 \bmod 1343 = 1$. So -470 is a multiplicative inverse for 6735 mod 1343. If we want a positive inverse, we just use $-470 \bmod 1343 = 1343 - 470 = 873$.

6.8   Summary

In this chapter, we introduced the Division Algorithm and the prime number decomposition of positive integers. We defined the **gcd** (greatest common divisor) and **lcm** (least common multiple) of two integers. The Euclidean Algorithm provides a way to efficiently compute the $\gcd(a, b)$ and the Extended Euclidean Algorithm lets us efficiently compute the coefficients x and y in Bézout's Identity $xa + yb = \gcd(a, b)$. This, in turn, gives us a way to calculate the multiplicative inverse of $a \bmod n$ when it exists.

Exercises

Prime Number Decomposition

Exercise 6.1

Give the prime number decomposition for each of the following. You should not need a calculator.

    a. 162   **b.** 640   **c.** 363 **d.** 1024 **e.** 1000   **f.** 8800

    g. 102400 **h.** 8100 **i.** 29 **j.** 999 **k.** $256 \cdot 81$ **l.** $125 \cdot 49 \cdot 325$

Exercise 6.2

Give the prime number decomposition for each of the following. You should not need a calculator.

    a. 8! **b.** 9!   **c.** 10! **d.** $\frac{6!}{2^4}$ **e.** $\frac{10!}{2^4 \cdot 3^3}$ **f.** $(6!)^3$

    g. $\frac{8!}{4!}$ **h.** $\frac{8!}{4!4!}$ **i.** $\frac{10!}{3!}$ **j.** $\frac{10!}{7!}$ **k.** $\frac{10!}{3!7!}$ **l.** $\frac{2^5 \cdot 3^7 \cdot 5^9 \cdot 7^6}{2^2 \cdot 3^4 \cdot 7^6}$

Greatest Common Divisor and Least Common Multiple

Exercise 6.3

Evaluate the following. You should not need a calculator.

  a. $gcd(60, 80)$

  b. $lcm(60, 80)$

  c. $gcd(256, 162)$

  d. $gcd(512, 1024)$

  e. $lcm(512, 1024)$

  f. $gcd(6!, 8!)$

  g. $lcm(6!, 8!)$

h. $gcd(2^3 \cdot 3^5 \cdot 5^4, 2^2 \cdot 3^7 \cdot 5^2)$

i. $lcm(2^3 \cdot 3^5 \cdot 5^4, 2^2 \cdot 3^7 \cdot 5^2)$

Exercise 6.4

Use the Euclidean Algorithm to find each of the following. Show your work.

a. $gcd(612, 588)$

b. $gcd(488, 183)$

c. $gcd(217, 124)$

Exercise 6.5

Use the Extended Euclidean Algorithm to solve $ax + by = gcd(a, b)$. If the gcd is 1, also give the multiplicative inverse of a mod b as a number from 1 to $b - 1$.

a. $a = 24$, $b = 119$

b. $a = 20$, $b = 151$

CHAPTER 7

The RSA (Rivest-Shamir-Adelman) Cryptosystem

7.1 Introduction

The RSA cryptosystem is a public-key cryptosystem widely used for secure communication and e-commerce applications. It is often used to encrypt messages sent between two communicating parties so that an eavesdropper who overhears the conversation cannot decode them easily. It also enables a party to append an unforgeable signature to the end of a message. This signature cannot be "easily" forged and can be checked by anyone.

7.2 How Do Public-key Cryptosystems Work?

Consider our protagonists Alice and Bob who want to communicate with each other securely. Suppose Bob wants to send a message to Alice. In a typical public-key cryptosystem Alice has two keys: a secret (or private) key that only Alice knows and a public key that Alice advertises to the whole world. Each key yields a function that maps a message to another message: the public key yields a public *encryption function*—let us call it P_A—and the secret key yields a secret *decryption function* S_A. A typical message exchange proceeds as follows.

Bob encrypts his message M using P_A and sends the message $P_A(M)$ to Alice.

If Alice receives $P_A(M)$, she applies S_A and obtains $S_A(P_A(M)) = M$.

So we want two functions S_A and P_A such that $S_A(P_A(M)) = M$ for all permissible messages M. Furthermore, our selection of S_A and P_A should be such that any eavesdropper who can read message $P_A(M)$ cannot "efficiently" extract M from this; or, ideally, cannot "efficiently" extract any reasonable information from this.

7.3   How Does RSA Work?

The basic RSA cryptosystem is completely specified by the following sequence of steps.

1. Alice selects at random two large primes p and q.

2. Alice computes $n = pq$.

3. Alice selects a small odd integer e that is relatively prime to $(p-1)(q-1)$.

4. Alice sets d so that de mod $(p-1)(q-1)$ equals 1.

5. Alice publishes the pair (e, n) as the public key, with $P_A(M) = M^e$ mod n.

6. Alice stores the pair (d, n) as the secret key, with $S_A(E) = E^d$ mod n.

   In order to send message M in $\{0, 1, \ldots, n-1\}$, Bob sends $P_A(M) = M^e$ mod n. Upon receiving the encrypted message Alice computes $S_A(P_A(M)) = M^{de}$ mod n. Our choices of d, e, and n ensure that M^{de} mod n equals M.

   To prove that this works, we need to understand the mathematical underpinnings of RSA, which we will do in Section 7.4. But first, let us do a couple of examples.

Example 7.1

 Take

$$p = 5, q = 3$$
$$\text{then } n = 5 \cdot 3 = 15, (p-1)(q-1) = 4 \cdot 2 = 8, \text{ and let } e = 3.$$

We need to find the multiplicative inverse of 3 mod 8. Well, $3 \cdot 3 = 9$ mod $8 = 1$. So $d = 3$.

Example 7.2

 Now take

$$p = 7, q = 11$$
$$\text{then } n = 7 \cdot 11 = 77, (p-1)(q-1) = 6 \cdot 10 = 60, \text{ and let } e = 13.$$

What is d? Note that d is the multiplicative inverse of e mod 60. We can calculate it using the Extended Euclidean Algorithm to obtain 37; you can verify that $37 \cdot 13$ mod $60 = 1$.

Suppose the message $M = 2$. Then the encrypted message is 2^{13} mod 77. We calculate it as follows:

$$
\begin{aligned}
2^2 \bmod 77 &= 4 \\
2^4 \bmod 77 &= 16 \\
2^8 \bmod 77 &= 256 \bmod 77 = 25 \\
2^{13} \bmod 77 &= (25 \cdot 16 \cdot 2) \bmod 77 = 800 \bmod 77 = 30.
\end{aligned}
$$

To decrypt, Alice computes 30^{37} mod 77, which can be calculated as follows.

$$
\begin{aligned}
30^2 \bmod 77 &= 900 \bmod 77 = 53 \\
30^4 \bmod 77 &= 53^2 \bmod 77 = 2809 \bmod 77 = 37 \\
30^8 \bmod 77 &= 37^2 \bmod 77 = 1369 \bmod 77 = 60 \\
30^{16} \bmod 77 &= 60^2 \bmod 77 = 3600 \bmod 77 = 58 \\
30^{32} \bmod 77 &= 58^2 \bmod 77 = 3364 \bmod 77 = 53 \\
30^{37} \bmod 77 &= (30^{32} \cdot 30^4 \cdot 30) \bmod 77 = (53 \cdot 37 \cdot 30) \bmod 77 = 2.
\end{aligned}
$$

7.4   Why Does RSA Work?

We can prove that RSA works by showing that for any M in $\{0, \ldots, n-1\}$, the following equation holds.

$$
M^{de} \bmod n = M \tag{7.1}
$$

We establish the above equation using a nice theorem proved by the French mathematician Pierre Fermat; it is called *Fermat's Little Theorem*.

Theorem 10 (Fermat's Little Theorem) *If p is prime, then for all $1 \leq a < p$, we have*

$$
a^{p-1} \bmod p = 1.
$$

Proof: Consider $a \cdot x$ and $a \cdot y$ for $x \neq y$, $1 \leq x, y < p$. We claim they are different $\bmod\, p$ since otherwise, p divides a or $x - y$, both not possible. So, $a \cdot 1 \bmod p,\, a \cdot 2 \bmod p,\, \ldots,\, a \cdot (p-1) \bmod p$

are all different numbers in $\{1, 2, ..., p - 1\}$. Thus, we have

$$(a \cdot 1) \cdot (a \cdot 2) \cdots (a \cdot (p - 1)) = a^{p-1} \cdot (p - 1)! = (p - 1)! \bmod p.$$

Thus, p either divides $a^{p-1} - 1$ or divides $(p - 1)!$. The latter is not possible, hence the claim.   □

We now establish Equation 7.1. Recall that

$$de \bmod (p - 1)(q - 1) = 1.$$
$$\text{So } de = k(p - 1)(q - 1) + 1 \text{ for some integer } k.$$

We will show that $M^{(p-1)(q-1)} \bmod n$ is equal to 1. Note that this immediately implies that $M^{de} \bmod n = M$.

We consider two cases. In the first case, M is relatively prime to both p and q; in the second, M has a common factor with either p or q.

1. Let us consider the first case. By Fermat's Little Theorem, we know that $M^{p-1} \bmod p = 1$ and $M^{q-1} \bmod q = 1$. Therefore, we have $M^{(p-1)(q-1)} \bmod p$ and $M^{(p-1)(q-1)} \bmod q$ are both 1. Thus, $M^{(p-1)(q-1)}$ is of the form $k_1 p + 1$ as well as of the form $k_2 q + 1$ for some integers k_1 and k_2. This implies that $k_1 p = k_2 q$; since p and q are different primes, this can hold only if k_1 is a multiple of q and k_2 is a multiple of p. It thus follows that $M^{(p-1)(q-1)}$ is of the form $kpq + 1 = kn + 1$ for some integer k. In other words, $M^{(p-1)(q-1)} \bmod n$ equals 1. This completes the proof for the first case.

2. We now consider the case where M shares a common factor with either p or q. In this case, M is a multiple of p or q. Suppose, without loss of generality $M = kp$ for some integer k. Let us consider what $M^{de} \bmod p$ and $M^{de} \bmod q$ are. Since M is a multiple of p, $M^{de} \bmod p = 0$. So M^{de} is a multiple of p. We now calculate $M^{de} \bmod q$ as follows. Since $M < n$, it follows that $k < q$; so M is relatively prime to q. By Fermat's Little Theorem, we then have $M^{q-1} \bmod q = 1$. Therefore, we also have $M^{(p-1)(q-1)} \bmod q = 1$, implying that $M^{de} \bmod q = M \bmod q$. We thus have

$$M^{de} \bmod p = 0; M^{de} \bmod q = M \bmod q.$$

Let M_1 denote $M^{de} \bmod pq$. It follows that

$$M_1 \bmod p = 0; M_1 \bmod q = M \bmod q.$$

Thus M_1 is of the form ℓp for some integer $\ell < q$. But since q divides $M - M_1 = (k - \ell)p$ for nonnegative integers $k, \ell < q$, it follows that $k = \ell$, implying that $M_1 = M$.

We have thus shown that the decryption function of RSA, when applied to an encrypted message, yields the original unencrypted message as desired.

7.5   Is RSA Secure and Efficient?

What are the individual steps in RSA? Which of these can be executed efficiently? How secure is RSA? Here is a brief discussion on the efficiency and security of RSA.

- Generating two large random primes: How do we perform this? Well, one way to do it is to generate a random number and then test whether it is prime. How do we test whether it is prime? Our naive scheme (that works in time proportional to the square root of the number) is too slow and inefficient. Fortunately, there are faster, efficient ways to do it.

- We need to raise a number to a (potentially) large power in modular arithmetic. We have seen how to do this efficiently using the repeated squaring method.

- We also need to find a multiplicative inverse in modular arithmetic. This can be done efficiently using the Extended Euclidean Algorithm.

- We do not want the number n (used in the RSA private and public key) to be easily factored into its prime factors p and q. A naive algorithm takes time proportional to the square root of n. Fortunately, there is *no* efficient way known to do this factoring.

- As stated, RSA is a deterministic encryption system; i.e., a particular message is encrypted the same way every time. This is prone to easy attacks, referred to as plaintext attacks, where the attacker may be aware that the message being sent is one of a small number of possibilities and can try the public encryption system with different possibilities. One way to avoid this attack is making the system randomized—for instance by adding a fixed-size random pad to the plaintext message and encrypting the padded message. The random pad is chosen independently at every step, thus making the above plaintext attack more difficult.

7.6   Summary

Public-key cryptosystems require two separate keys, one of which is secret (or private) and one of which is public. **RSA** is one of the first practical public-key cryptosystems and it is still widely used for secure data transmission and e-commerce applications. In this chapter, we applied modular arithmetic to show how to perform RSA encryption and decryption. We also learned Fermat's Little Theorem and used it to prove that RSA really works.

Exercises

The RSA Cryptosystem

Exercise 7.1
As in example 7.1,

Let $p = 5$ and $q = 3$ so $n = 5 \cdot 3 = 15$ and $(p-1)(q-1) = 4 \cdot 2 = 8$.

With $e = 3$, we have seen that $d = 3$.

a. What is the RSA encryption of $M = 2$?

b. Verify that $(M^e)^d \bmod n = M$ when $M = 2$.

Exercise 7.2
As in example 7.2,

Let $p = 7$ and $q = 11$ so $n = 7 \cdot 11 = 77$ and $(p-1)(q-1) = 6 \cdot 10 = 60$.

a. List all the values of e that Alice can use for her encryption key.

b. If $e = 17$, what is the RSA encryption of $M = 2$?

c. What is d when $e = 17$?

Exercise 7.3
Suppose we have an RSA cryptosystem with $p = 23$ and $q = 41$.

a. Compute n.

b. Compute $(p-1)(q-1)$.

c. If $e = 3$, what is d?

Part III

Combinatorics: Sets, Counting, and Probability

CHAPTER 8

Sets

Combinatorics is a field of mathematics that includes counting the structures of a given kind and size. Counting is something most of us started doing as young children. In elementary school, we often used arithmetic to count things, for example, "If I have three boxes of candy and each box has 12 candies, how many candies do I have altogether?" We learned to estimate things we couldnt count exactly like, "How many Canada geese are there in Massachusetts?"

There are many things we have to count in computer and information science. If we are designing a game, we might want to count the number of different ways we can arrange the hazards at each level and how many of those layouts will allow some way for the player to succeed. Counting provides a way to estimate the security of passwords. Four-digit PINs or passwords might be fine for a mechanical device like a door or a bicycle lock but not very useful as online passwords where a computer program could try all the possibilities (10,000) in a fraction of a second. As programmers, we often want to know, "How long will it take my code to run?" We can often answer this question by counting the number of times certain lines of code will be executed during the run of the program.

To get started, we need some mathematical language to describe the things we want to count. Thats the language of sets.

8.1 Set Definition and Examples

A *set* is an unordered collection of objects. The objects are called *elements* of the set.

Many of the sets we talk about in discrete structures are sets of numbers.

Example 8.1

Some Sets of Numbers:

$$\mathbb{N} = \{0, 1, 2, 3, ...\} \qquad \text{natural numbers }^1$$
$$\mathbb{Z} = \{... -2, -1, 0, 1, 2, ...\} \qquad \text{integers}$$
$$\mathbb{Z}^+ = \{1, 2, 3, ...\} \qquad \text{positive integers}$$
$$\mathbb{Q} = \{p/q | p \text{ in } \mathbb{Z}, q \text{ in } \mathbb{Z}, q \neq 0\} \quad \text{rational numbers}$$
$$\mathbb{R} \qquad \text{real numbers}$$
$$S = \{1, 2, 3\} \qquad \text{the set containing the three numbers: } 1, 2, 3.$$

We use braces (also called curly brackets) to show the elements of a set. The elements of a set do not have to be numbers. We can talk about the set of all freshmen computer science majors or just those freshmen who showed up for class today. Here are some other sets.

Example 8.2

Some Other Sets:

Letters $= \{a, b, c, d, e, f, g, h, i, j, k, l, m, n, o, p, q, r, s, t, u, v, w, x, y, z\}$

Vowels $= \{a, e, i, o, u\}$

Nibbles $= \{0000, 0001, 0010, 0011, 0100, 0101, 0110, 0111, 1000, 1001, 1010, 1011, 1100, 1101, 1110, 1111\}$

$\{$George, textbook, a piece of chalk, $6\}$ This is a weird set.

8.2   Set Basics

If x is an element of S, we write $x \in S$ which may also be read as "x is in S."

If x is not in S, we write $x \notin X$.

Two sets are equal if and only if they have the same elements.

$$\{a, b, c\} = \{b, c, a\} = \{b, a, c, b\}$$

We do not usually write a element twice, as in $\{b, a, c, b\}$ but sometimes it just happens. We might, for example, compute $\{2x, x^2, x^3 - 4\}$ for some values of x. Here's what we get for a few small values of x.

$x = 1$: $\{2x, x^2, x^3 - 4\} = \{2, 1, -3\}$

$x = 3$: $\{2x, x^2, x^3 - 4\} = \{6, 9, 23\}$

$x = 0$: $\{2x, x^2, x^3 - 4\} = \{0, 0, -4\} = \{0, -4\}$

$x = 2$: $\{2x, x^2, x^3 - 4\} = \{4, 4, 4\} = \{4\}$

If a set has a finite number of elements, we say it is a *finite set* and the *cardinality* or *size* of the set is the number of elements it contains. We use the notation $|S|$ to denote the cardinality of S. If $S = \{1, 2, 5, 7\}$, then $|S| = 4$. Cardinality is also defined for infinite sets, i.e. sets with infinitely many elements. Though both $\mathbb{R}$ and $\mathbb{Z}$ have infinitely many elements, they do not have the same cardinality. In fact, there are an infinite number of different infinities. You will learn about this in Theory of Computation, if not sooner.

A set may also have no elements at all. We call a set with no elements the *empty set* and denote it by $\emptyset$ or by $\{\}$. This may seem silly but the empty set is very important. In a way, it is a place-keeper like the number zero. When you declare a set variable in computing, it is an empty set until you put something in it. If we compute

$$S = \{x \in \mathbb{R} | x^2 + 4x + c = 0\}$$

for various values of c, then when

$$
\begin{aligned}
c &= 0, \quad S = \{-4, 0\} \\
c &= 4, \quad S = \{-2\} \\
c &= 6, \quad S = \{\}.
\end{aligned}
$$

8.3   Set-Builder Notation

Sometimes we define a set by listing all the elements of the set inside curly brackets as we did above for $S = \{1, 2, 3\}$. We also do this for infinite sets as in $\mathbb{Z}^+ = \{1, 2, 3, \ldots\}$ or $= \mathbb{Z} = \{\ldots -2, -1, 0, 1, 2, \ldots\}$. When we need to describe which elements are in the set instead of just leaving it to the reader to figure out how to continue a list, we use *set-builder notation*. A set description in set-builder notation looks like

$$\{v| \text{ condition on } v\} \text{ or } \{v \in S| \text{ condition on } v\}$$

where v is a variable and S is a set. The braces "{" and "}" tell us to say "the set of" and the vertical bar "|" is read as "such that." We sometimes use a colon ":" in place of the vertical bar.

$\{v| \text{ condition on } v\}$ is read as "the set of v such that" the condition on v holds.

$\{v \in S| \text{ condition on } v\}$ is read as "the set of v in S such that" the condition on v holds. The examples below should explain how set builder notation works.

Example 8.3
Set-Builder Examples:

$\{x | x \in \mathbb{Z} \text{ and } |x| < 5\}$ means "the set of x in $\mathbb{Z}$ such that $|x|$ is less than 5" which is equal to $\{-4, -3, -2, -1, 0, 1, 2, 3, 4\}$. We might also write $\{x \in \mathbb{Z} | |x| < 5\}$.

$\{x \in \mathbb{Z} | x^2 < 10\}$ = the set of integers such that $x^2 < 10 = \{-3, -2, -1, 0, 1, 2, 3\}$.

$\{x \in \mathbb{N} | x^2 < 10\}$ = the set of natural numbers such that $x^2 < 10 = \{0, 1, 2, 3\}$.

$\{z | z = 2k$ and $k \in \mathbb{N}\}$ = the set of z such that $z = 2k$ where k is a natural number $= \{0, 2, 4, 6, \ldots\}$ = the positive even integers.

8.4   Venn Diagrams

Venn diagrams are a way of using pictures to describe sets and set operations. The first thing we do is draw a *universe* or *universal set*, U. The set U contains all the objects that we might want to be in the sets we are talking about: for example, U might be all real numbers or all people living today or all current Northeastern University students. We use a rectangle to show U.

We then show a single set S with elements in the universe U like this.

If two sets A and B with elements from the universe U have no elements in common, we say A and B are *disjoint*. Here is a Venn diagram showing the relationship between disjoint sets A and B.

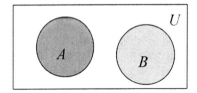

We say A *is a subset of* B (or A *is included in* B or B *includes* A) if every element of A is also an element of B. We write

$A \subseteq B$ if A is a subset of B. In this case, A might be equal to B.

$A \subset B$ if A is a subset of B but A is not equal to B. This means that every element of A is an element of B but there is at least one element of B that is not an element of A. We say A is a *proper subset* of B.

Here is a Venn diagram that shows $A \subseteq B$ or $A \subset B$.

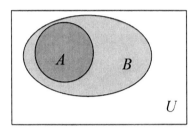

8.5 Set Operations

Just like we use arithmetic operations, e.g. $+$, $-$, $\times$, $/$, to combine numbers to yield new numbers, we use set operations to combine sets to form new sets. The basic set operations follow with definitions, corresponding Venn diagrams, and examples.

8.5.1 $\cup$ Union

$A \cup B = \{x | x \in A \text{ or } x \in B\}$

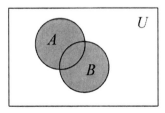

Let $A = \{1, 2, 3, 4\}$, $B = \{2, 3, 4, 6, 7, 9\}$, and $C = \{1, 2, 9\}$. Then

$A \cup B = \{1, 2, 3, 4, 6, 7, 9\}$

$B \cup C = \{1, 2, 3, 4, 6, 7, 9\}$

$A \cup C = \{1, 2, 3, 4, 9\}$

For any set S, $S \cup \emptyset = S$ and $S \cup U = U$ where U is the universe.

8.5.2   ∩ Intersection

$A \cap B = \{x | x \in A \text{ and } x \in B\}$

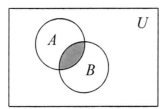

Let $A = \{1, 2, 3, 4\}$, $B = \{2, 3, 4, 6, 7, 9\}$, and $C = \{1, 2, 9\}$. Then

$A \cap B = \{2, 3, 4\}$

$B \cap C = \{2, 9\}$

$A \cap C = \{1, 2\}$

For any set S, $S \cap \emptyset = \emptyset$ and $S \cap U = S$ where U is the universe.

Sets A and B are disjoint if and only if $A \cap B = \emptyset$.

Theorem 11 Inclusion-exclusion Principle *If A and B are finite sets, the cardinality of $A \cup B$ is given by $|A \cup B| = |A| + |B| - |A \cap B|$.*

Proof: When we add up $|A| + |B|$, we have counted all the elements of A and all the elements of B but we have counted the elements in $A \cap B$ twice so we must subtract that number to get the correct result.   □

This statement seems obvious but often proves to be a stumbling block in the counting problems.

8.5.3 $\overline{A}$ Complement

$\overline{A} = \{x | x \in U \text{ and } x \notin A\}$

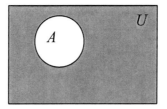

Let $A = \{1, 2, 3, 4\}$, $B = \{2, 3, 4, 6, 7, 9\}$, $C = \{1, 2, 9\}$ and $U = \{0, 1, 2, 3, 4, 5, 6, 7, 8, 9\}$. Then

$\overline{A} = \{0, 5, 6, 7, 8, 9\}$

$\overline{B} = \{0, 1, 5, 8\}$

$\overline{C} = \{0, 3, 4, 5, 6, 7, 8\}$

The empty and universal sets are related by $\overline{\emptyset} = U$ and $\overline{U} = \emptyset$.

8.5.4   Difference

$A - B = \{x | x \in A \text{ and } x \notin B\}$

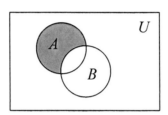

Let $A = \{1, 2, 3, 4\}$, $B = \{2, 3, 4, 6, 7, 9\}$, and $C = \{1, 2, 9\}$. Then

$A - B = \{1\}$

$B - A = \{6, 7, 9\}$

$B - C = \{3, 4, 6, 7\}$

$C - B = \{1\}$

$A - C = \{3, 4\}$

$C - A = \{9\}$

For any set S, $S - \emptyset = S$ and $S - U = \emptyset$ where U is the universe.

8.5.5   Symmetric Difference

$A \triangle B = \{x | x \in A \text{ and } x \notin B\} \cup \{x | x \in B \text{ and } x \notin A\}$

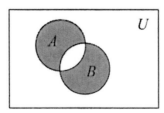

Let $A = \{1,2,3,4\}$, $B = \{2,3,4,6,7,9\}$, and $C = \{1,2,9\}$. Then

$A \triangle B = \{1,6,7,9\}$

$B \triangle A = \{1,6,7,9\}$

$B \triangle C = \{1,3,4,6,7\}$

$C \triangle B = \{1,3,4,6,7\}$

$A \triangle C = \{3,4,9\}$

$C \triangle A = \{3,4,9\}$

All of the set operations introduced above yield sets in the same universe as the original sets. We now look at two ways of building sets from a given set or sets that result in a set with elements from a different universe.

8.5.6 Power Set

If A is a set, the power set $\mathfrak{P}(A)$ is the set of all subsets of A. We often need to use subsets of a set when we model a real problem, e.g. if the universe is all Northeastern students, we may want to consider possible subsets of students in particular classes, or dorms, or teams.

If $A = \{1,2\}$ then $\mathfrak{P}(A) = \{\emptyset, \{1\}, \{2\}, \{1,2\}\}$. The elements of $\mathfrak{P}(A)$ are sets, not numbers. In general, the cardinality of the power set $|\mathfrak{P}(A)| = 2^{|A|}$ and sometimes we use 2^A instead of $\mathfrak{P}(A)$ to denote the power set of A.

Example 8.4
Examples of Power Sets

If $A = \{a,b,c\}$ then $\mathfrak{P}(A) = \{\emptyset, \{a\}, \{b\}, \{c\}, \{a,b\}, \{a,c\}, \{b,c\}, \{a,b,c\}\}$.

$\mathfrak{P}(\emptyset) = \{\emptyset\}$ which is not the same as $\emptyset$. The empty set $\emptyset$ has no elements but it does have one subset, $\emptyset$.

If $S = \{x\}$, $\mathfrak{P}(S) = \{\emptyset, \{x\}\}$ and $\mathfrak{P}(\mathfrak{P}(S)) = \{\emptyset, \{\emptyset\}, \{\{x\}\}, \{\emptyset, \{x\}\}\}$. Note that $|S| = 1$, $|\mathfrak{P}(S)| = 2 = 2^{|S|}$, and $|\mathfrak{P}(\mathfrak{P}(S))| = 4 = 2^{|\mathfrak{P}(S)|}$.

8.5.7 Cartesian Product

You learned about one particular Cartesian product $\mathbb{R} \times \mathbb{R}$ back in high school when you drew graphs of functions. $\mathbb{R} \times \mathbb{R} = \{(x,y)|x,y \in \mathbb{R}\}$ and it is usually visualized as a plane.

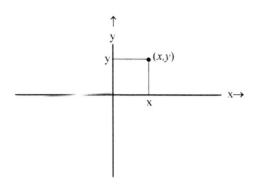

Points correspond to order pairs (x, y). Unlike sets, order matters when we write an ordered pair. The ordered pairs $(1, 2)$ and $(2, 1)$ are not equal whereas the sets $\{1, 2\}$ and $\{2, 1\}$ are equal. The Cartesian product is named after Rene Descartes.

We can define the *Cartesian product* of any two sets, A and B, in a similar way.

$$A \times B = \{(x, y) | x \in A \text{ and } y \in B\}$$

Let $A = \{1, 2, 3\}$ and $B = \{a, b\}$, then $A \times B = \{(1, a), (1, b), (2, a), (2, b), (3, a), (3, b)\}$. We can visualize $A \times B$ similarly to the way we visualized $\mathbb{R} \times \mathbb{R}$.

$$
\begin{array}{c|ccc|l}
b & \cdot & \cdot & \cdot & A \times B \\
  & (1,b) & (2,b) & (3,b) & \\
a & \cdot & \cdot & \cdot & \\
  & (1,a) & (2,a) & (3,a) & \\
\hline
  & 1 & 2 & 3 &
\end{array}
$$

In general, the cardinality of $A \times B = |A \times B| = |A| \times |B|$.

We often need the Cartesian product of many sets, e.g. $A \times B \times C$. The elements of the Cartesian product $A \times B \times C$ are similar to ordered pairs but they have three components instead of two, e.g. (a, b, c). As with ordered pairs, the order matters. We call such an ordered triple a *3-tuple*. An *n-tuple* has n components.

Example 8.5
Tuples

   $(7, 5, 0, -3, 11, 4)$ is a 6-tuple of integers.

   (Fell, Felleisen, Aslam) is a 3-tuple of professors.

   (Aslam, Felleisen, Fell) is a different 3-tuple of professors.

Example 8.6

Cartesian Products

$\mathbb{R} \times \mathbb{R} \times \mathbb{R} = \{(x, y, z) | x, y, z \in \mathbb{R}\}$ is usually used to represent 3-dimensional space

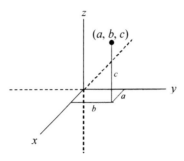

If $A = \{1, 2\}$, $B = \{a, b\}$, and $C = \{X, Y\}$ then

$$A \times B \times C = \{(1, a, X), (1, a, Y), (1, b, X), (1, b, Y), (2, a, X), (2, a, Y), (2, b, X), (2, b, Y)\}$$

In general, the cardinality $|A_1 \times A_2 \times \cdots \times A_n| = |A_1| \times |A_2| \times \cdots \times |A_n|$.

8.6   Computer Representation of Sets

Just like numbers, sets can be represented on a computer by 0^s and 1^s. First, we order the elements of the universe. We use bit strings with length equal to the cardinality of the universe U to represent the subsets of U. Each position in the bit string corresponds to an element of U. A one in some position means the corresponding element is in the set while a zero means the element is not in the set.

Example 8.7

Let $U = \{0, 1, 2, 3, 4, 5, 6, 7, 8, 9\}$. Here are some subsets of U.

$U = \{0, 1, 2, 3, 4, 5, 6, 7, 8, 9\}$ 1111111111

        All elements are in U.

$S = \{1, 2, 5, 6, 7, 9\}$ 0110011101

$\overline{S} = \{0, 3, 4, 8\}$ 1001100010

        This is the bit-wise complement of the bit string for S.

$A = \{2, 5, 6, 7, 9\}$ 0010011101

$B = \{1, 4, 6, 8, 9\}$ 0100101011

$A \cap B$ 0000001001

        This is the bit-wise **and** of the bit strings for A and B.

$A \cup B$ 0110111111

        This is the bit-wise **or** of the bit strings for A and B.

Further Thoughts

Think about the set R of all sets that are not members of themselves.

     See Wikipedia on Russell's Paradox

8.7 Summary

In this chapter, we introduced *sets* as a way of formally describing the collections of things we might want to count. We met the *universal set U*, and the *empty set ∅*. Along with basic notation for sets, we have seen ways of combining sets using the set operations *union $A \cup B$*, *intersection $A \cap B$*, *complement $\overline{A}$*, *difference $A - B$*, and the *symmetric difference $A \triangle B$*. The **inclusion-exclusion principle** tells us how to compute the cardinality of $A \cup B$ when A and B are finite sets.

Power sets let us talk about all the subsets of a set and *Cartesian products* describe sets of *ordered pairs* or *n-tuples* of set elements.

We ended this chapter with a brief discussion of how sets can be represented on a computer.

Exercises

Set Builder Notation

Exercise 8.1
Show or describe the elements in each set.

  a. $A = \{n \in \mathbb{Z} \mid 1 \le |2 \times n| \le 6\}$

  b. $B = \{n \in \mathbb{N} \mid 1 \le |2 \times n| \le 6\}$

  c. $C = \{n \in \mathbb{Z} \mid n \le 4\}$

  d. $D = \{n \in \mathbb{Z} \mid n^2 \le 4\}$

  e. $E = \{n^2 \in \mathbb{Z} \mid |n| \le 4\}$

  f. $F = \{n \in \mathbb{R} \mid n \le 4\}$

  g. $G = \{n \in \mathbb{R} \mid n^2 \le 4\}$

  h. $H = \{n^2 \in \mathbb{R} \mid n \le 4\}$

Venn Diagrams

Exercise 8.2
Create a Venn diagram for each of the sets below.

  a. $A \cup B \cup C$

  b. $A \cap B \cap C$

  c. $A \cap (\overline{B} \cup C)$

  d. $(\overline{A} \cup B) \cap C$

Set Operations

Exercise 8.3
Let $A = \{2, 3, 4, 7, 9\}$, $B = \{0, 6, 7\}$, $C = \{0, 4, 9\}$ and $U = \{0, 1, 2, 3, 4, 5, 6, 7, 8, 9\}$. Evaluate the following.

a. $A \cup B$	b. $A \cap B$	c. $A - B$	d. $B - A$	e. $A \triangle B$
f. $C \cup B$	g. $C \cap B$	h. $C - B$	i. $B - C$	j. $C \triangle B$
k. $A \cup C$	l. $A \cap C$	m. $A - C$	n. $C - A$	o. $A \triangle C$

Exercise 8.4

Let $A = \{0,1,2,3,4\}$, $B = \{5,6,7,8,9\}$, $C = \{3,4,5,6\}$ and $U = \{0,1,2,3,4,5,6,7,8,9\}$.
Evaluate the following.

    a. $A \cup B$ **b.** $A \cap B$ **c.** $A - B$ **d.** $B - A$ **e.** $A \triangle B$

    f. $C \cup B$ **g.** $C \cap B$ **h.** $C - B$ **i.** $B - C$ **j.** $C \triangle B$

    k. $A \cup C$ **l.** $A \cap C$ **m.** $A - C$ **n.** $C - A$ **o.** $A \triangle C$

Exercise 8.5

Let $A = \{0,1,2\}$, $B = \{3,4,5,6\}$, $C = \{7,8,9\}$ and $U = \{0,1,2,3,4,5,6,7,8,9\}$. Evaluate the
following.

    a. $A \cup B$ **b.** $A \cap B$ **c.** $A - B$ **d.** $B - A$ **e.** $A \triangle B$

    f. $C \cup B$ **g.** $C \cap B$ **h.** $C - B$ **i.** $B - C$ **j.** $C \triangle B$

    k. $A \cup C$ **l.** $A \cap C$ **m.** $A - C$ **n.** $C - A$ **O.** $A \triangle C$

Power Set

Exercise 8.6

Give the power set for each of these sets.

    a. $\{1\}$ **b.** $\{X\}$ **c.** $\{21\}$ **d.** $\{\alpha\}$

    e. $\{1,2\}$ **f.** $\{X,Y\}$ **g.** $\{21,33\}$ **h.** $\{\alpha,\beta\}$

    i. $\{1,2,3\}$ **j.** $\{X,Y,Z\}$ **k.** $\{21,33,42\}$ **l.** $\{\alpha,\beta,\gamma\}$

    m. $\{1,2,3,4\}$ **n.** $\{W,X,Y,Z\}$ **o.** $\{21,33,42,56\}$ **p.** $\{\alpha,\beta,\gamma,\delta\}$

    q. $\mathfrak{P}(\{1\})$ **r.** $\mathfrak{P}(\{X\})$ **s.** $\mathfrak{P}(\{21\})$ **t.** $\mathfrak{P}(\{\alpha\})$

    u. $\mathfrak{P}(\{1,2\})$ **v.** $\mathfrak{P}(\{X,Y\})$ **w.** $\mathfrak{P}(\{21,33\})$ **x.** $\mathfrak{P}(\{\alpha,\beta\})$

Cartesian Product

Exercise 8.7

Let $A = \{1,2\}$, $B = \{X,Y,Z\}$, and $C = \{\alpha,\beta,\gamma\}$. Show each Cartesian product below.

    a. $A \times B$ **b.** $B \times A$ **c.** $B \times C$ **d.** $C \times B$

    e. $A \times C$ **f.** $C \times A$ **g.** $A \times A$ **h.** $A \times B \times A$

    i. $A \times A \times A$ **j.** $B \times \emptyset$ **k.** $B \times \{\emptyset\}$ **l.** $\{\emptyset,0\} \times B$

Cardinality

Exercise 8.8

Let $A = \{1,2\}$ and $B = \{X,Y,Z\}$. Give the cardinality of each set below.

    a. $A \times B$ **b.** $A \times A \times A$ **c.** $B \times B \times B$ **d.** $A \times \mathfrak{P}(A)$

    e. $\mathfrak{P}(A) \times \mathfrak{P}(A)$ **f.** $\mathfrak{P}(A) \times \mathfrak{P}(B)$ **g.** $\mathfrak{P}(\mathfrak{P}(A))$ **h.** $\mathfrak{P}(\mathfrak{P}(B))$

    i. $\mathfrak{P}(\mathfrak{P}(A \times B))$ **j.** $\mathfrak{P}(\mathfrak{P}(A) \times \mathfrak{P}(B))$ **k.** $\mathfrak{P}(\mathfrak{P}(\emptyset)) \times B$ **l.** $\mathfrak{P}(\mathfrak{P}(A) \times \mathfrak{P}(\mathfrak{P}(B)))$

Computer Representation of Sets

Exercise 8.9

Let the universal set $U = \{0, 1, 2, 3, 4, 5, 6, 7, 8, 9\}$. Let $A = \{1, 3, 5, 7, 8, 9\}$ and $B = \{0, 2, 4, 6, 8, 9\}$. Using the representation of sets shown in Section 8.6, give the representation for each of these sets.

    a. A **b.** B **c.** $A \cup B$ **d.** $A \cap B$

    e. $\overline{A}$ **f.** $\overline{B}$ **g.** $\overline{A} \cup \overline{B}$ **h.** $\overline{A} \cap \overline{B}$

    i. $A \cup \overline{B}$ **j.** $A \cap \overline{B}$ **k.** $B \cup \overline{A}$ **l.** $B \cap \overline{B}$

Counting

Combinatorics is the branch of mathematics largely concerned with *counting* discrete objects, and counting plays a central role in many aspects of computer science. We often use computers to solve problems that involve *counting* possible solutions, *enumerating* those solutions, or finding the *optimal* solution among a candidate set. The algorithms for finding such solutions, and the analysis of these algorithms, all depend on counting.

As a simple example, consider the problem of planning a party. Suppose that you have 20 friends, and you wish to invite eight of them over for dinner. You also want to discuss possible invitation lists with your best friend. How many possible invitation lists are there? The answer is a surprisingly large number: 125,970.

Once you have selected the eight invitees, you may want to arrange them at the dinner table in a particular order—some pairs of your guests may have much more fun sitting next to each other than others. To model this problem, you might start by assigning each pair of partygoers a *conviviality index*, e.g., a number in the range 1 to 10 indicating how much fun this pair would have sitting next to each other at dinner. How many such conviviality indices must be computed? You might naively construct a 9×9 table, where each row is labeled with one of the nine partygoers (eight guests plus yourself) and each column is similarly labeled with one of the partygoers; the (i, j) entry would then contain the conviviality index for the corresponding pair of partygoers. However, this table containing 81 entries is clearly excessive: each conviviality index appears twice, once as (i, j) and once as (j, i), and the (i, i) indices are not needed (we trust that everyone gets along with themselves!). How many conviviality indices are actually needed? The answer is significantly smaller: 36.

Finally, given any arrangement of partygoers around a table, you could compute the total conviviality by simply adding the conviviality indices for each pair of partygoers sitting next to each other; your goal would be to find such an arrangement that maximizes the total conviviality. One naive approach would be to simply enumerate all possible arrangements, compute the total conviviality for each arrangement, and output the arrangement with maximum total conviviality. How many such arrangements must be considered? The number of arrangements is surprisingly large: 20,160.

The example above illustrates how counting can and does play a role in solving problems and/or analyzing the efficiency of such solutions. Creating invitation lists and computing conviviality indices are related to the counting paradigm of *combinations* which we shall explore in Section 9.5. Arranging partygoers around a table is related to the counting paradigm of *permutations* which we shall explore in Section 9.4. We begin by discussing some basic rules from which one can derive formulae for counting combinations, permutations, and other discrete objects.

9.1   Basic Rules

In order to count or enumerate a collection of discrete objects, one can consider the *choices* that need to be made in order to *generate* the objects in the collection, and then count the number of objects that can be generated based on those choices and a few basic rules. We illustrate two basic rules through an example below.

Alice and Bob often eat lunch together at a local deli. Alice eats a big breakfast every day, so she has a light lunch; she always orders either a soup or a sandwich, never both. Bob skips breakfast every day, so he has a big lunch; he always orders both a soup and a sandwich. On an average day, the deli might offer six different soups and twelve different sandwiches.

How many different meals can Alice order?

How many different meals can Bob order?

Though the questions look similar and the underlying numbers are the same, the answers are quite different. Bob must choose one soup and one sandwich. He has 6 ways to choose a soup and 12 ways to choose a sandwich. Since any soup can be paired with any sandwich, there are $6 \cdot 12 = 72$ total different meals that he can order. Alice must choose either one of six soups or one of 12 sandwiches for a total of $6 + 12 = 18$ different meals.

The two different counting rules that we used can be generalized. Bob's meal choice problem generalizes to the **Product Rule**, and Alice's meal choice problem generalizes to the **Sum Rule**.

The Product Rule   *If A and B are finite sets then the number of ways of choosing an element from A and then an element from B is $|A \times B| = |A| \times |B|$.*

Note that A and B do not have to be disjoint. If $c \in A$ and $c \in B$, we might choose c to represent A and then choose c to represent B,

This corresponds to Bob's meal choice: he must choose a soup *and* a sandwich, and since there are six soups and 12 sandwiches, he can choose from among $6 \times 12 = 72$ possible meals. If in addition Bob were to choose a drink and there were eight possible drinks, Bob would then have $6 \times 12 \times 8 = 576$ possible meal choices. The product rule can clearly be extended to this more general case. If Bob is at a counter in the food court where he must choose one of 3 meat options and two of 5 vegetable options that could be the same (e.g. double French fries), then he has $3 \times 5 \times 5 = 75$ choices for his meal.

The General Product Rule   *If $A_1, A_2, \ldots, A_n$ are finite sets, then the number of ways of choosing an element from A_1, an element from A_2, $\ldots$, and an element from A_n is $|A_1 \times A_2 \times \cdots \times A_n| = |A_1| \times |A_2| \times \cdots \times |A_n|$.*

The product rule is applicable when one must make two (or more) consecutive choices from sets of alternatives; for example, Bob must first choose a soup and then choose a sandwich. Conversely, the sum rule is applicable when one must make *one* choice from the union of two (or more) sets of alternatives; for example, Alice must choose a meal from the union of the set of soups and sandwiches.

The Sum Rule   *If A and B are **disjoint** finite sets then the number of ways of choosing a single element from A or B is $|A \cup B| = |A| + |B|$.*

Like the product rule, the sum rule can be generalized to more than two sets of alternatives in an obvious way.

The General Sum Rule   *If $A_1, A_2, \ldots, A_n$ are **mutually disjoint** finite sets then the number of ways of choosing a single element from A_1, A_2, $\ldots$, or A_n is $|A_1 \cup A_2 \cup \cdots \cup A_n| = |A_1| + |A_2| + \cdots + |A_n|$.*

Example 9.1

Personal Identification Numbers or PINs are entered on a numeric keypad and, hence made up entirely of digits.

The PINs on our office locks are required to be exactly 4 digits. How many different PINs are possible?

The set of digits, $D = 0, 1, 2, 3, 4, 5, 6, 7, 8, 9$ has cardinality 10. Each PIN corresponds to an element of $D \times D \times D \times D$. There are $10^4 = 10,000$ different PINs.

How many different 7 digit PINs are there?

$10^7 = 10,000,000.$

How many different PINs with 4 to 7 digits are there?

A single PIN has either 4 or 5 or 6 or 7 digits. We use the product rule to separately count the sets of 4-digit, 5-digit, 6-digit, and 7-digit passwords then use the sum rule to count the union of these sets. The number of PINs with 4 to 7 digits is $10^4 + 10^5 + 10^6 + 10^7 = 11,110,000.$

Example 9.2

Passwords are often composed of alpha-numeric characters, $a, b, ..., z, 0, 1, 2, ..., 9$ on systems that are not case-sensitive or $A, B, ..., Z, a, b, ..., z, 0, 1, 2, ..., 9$ on systems that are case-sensitive.

How many 4-character alpha-numeric passwords are there if you can use uppercase and lowercase letters and digits (i.e. case-sensitive)?

There are 26 uppercase letters, 26 lowercase letters, and 10 digits for a character set C of size 62. The total number of possible passwords is $|C \times C \times C \times C| = (62)^4 = 14,776,336.$

If a hacker has code that can try out passwords on a system at a rate of 1 per second, how long would it take her to break into a system that

a) uses 4-digit passwords?

10,000 seconds = 2 hours 46 minutes 40 seconds.

b) uses 4-character case-sensitive, alpha-numeric passwords?

14,776,336 seconds = 171 days 32 minutes 16 seconds

Example 9.3

Bit strings are strings composed of 0s and 1s.

How many bit strings are there with 8 bits?

$2^8 = 256.$

How many bit strings are there with 16 bits?

$2^{16} = 65,536.$

What is the largest integer that can be represented in 16-bit two's complement?

Since positive integers in two's complement must have a 0 in the leftmost position, we have only 15 places to represent the magnitude of the integer. The largest integer we can represent is 0111 1111 1111 1111 $= 2^{15} - 1 = 32767.$

Example 9.4

Picking Students Suppose that there are three sections of a discrete structures class containing 73, 64, and 41 students, respectively.

a) How many distinct ways are there of choosing one discrete structures student to write up a sheet of notes for everyone to use at the final?

The sum rule applies, yielding $73 + 64 + 41 = 178$ possibilities.

b) How many distinct ways are there of choosing one discrete structures student from each class to form an advisory committee?

The product rule applies, yielding $73 \cdot 64 \cdot 41 = 191,552.$

c) How many distinct ways are there of listing six different discrete structures students from a 41 person section to go to the board one after the other to present problem solutions?

Consider the choices that must be made in generating such a section. There are 41 students to choose from as the first presenter, but then there are only 40 students to choose from as the second presenter, 39 as the third presenter and so on. Note that *multiple* choices must be made (so the product rule applies) and the size of the sets of alternatives (from which these choices must be made) shrinks with each successive choice.The result is

$$41 \cdot 40 \cdot 39 \cdot 38 \cdot 37 \cdot 36 = 3,237,399,360.$$

This is an example of *permutations*, which we discuss in more detail in Section 9.4.

d) How many distinct ways are there of choosing six discrete structures students to form the course volleyball team?

Now we have to choose a set of six students out of the 178 discrete structures students. If we count the ways to make a list of 6 students, as in c, we get

$$178 \cdot 177 \cdot 176 \cdot 175 \cdot 174 \cdot 173 \text{ possible ordered lists of 6 students.}$$

Each set of 6 students appears in this list $6! = 6 \cdot 5 \cdot 4 \cdot 3 \cdot 2 \cdot 1$ times so the number of sets is of six students out of the 178 is

$$\frac{178 \cdot 177 \cdot 176 \cdot 175 \cdot 174 \cdot 173}{6 \cdot 5 \cdot 4 \cdot 3 \cdot 2 \cdot 1} = \frac{178!}{172! \cdot 6!}$$

This is an example of *combinations*, which is discussed in more detail in Section 9.5.

Example 9.5

More Passwords Suppose passwords are restricted to 6 case-sensitive alpha-numeric characters and must contain at least 1 digit and at least 1 letter. How many are there?

There are $(62)^6$ passwords composed of 6 case-sensitive alpha-numeric characters with no other restrictions. Of these, $(52)^6$ are composed of letters only and $(10)^6$ are composed of digits only. All the others have at least one digit and at least one letter. So the answer is $[(62)^6 - (52)^6 - (10)^6]$.

Suppose passwords may have 6 to 10 case-sensitive alpha-numeric characters and must contain at least 1 digit and at least 1 letter. How many are there?

Since a password may have 6 or 7 or 8 or 9 or 10 letters, we can count each of these possibilities separately and apply the sum rule to get the result.

$$[(62)^6-(52)^6-(10)^6]+[(62)^7-(52)^7-(10)^7]+[(62)^8-(52)^8-(10)^8]+[(62)^9-(52)^9-(10)^9]+[(62)^{10}-(52)^{10}-(10)^{10}]$$

9.2 Inclusion-exclusion Principle

In our description of the sum rule above, we assumed that the sets of alternatives from which one must make a single choice were *mutually disjoint*, i.e., that they did not share any common elements. In our lunch example with Alice and Bob, the sets of soups, sandwiches, and drinks are clearly mutually disjoint. However, one often encounters situations when a single choice must be made from sets of alternatives that are *not* disjoint. For example, suppose that Alice and Bob's deli has both a lunch menu and a dinner menu, and that one is allowed to order off either menu at lunchtime. Furthermore, suppose that some sandwiches that are available for lunch are also available for dinner. In how many ways can Bob pick his sandwich? In

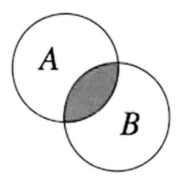

Figure 9.1: $|A|+|B|$ counts the elements in A and the elements in B, but the elements of $A \cap B$ (the red/shaded ones) are counted twice. The proper total count is $|A \cup B| = |A|+|B|-|A \cap B|$ as dictated by the inclusion-exclusion principle.

mathematical terms, let S_l denote the set of lunch sandwiches, and let S_d denote the set of dinner sandwiches. Applying the sum rule, the total number of sandwich choices is $|S_l \cup S_d|$ which is $|S_l|+|S_d|$ *if the sets S_l and S_d are disjoint.* If S_l and S_d are *not* disjoint, then $|S_l|+|S_d|$ will double-count those sandwiches that are in both S_l and S_d, i.e., available for both lunch and dinner. To avoid this double counting, we must *subtract* a quantity that corresponds to the number of sandwiches that are double-counted; this is precisely $|S_l \cap S_d|$. This is the essence of the inclusion-exclusion principle, as defined below and shown graphically in Figure 9.1.

Inclusion-exclusion Principle   *If A and B are finite sets then $|A \cup B| = |A|+|B|-|A \cap B|$.*

Example 9.6
How many strings of 6 uppercase letters start with A or end with Z?

> 26^5 start with A. 26^5 end with Z. 26^4 start with A and end with Z and they were counted twice. The answer is $26^5 + 26^5 - 26^4$.

Example 9.7
How many positive integers less than 100 are divisible by 2 or 5 or 7?

> It is clear that 50 of these integers are divisible by 2 and 20 are divisible by 5. $7 \times 14 = 98$ so 14 of these integers are divisible by 7.

To count up the integers in this range divisible by 2 or 5 or 7, we first add $50+20+14 = 84$.

We have doubly counted the integers divisible by both 2 and 5 (i.e. by 10) and there are 10 of those. Similarly, we doubly counted the integers divisible by both 2 and 7 (i.e. by 14) and there are 7 of those and the integers divisible by both 5 and 7 (i.e. by 35); there are 2 of those. So it look like our count is $50+20+14-10-5-2 = 84-17 = 67$.

But we have to make one more correction. There is one positive integer less than 100 divisible by 2 and 5 and 7, the integer 70. We first counted that three times as divisible by 2, and by 5, and by 7. Then we removed it from our count three times since it is divisible by 10, and 14, and 35. We must add 1 to our count to cover this triple intersection. There are 68 integers between 1 and 100 divisible by 2 or 5 or 7.

This is an example of the inclusion-exclusion principle for three sets, as stated below and shown graphically in Figure 9.2.

Inclusion-exclusion Principle - for three sets   *If A, B, and C are finite sets then $|A \cup B \cup C| = |A| + |B| + |C| - |A \cap B| - |A \cap C| - |B \cap C| + |A \cap B \cap C|$.*

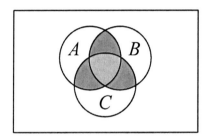

Figure 9.2: $|A| + |B| + |C|$ counts the elements in A, the elements in B, and the elements in C but the elements of $A \cap B$ are counted twice as are the elements of $A \cap C$ and $B \cap C$. The elements of $A \cap B \cap C$ are counted three times. The proper total count is $|A| + |B| + |C| = |A| + |B| + |C| - |A \cap B| - |A \cap C| - |B \cap C| + |A \cap B \cap C|$ as dictated by the inclusion-exclusion principle.

The inclusion-exclusion principle can be generalized to n finite sets. The cardinality of their union is given by the sum of their cardinalities take away the sum of the cardinalities of their pairwise intersections, plus the sum of the cardinalities of their triple intersection, take away the sum of the cardinalities of their quadruple intersections, ...

9.3   Pigeonhole Principle

Pigeons like to roost between the rafters in the eaves of overhanging roofs. Suppose that there are 10 such locations, and suppose that 11 or more pigeons decide to roost there. Then there must exist a location with two or more roosting pigeons. This is the essence of the pigeonhole principle.

Pigeonhole Principle   *If $k + 1$ or more objects are placed in k boxes, then there must exist a box that contains two or more objects.*

This simple and seemingly obvious principle shows up quite often in counting problems, primarily to show that some property of a collection of objects must exist. For example, if 13 or more people gather in a room, then it is *guaranteed* that at least two of them share the same birth month. While this *may* happen in a gathering of 12 or fewer people, it is not guaranteed.

Example 9.8

Suppose that there are 102 students in two sections of discrete structures. If they all take the final, will at least two of them get the same grade?

> There are 101 possible grades $0, 1, \ldots, 100$ so the result follows from the pigeonhole principle.

Example 9.9

If I use the last two digits of their social security numbers as a code to post grades in anonymity, will at least two students get the same code?

> There are 100 2-digit codes, 00 through 99 so by the time I list the first 101 students there will be two with the same code.

Example 9.10

If a drawer contains 12 red socks and 12 blue socks and I pull some socks out in the dark,
a) how many must I pull out to be sure of having a pair?

> 3 because there are only 2 colors.

b) how many must I pull out to be sure of having a pair of red socks?

> 14 because I might pull out all the blue ones and just 2 red ones.

c) how many must I pull out to be sure of having at least one of each color?

> 13 because I might pull out all 12 of one color and just one of the other color.

Example 9.11

Every integer n has a multiple that has only 0s and 1s in its decimal expansion.

> **Proof**
>
> Consider the $n + 1$ numbers $1, 11, \ldots, 11111\ldots11$ where the last number has $(n + 1)$ ones. If we evaluate each of these numbers $\bmod n$, two of them must give the same value as there are only n possible results, $0, \ldots, n - 1$. So take the two numbers that result in the same value and subtract the smaller from the larger. The result is a

multiple of n and has only 0s and 1s in its decimal expansion. Here's an example.
Take $n = 6$.

$1 \bmod 6 = 1$

$11 \bmod 6 = 5$

$111 \bmod 6 = 3$

$1111 \bmod 6 = 1$

so $1111 - 1 = 1110$ is a multiple of 6.

Example 9.12

In any set of $n + 1$ positive integers not exceeding $2n$, there must be one integer that divides another.

> Write each of the $n + 1$ integers as a power of 2 times an odd integer, $a_j = 2^{e_j} q_j$.
> Then $q_1 \ldots q_{n+1}$ are $n+1$ odd integers less than $2n$. Two of them must be the same.
> One of the corresponding a_j's divides the other.

9.3.1   Generalized Pigeonhole Principle

The pigeonhole principle can be generalized in an obvious way: Suppose that 21 or more pigeons attempt to roost in 10 locations; then there must exist a location that contains three or more pigeons. This is a special case of a more general result. Suppose that $\{x_1, x_2, \ldots, x_n\}$ is a collection of n numbers, and let $\bar{x}$ be the *average* of these numbers, i.e.,

$$\bar{x} = \frac{x_1 + x_2 + \cdots + x_n}{n}.$$

Then it clearly cannot be the case that *every* number is less than the average; in other words, there must exist at least one number that is at least as large as the average. Returning to our pigeonhole example, suppose that 21 pigeons attempt to roost in 10 locations. The *average* number of pigeons per location is $21/10 = 2.1$, and by our argument above, it cannot be the case that *every* location contains fewer than the average number of pigeons. Thus, at least one location must contain at least 2.1 pigeons. Since pigeons are discrete objects (we can't have $1/10$ of a pigeon!), there must exist a location with $\lceil 2.1 \rceil = 3$ pigeons. This is the essence of the generalized pigeonhole principle.

Generalized Pigeonhole Principle   *If N objects are placed in k boxes, then there must exist a box that contains $\lceil N/k \rceil$ or more objects.*

Example 9.13

Suppose that there are 51 students in a discrete structures class. How many students are guaranteed to have birthdays in the same month? (In particular, what is the *largest* number of students that are guaranteed to have the same birth month?)

$\left\lceil \frac{51}{12} \right\rceil = 5$ students are guaranteed to have birthdays in the same month.

9.4   Permutations

A *permutation* is an ordered arrangement of a set (or subset) of objects. Suppose, for example, that one had to run four errands, a trip each to (1) the grocery store, (2) the dry cleaners, (3) the hardware store, and (4) the post office. One would have to decide in which order these errands would be performed. Any such ordering of these errands is a permutation. Each permutation may have an associated cost (e.g., the total driving distance if the errands are processed in a specific order), and one often wants to minimize this cost. A brute force approach would be to list all possible permutations, determine each associated cost, and pick the permutation with the least cost. How many such permutations are there? One could choose any of the four errands to start with, then any of the three remaining errands second, then either of the two remaining errands third, and finally the last remaining errand fourth. Note that these choices are made consecutively, so the Product Rule applies: There are four possibilities for the first choice, three for the second, two for the third, and one choice for the last, for a total of $4 \cdot 3 \cdot 2 \cdot 1 = 4! = 24$ total possibilities (permutations). If there were n errands to run (or n objects to order), the number of possible permutations is $n!$.

Counting Permutations   *The number of permutations of n distinct elements is*

$$n! = n \cdot (n-1) \cdot (n-2) \cdots 1.$$

Now suppose that one only had time to run two of the four errands. How many ordered arrangements of two of the four errands are there? Applying our analysis from above, there are four choices for the first errand and three remaining choices for the second, yielding $4 \cdot 3 = 12$ possible arrangements. More generally, an ordered arrangement of r objects from a collection is referred to as an *r-permutation* and denoted by $P(n, r)$; calculators often use the notation nPr. Applying the above analysis to the general case yields the number of such arrangements.

Counting r-permutations *The number of r-permutations of n distinct elements is*

$$P(n,r) = \overbrace{n \cdot (n-1) \cdot (n-2) \cdots (n-r+1)}^{r\text{ terms}} = \frac{n!}{(n-r)!}.$$

Note that r-permutations are a generalization of permutations; indeed, and n-permutation is an ordered arrangement of all n out of n objects, and the number of such n-permutations is $P(n,n) = n!/0! = n!$.

Example 9.14

A wedding party consists of the bride, the groom, the bride's mother and father, the groom's mother and father, the best man, the maid of honor, two ushers, and two bridemaids.

a. How many ways are there of arranging all of them in a row for a picture?

There are 12 people in the wedding party so there are $P(12,12) = 12!$ ways of arranging them in a row.

b. How many ways if the bride and groom stand together on the left side of the line?

There are 2 ways to arrange the bride and groom on the far left side of the line and $P(10,10) = 10!$ ways of arranging the rest of the party so $2 \cdot 10!$ possible arrangements.

c. How many ways if the bride and groom are together but anywhere in the line?

There are $P(10,10) = 10!$ ways of arranging the rest of the party without the bride and groom. Then the bride and groom together can be placed between any two of the other people in the line or to the left or to the right of all of them. That's 11 different positions. There are 2 ways to arrange the bride and groom. The total number of arrangements is $10! \cdot 11 \cdot 2$.

d. How many ways can 5 members of the wedding party line up for a picture?

We must line up 5 people out of 12 so $P(12,5) = 12 \cdot 11 \cdot 10 \cdot 9 \cdot 8$.

Example 9.15

On the trip I am about to take, I must visit Florence, Milan, Venice, London, Bristol, and Warwick.

a. How many different itineraries are possible?

There are 6 cities so $6!$ possible itineraries.

b. How many itineraries are possible if all the British cities are consecutive and all the Italian cities are consecutive?

Florence, Milan, and Venice are in Italy. London, Bristol, and Warwick are in England. There are 3! orders for the Italian cities and 3! orders for the British cities. I can go to Italy first or to England first so there are $3! \cdot 3! \cdot 2 = 72$ possible itineraries.

Example 9.16

a. How many permutations are there of the letters A B C D E F G H I J?

$P(10, 10) = 10!$.

b. How many of them contain the block

i. HEAD

First arrange the other letters, B, C, F, G, I, J. There are 6! arrangements. Then place the block HEAD between two of the arranged letters or at one of the ends. There are 7 places it can go. That makes a total of $7 \cdot 6!$ strings. You can also think of this as gluing the H,E,A,D together to form one block and then counting all the arrangements of the 7 blocks, HEAD, B, C, F, G, I, J to get 7!.

ii. HJF

This is just like part i but you must arrange the other 7 letters and then there are 8 places where HJF can go.

iii. BIGFACEDHJ

Just one.

9.5 Combinations

An r-permutation is an *ordered arrangement* or r out of n elements, while an r-combination is an *unordered subset* of r out of n elements. Consider our "errands" examples from the previous section. If one had to choose two out of four possible errands, there are $P(4, 2) = 4 \cdot 3 = 12$ such ordered arrangements (r-permutations). Note that such permutations distinguish between identical subsets of errands if they appear in a different order; e.g., (grocery store, post office) is different from (post office, grocery store) since the errands are processed in a different order. If order did not matter, then these two "arrangements" would be identical and denoted with set notation {grocery store, post office}. Such a subset is a 2-combination. More generally, an unordered subset of r elements out of n is an r-combination, and the number of such combinations is denoted $C(n,r) = \binom{n}{r}$. Calculators often use the notation nCr analogous to nPr for r-permutations. Finally, $\binom{n}{r}$ is often referred to as a *binomial coefficient* for reasons that will be explained in Section 9.6.

Counting r-combinations   *The number of r-combinations of n distinct elements is*

$$C(n,r) = \binom{n}{r} = \frac{n!}{r! \cdot (n-r)!}.$$

Proof: $P(n,r) = C(n,r) \cdot P(r,r)$. That is, to create an ordered list of r elements from a set of n elements, first choose r elements from the set (there are $C(n,r)$ ways to do this) and then choose an ordering of the r elements (there are $P(r,r)$ ways to do this). Since we already know that $P(n,r) = n!/(n-r)!$ and $P(r,r) = r!$, the result follows. $\square$

Note that choosing r out of n elements to be included in a subset is equivalent to choosing the $n - r$ elements that should be *left out* of the subset. Therefore, every r-combination has a unique associated $(n-r)$-combination, and thus the number of r-combinations is equivalent to the number of $(n-r)$-combinations. Mathematically, we have

$$C(n,r) = \binom{n}{r} = \frac{n!}{r! \cdot (n-r)!} = \frac{n!}{(n-r)! \cdot r!} = \binom{n}{n-r} = C(n, n-r).$$

Example 9.17
Eight members of the wedding party (described above) are to do a traditional circle dance. How many different groups of eight can be selected?

There are 12 people in the wedding party so we can choose $C(12,8)$ different subsets of 8 people. $C(12,8) = \frac{12!}{(8!)(4!)} = \frac{12 \cdot 11 \cdot 10 \cdot 9}{4 \cdot 3 \cdot 2 \cdot 1} = 11 \cdot 5 \cdot 9 \cdot = 495.$

Example 9.18
Now that we have selected 8 people for the dance, how many ways can we arrange them in a circle?

This is a permutation problem, not a combination problem. It is similar, but not quite the same as finding the number of ways we can arrange 8 people in a line. There are $P(8,8) = 8!$ ways to do that. Each circular arrangement will appear 8 times as a linear arrangement. (A B C D E F G H forms the same circular arrangement as B C D E F G H A or C D E F G H A B ...) So there are $8!/8 = 7!$ possible circle dance arrangements.

Example 9.19

How many ways can I select 3 men and 3 women from the wedding party?

There are 6 men and 6 women in the wedding party. The number of ways of choosing 3 men (or 3 women) is $C(6,3) = 20$. The number of ways of selecting 3 men and 3 women from the wedding party is $20 \cdot 20 = 400$.

Example 9.20

How many ways can I select 6 students from this class of 51 students to get a grade of "A"?

$$C(51,6) = \frac{51!}{(45!)(6!)} = \frac{51 \cdot 50 \cdot 49 \cdot 48 \cdot 47 \cdot 46}{6 \cdot 5 \cdot 4 \cdot 3 \cdot 2 \cdot 1 \cdot} = 17 \cdot 10 \cdot 49 \cdot 2 \cdot 47 \cdot 46 = 36018920.$$

Really, we won't do it this way—we'll look at your grades.

9.6   Binomial Theorem

One important application of combinations is the Binomial Theorem which allows one to expand expressions of the form $(x + y)^n$ for any nonnegative integer n.

Binomial Theorem   *Let x and y be variables, and let n be a nonnegative integer. Then*

$$
\begin{aligned}
(x+y)^n &= \sum_{j=0}^{n} \binom{n}{j} x^{n-j} y^j \\
&= \binom{n}{0} x^n + \binom{n}{1} x^{n-1}y + \binom{n}{2} x^{n-2}y^2 + \cdots + \binom{n}{n-1} xy^{n-1} + \binom{n}{n} y^n
\end{aligned}
$$

Proof: Consider the product

$$(x+y)^n = \underbrace{(x+y) \cdot (x+y) \cdots (x+y)}_{n \text{ copies}}.$$

To expand this product, one could repeatedly apply the distributive law

$$(a+b) \cdot c = ac + bc.$$

Applying the distributive law to $(x+y)^n = (x+y) \cdot (x+y)^{n-1}$, one could choose first to expand via x in the first factor, obtaining the sub-expression $x \cdot (x+y)^{n-1}$, or one could expand via y, obtaining $y \cdot (x+y)^{n-1}$. Similarly for the remaining factors, one could choose to expand via x or y. The full expansion is the sum of all the expressions one obtains from making all such possible choices.

Suppose that one chooses to expand via y a total of j times, thus expanding via x the remaining $n-j$ times. What expression results? We have j y-factors and $n-j$ x-factors, thus obtaining the expression $x^{n-j}y^j$. How many such expressions can one obtain? There are n total $(x+y)$ factors, and one must choose j of them to expand via y (and thus $n-j$ to expand via x). This is a direct application of combinations—there are precisely $\binom{n}{j}$ ways of choosing j out of n factors to expand via y. Thus, the term $x^{n-j}y^j$ will appear $\binom{n}{j}$ times. The complete expansion is thus the sum of all $\binom{n}{j} x^{n-j}y^j$ terms for all possible j. $\qquad\square$

Note that the combination $\binom{n}{j}$ appears as the *coefficient* associated with each term of the form $x^{n-j}y^j$. For this reason, combinations $\binom{n}{j}$ are often referred to as *binomial coefficients*.

Example 9.21
Expand $(x+y)^4$.

$$
\begin{aligned}
(x+y)^4 &= \sum_{j=0}^{4} \binom{4}{j} x^{4-j}y^j \\
&= \binom{4}{0} x^4 + \binom{4}{1} x^3 y + \binom{4}{2} x^2 y^2 + \binom{4}{3} xy^3 + \binom{4}{4} y^4 \\
&= x^4 + 4x^3 y + 6x^2 y^2 + 4xy^3 + y^4
\end{aligned}
$$

Example 9.22
Expand $(2x + y^{-2})^3$.

$$
\begin{aligned}
(2x + y^{-2})^3 &= \sum_{j=0}^{3} \binom{3}{j} (2x)^{3-j}(y^{-2})^j \\
&= \binom{3}{0} (2x)^3 + \binom{3}{1} (2x)^2(y^{-2}) + \binom{3}{2} (2x)(y^{-2})^2 + \binom{3}{3} (y^{-2})^3 \\
&= (2x)^3 + 3(2x)^2(y^{-2}) + 3(2x)(y^{-2})^2 + (y^{-2})^3 \\
&= 8x^3 + 12x^2 y^{-2} + 6xy^{-4} + y^{-6}
\end{aligned}
$$

Example 9.23

Give the term in $(a + b)^{42}$ that contains the factor b^{17}.

$$\binom{42}{17} a^{25} b^{17}$$

9.6.1   Pascal's Triangle

Pascal's triangle is a geometric arrangement of the binomial coefficients in a triangle. It is named after Blaise Pascal, even though the ancient Chinese studied it centuries before him. The binomial coefficients $\binom{n}{0}, \binom{n}{1}, \ldots, \binom{n}{n-1}, \binom{n}{n}$ form the n-th row of Pascal's triangle. The rows are staggered so that each number inside the triangle lies diagonally below two other numbers.

Pascal's triangle arises as a consequence of the following fact concerning binomial coefficients.

Theorem   *If n is a positive integer and k is an integer such that $0 \leq k \leq n$, then*

$$\binom{n+1}{k} = \binom{n}{k} + \binom{n}{k-1}.$$

Proof: An intuitive proof proceeds as follows: To choose k out of $n+1$ objects, consider whether the first object is chosen or not. If the first object is *not* chosen, then the k objects must all be chosen out of the remaining n objects; there are $\binom{n}{k}$ such possibilities. If the first object *is* chosen, then an additional $k-1$ objects much be chosen from the remaining n objects; there are $\binom{n}{k-1}$ such possibilities. Thus, the total number of ways of choosing k objects from $n+1$ objects is $\binom{n}{k} + \binom{n}{k-1}$.

One can also prove this theorem by directly manipulating the binomial coefficients in their expanded factorial form.

$$
\begin{aligned}
\binom{n}{k} + \binom{n}{k-1} &= \frac{n!}{(n-k)! \cdot k!} + \frac{n!}{(n-(k-1))! \cdot (k-1)!} \\
&= \frac{(n-(k-1)) \cdot n!}{(n-(k-1)) \cdot (n-k)! \cdot k!} + \frac{k \cdot (n!)}{k \cdot (n-(k-1))! \cdot (k-1)!} \\
&= \frac{(n-(k-1)+k) \cdot n!}{(n-(k-1)) \cdot (n-(k-1))!} \\
&= \frac{(n+1) \cdot n!}{(n+1-k)! \cdot k!} \\
&= \frac{(n+1)!}{(n+1-k)! \cdot k!} \\
&= \binom{n+1}{k}
\end{aligned}
$$

$\square$

This theorem effectively says that one can compute an entry in Pascal's triangle by adding the two elements diagonally above it; see Figure 9.3.

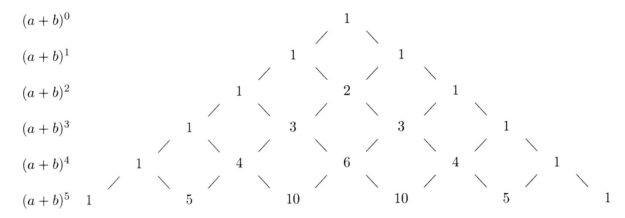

Figure 9.3: Rows 0 through 5 of Pascal's Triangle

9.7   Balls-in-Bins

Suppose that there are 60 students in a discrete math class, and we recorded each student's birthday. Surprisingly, a result in probability theory known as the Birthday Paradox states that there is a greater than 99% chance that at least two people will share the same birthday. Now suppose that we were to write down a tally of all 60 birthdays by date, for example

Date	Jan 1	Jan 2	Jan 3	$\cdots$	Dec 31
Count	1	0	2	$\cdots$	1

How many such tallies are there? Each tally corresponds to a unique sequence of 365 numbers whose sum is 60, such as the sequence $(1, 0, 2, \ldots, 1)$ above. This is a specific instance of what is generally known as a "balls-in-bins" problem: Imagine throwing 60 balls into 365 bins; how many ways can the 60 balls be placed in these 365 bins, where the only quantities of interest are the numbers of balls in each bin? In our example, we wish to calculate the number of ways of assigning 60 students to 365 possible birthdays, where birthday repetitions are allowed.

In order to count the number of such arrangements of balls-in-bins, we shall consider an alternate but equivalent representation of any such arrangement. Imagine that the bins are all adjacent, and that there is a divider between adjacent bins. Let "|" represent the dividers, and let "•" represent balls. Any arrangement of balls-in-bins can be encoded by a sequence consisting of one • for each ball in the first bin, followed by a divider |, followed by one • for each ball in the second bin, and so on. In our example arrangement above, the encoding would be

$$\bullet \mid \mid \bullet \bullet \mid \cdots \mid \bullet$$

Note the two adjacent dividers that represent the empty "bin" corresponding to Jan 2. Any such sequence will contain exactly 424 symbols: 60 • symbols corresponding to the balls and 364 | symbols corresponding to the bin dividers.[1] How many such sequences are there? We have 424 total symbols, and we must choose which 60 will be • symbols (and thus which 364 will be | symbols). This is a direct application of combinations, and thus the answer is $\binom{424}{60} = \binom{424}{364} \approx 6.57 \times 10^{73}$, an astronomically large number.[2] In the general case, we have the following result.

Balls-in-Bins *The number of arrangements of n balls placed in m bins is*

$$\binom{n + m - 1}{n} = \binom{n + m - 1}{m - 1}.$$

Balls-in-bins problems arise in many areas of computer science, including data structures (analysis of hashing), networking (analysis of congestion), and so on.

Note: You can also think of the balls as zeros and the dividers as ones. When you are trying to find the number of ways of placing n balls in m bins, think of each possibility as a binary

---

[1]There is always one less divider than the number of bins; for example, two bins require only one separating divider.

[2]It is estimated that there are 10^{58} atoms in our solar system and 10^{80} atoms in the entire observable universe.

number with n 0s (the balls) and $m-1$ 1s (the dividers). So you are just counting the number of $n+m-1$ bit binary numbers with exactly $m-1$ 1s or exactly n 0s.

9.8 Summary

This chapter introduced many techniques for counting the number of objects in a **finite** collection.

Product Rule The ways of choosing an element from A and then one from $B = |A| \times |B|$.

Sum Rule The ways of choosing a single element from disjoint sets A and $B = |A| + |B|$.

Inclusion-exclusion Principle $|A \cup B| = |A| + |B| - |A \cap B|$.

Pigeonhole Principle If $k+1$ or more objects are placed in k boxes, at least one box has two or more objects.

r-Permutations The ways of arranging r of n distinct elements is given by

$$P(n,r) = \overbrace{n \cdot (n-1) \cdot (n-2) \cdots (n-r+1)}^{r \text{ terms}} = \frac{n!}{(n-r)!}$$

.

r-Combinations The ways of choosing r of n distinct elements is $C(n,r) = \binom{n}{r} = \frac{n!}{r! \cdot (n-r)!}$.

Balls-in-Bins The number of arrangements of n balls placed in m bins is $\binom{n+m-1}{n} = \binom{n+m-1}{m-1}$.

The **Binomial Theorem** shows us how to expand $(x+y)^n$ as a sum of terms, $\binom{n}{0} x^n + \binom{n}{1} x^{n-1}y + \binom{n}{2} x^{n-2}y^2 + \cdots + \binom{n}{n-1} xy^{n-1} + \binom{n}{n} y^n$ and **Pascal's Triangle** relates the (binomial) coefficients of the terms, $\binom{n+1}{k} = \binom{n}{k} + \binom{n}{k-1}$.

Exercises

Simple Counting

Exercise 9.1
If you roll a pair of six sided dice, one red and one black, there are 36 possible rolls, e.g. the red die comes up 3 and the black die comes up 5. For each of the following, tell how many of these rolls satisfy the condition.

a. The total is 2.

b. The total is 4.

c. The total is 7.

d. The total is 10.

e. The total is between 5 and 8. (5 and 8 included)

f. The total is between 2 and 12. (2 and 12 included)

g. The red die is 3.

h. The red die is 3 and the black die is 6.

i. The sum is less than 5.

j. The red die is less than the black die.

k. The two dice are equal.

l. The two dice are different.

Exercise 9.2

Some games use octahedral dice. They have 8 sides numbered from 1 to 8. How many possible outcomes are there if you roll a pair of octahedral dice?

Answer each of the questions in Exercise 9.1, assuming the dice are 8-sided instead of 6-sided.

Exercise 9.3

If you draw a card from a standard deck of 52 cards, how many different ways are there to do each of the following?

a. Draw a card.

b. Draw a jack.

c. Draw a heart.

d. Draw a face card.

e. Draw the ace of spades.

f. Draw the 2 of diamonds.

g. Draw a card that is not a face card or an ace.

h. Draw a joker.

i. Draw a black card.

j. Draw a 10 or an 8.

Sum and Product Rules

Exercise 9.4

a. For Mother's Day, Eloise's daughter always sends her a balloon or flower arrangement from lastminutegifts.com. They offer 10 different balloon arrangements and 45 different flower arrangements. How many different gifts can she choose from?

b. Eloise always sends her mother a balloon arrangement and a flower arrangement, both from ftd.com. How many ways can Eloise select her gift?

Exercise 9.5

In History 101: The Olden Days, students are given a list of 7 historical novels and a list of 15 essay topics.

a. In the regular sections, students must turn in a book report on one of the novels or a five-page essay on one of the listed topics. How many ways can a student complete the assignment?

b. In the honors sections, students must turn in a book report and an essay. How many ways can an honors student complete the assignment?

Exercise 9.6

a. In the cafeteria at the National Computer Science Research Institute (INRIA) in Rocquencourt, France, a lunch ticket entitles you to one hors d'œuvre, one entrée, one salad, one cheese, and one dessert. If there are 7 choices of hors d'œuvre, 3 choices of entrée, 2 choices of salad, 11 choices of cheese and 5 choices of dessert, how many different 5-course meals can one choose for lunch?

b. In the cafeteria at NotEastern U., a meal ticket lets you choose one item from 3 different sushi boxes, 5 different sandwiches (wrapped in plastic), 2 soups, or a box of carrots with cheese dip. How many different lunches can one get at this cafeteria?

Exercise 9.7

NSF (National Science Foundation) Fast-Lane Passwords have 6 to 10 alpha-numeric characters where uppercase and lowercase are distinguished. They must contain at least 2 digits and at least 2 letters. How many are there?

Exercise 9.8

Regular Massachusetts license plates have either three digits followed by three letters, e.g. 924 XVA, or four digits followed by two letters, e.g. 2007 CS. How many possible license plates are there?

Exercise 9.9

Members of the Secret Superwoman Society each have a password composed of **different** letters from the word "SUPERWOMAN."

    a. How many different 10-letter passwords can they form?

    b. How many different 5-letter passwords can they form?

    c. How many 5-letter passwords can they form if the middle letter must be a vowel?

    d. How many 5-letter passwords can they form if the first letter must be "W"?

    e. How many 5-letter passwords can they form if the first letter must be "W" and the middle letter must be a vowel?

Inclusion-exclusion Principle

Exercise 9.10

Still referring to the Secret Superwoman Society as in Exercise 9.9, how many 5-letter passwords can they form if the first letter must be "W" or the middle letter must be a vowel?

Exercise 9.11

At State University, many students are majoring in two or more subjects. In all, there are 320 computer science majors, 145 math majors, and 580 business majors. There are 35 students majoring in both computer science and math, 20 students majoring in business and math, 90 students majoring in business and computer science, and 10 students majoring in all three subjects.

    a. How many students are majoring in computer science or math?

    b. How many students are majoring in computer science or business?

    c. How many students are majoring in business or math?

    d. How many students are majoring in computer science, business, or math?

Pigeonhole Principle

Exercise 9.12

The Geek Dormitory has 75 rooms numbered 0 to 74. Each student is assigned a room whose number is the student's ID number modulo 75.

    a. How many students must there be to insure that at least 2 students will be sharing some room?

    b. How many students must there be to insure that at least 3 students will be sharing some room?

    c. If 150 students are assigned to Geek Dormitory, can we be sure that there will not be three or more students assigned to the same room?

    d. If 150 students are assigned to Geek Dormitory, what is the largest number of students that might end up assigned to one room?

Exercise 9.13

The New Village Cinema shows 6 different movies in 6 300-seat theaters. Exactly 1111 people come to the theater on Saturday night.

    a. "I know that at least N people will view the same movie." What is the largest value N can have for that statement to necessarily be true?

    b. If one of the theaters s closed for renovation, what is the largest value N can have for the statement to necessarily be true?

Exercise 9.14

A salesman regularly takes trips through the same 11 cities. On any given trip, he may stay overnight in a city more than once and he need not stay in every city.

    a. How many nights must he be out to require that he stays in some city at least twice?

b. How many nights must he be out for it to be possible that he stays in some city at least twice?

c. How many nights must he be out to require that he stays in some city at least three times?

d. How many nights must he be out for it to be possible that he stays in some city at least three times?

e. If he takes a trip that has 30 nights out, what the largest number of nights that he knows he must stay in the same city?

Permutations

Exercise 9.15

Evaluate

a. $P(5,2)$	**b.** $P(5,3)$	**c.** $P(5,4)$
d. $P(6,2)$	**e.** $P(6,3)$	**f.** $P(6,4)$
g. $P(10,2)$	**h.** $P(10,3)$	**i.** $P(11,3)$
j. $P(1234,0)$	**k.** $P(1234,1)$	**l.** $P(10000,2)$

Exercise 9.16

A salesman regularly takes trips through the same 6 cities.

a. If he visits each city exactly once on a trip, how many different itineraries could he have?

b. If he always visits Springfield first and the other five in any order, how many different itineraries could he have?

c. If he always visits Springfield first, Worcester last, and the other four in any order, how many different itineraries could he have?

Exercise 9.17

a. How many ways can you arrange all the letters of the word JUPITER?

b. How many 5-letter strings of distinct letters can you make from the letters in JUPITER?

c. How many 3-letter strings of distinct letters can you make from the letters in JUPITER?

d. (optional) How many of the 3-letter strings of distinct letters from the letters in JUPITER are legitimate Scrabble™ words?

Exercise 9.18

A mountain bike, a tennis racket, a baseball mitt, and a math book are the prizes offered in a school lottery. If 130 students each bought one raffle ticket, how many different ways might the prizes be distributed?

Combinations

Exercise 9.19

Evaluate

a. $C(5,2)$	**b.** $C(5,3)$	**c.** $C(5,4)$
d. $C(6,2)$	**e.** $C(6,3)$	**f.** $C(6,4)$
g. $C(10,2)$	**h.** $C(10,3)$	**i.** $C(11,3)$
j. $C(1234,0)$	**k.** $C(1234,1)$	**l.** $C(10000,2)$

Exercise 9.20

Acme Vacuum Cleaner Company sells its wares in 60 cities. Each salesperson is assigned 6 cities to cover.

a. How many different assignments might Sally get?

b. If Sally decides to work double time, she will have to cover 12 cities. How many different assignments might she get?

Exercise 9.21

A poker hand consists of 5 cards drawn from a deck of 52 cards (no Jokers).

a. How many different poker hands are there?

b. How many poker hands include the Ace of Spades?

c. How many poker hands include four Aces?

d. How many poker hands include only face cards (Jack, King Queen) or Aces?

e. How many poker hands include no face cards (Jack, King Queen) or Aces?

Exercise 9.22

Four $25 prizes are offered in a school lottery. If 130 students each bought one raffle ticket, how many different ways might the prizes be distributed?

Binomial Theorem

Exercise 9.23

Expand each of the following.

a. $(x+y)^3$ **b.** $(x+y)^5$ **c.** $(x+y)^6$

d. $(2x+y)^3$ **e.** $(x+3y)^4$ **f.** $(\frac{1}{x}+3y)^4$

g. $(x-y)^5$ **h.** $(1+n)^6$ **i.** $(x^2+y^{-2})^5$

Exercise 9.24

Use the Binomial Theorem to show the following.

a.

$$1 \cdot \binom{n}{0} + 2 \cdot \binom{n}{1} + 4 \cdot \binom{n}{2} + 8 \cdot \binom{n}{3} + \cdots + 2^n \cdot \binom{n}{n} = 3^n.$$

b.

$$\binom{10}{0} - \binom{10}{1} + \binom{10}{2} - \binom{10}{3} + \cdots - \binom{10}{7} + \binom{10}{8} - \binom{10}{9} + \binom{10}{10} = 0.$$

Pascal's Triangle

Exercise 9.25

Below is the 16th row of Pascal's triangle. Use it to compute the 15th and 17th rows of Pascal's triangle.

1 16 120 560 1820 4368 8008 11440 12870 11440 8008 4368 1820 560 120 16 1

Exercise 9.26

Fill in rows 0 through 9 of Pascal's triangle in an hexagonal grid, as shown below. You can find hexagonal graph paper at (`http://incompetech.com/graphpaper/hexagonal/`). Then add the numbers along the shallow diagonals as shown by the dotted lines in the picture. Do these numbers look familiar?

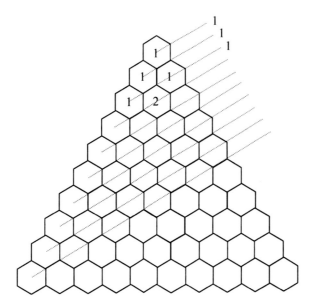

Balls-in-Bins

Exercise 9.27

I have a box with 50 Snickers candy bars. 8 kids come over on Halloween night to trick-or-treat.

a. How many ways can I distribute all 50 Snickers candy bars to the 8 kids?

b. How many ways can I distribute all 50 Snickers candy bars to the 8 kids if every kid gets at least 2 candy bars?

CHAPTER 10

Probability

The mathematical theory of probability is a way of formally representing and reasoning about uncertain events. In 1654, mathematicians Blaise Pascal and Pierre de Fermat corresponded about the odds for gambling outcomes and thus became co-founders of the theory of probability. In 1774, Pierre-Simon Laplace defined the probability of an event as the ratio of the number of favorable outcomes to the total number of possible outcomes. This definition only applies if all outcomes are equally likely; e.g., heads and tails are equally likely outcomes when we toss a fair coin but not equally likely when we toss a biased coin. In this chapter, we will primarily follow Laplace and mostly consider events where all outcomes are equally likely. This is a pretty common occurrence and when it happens, the task of computing probabilities reduces to a task of counting.

10.1 Definitions and Basic Properties

An *experiment or random experiment* yields one of a possible set of outcomes. The sample space is the set of all possible outcomes. We will assume that all outcomes are equally likely. An event is a subset of the sample space, i.e. a set of outcomes.

The probability of an event E that is a subset of a finite sample space S is $\Pr[E] = \frac{|E|}{|S|}$.

Let E_1, E_2, and E_3 be events in sample space S.

$$\Pr[\overline{E}] = 1 - \Pr[E]$$

137

The inclusion-exclusion principle tells us that

$$\Pr[E_1 \cup E_2] = \Pr[E_1] + \Pr[E_2] - \Pr[E_1 \cap E_2]$$

10.2   Examples

10.2.1   Dice

The study of probability did, after all, start with gambling.

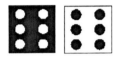

Experiment: Roll a pair of fair dice once.

i) What is the size of the sample space?

> There are 6 possibilities for the black die and 6 for the white one. By the product rule, there are a total of $6 \cdot 6 = 36$ possible tosses.

What is the probability of each of these events?

ii) The total is 6.

> There are exactly 5 ways that the two dice that result in a sum of 6.

Black	1	2	3	4	5
White	5	4	3	2	1

So the probability of the sum being 6 is 5/36.

iii) The total is 9.

> There are exactly 4 ways that the two dice that result in a sum of 9.

Black	3	4	5	6
White	6	5	4	3

So the probability of the sum being 9 is $4/36 = 1/9$.

iv) The total is greater than 8.

> There are exactly 4 ways that the two dice result in a sum of 9,

Black	3	4	5	6
White	6	5	4	3

exactly 3 ways that the two dice result in a sum of 10,

Black	4	5	6
White	6	5	4

exactly 2 ways that the two dice result in a sum of 11,

Black	5	6
White	6	5

exactly 1 way that the two dice result in a sum of 12,

Black	6
White	6

So the probability of a sum greater than 8 is $(4 + 3 + 2 + 1)/36 = 10/36 = 5/18$.

v) The total is 7 or 11.

There are exactly 2 ways that the two dice result in a sum of 11

Black	5	6
White	6	5

and 6 ways that the sum can be 7.

Black	1	2	3	4	5	6
White	6	5	4	3	2	1

So the probability a 7 or 11 is $(2 + 6)/36 = 8/36 = 2/9$.

vi) Both dice have the same number.

There are 6 ways that the numbers can be the same.

Black	1	2	3	4	5	6
White	1	2	3	4	5	6

So the probability that the numbers are the same is $6/36 = 1/6$.

vii) The numbers are 4 and 3.

There are exactly 2 ways this can happen so the probability is $2/36 = 1/18$.

Black	3	4
White	3	4

viii) Snake-eyes.

There is only one way this can happen so the probability is $1/36$.

Black	1
White	1

10.2.2 Cards

- still gambling

Experiment: Draw a single card from a normal 52 card deck.

i)What is the size of the sample space?

Each card is a possible event. The size of the sample space is 52.

What is the probability of each of these events?

ii) The card is a face card.

There are 12 face cards (4 jacks, 4 queens, 4 kings) so the probability of a face card is $12/52 = 3/13$.

iii) The card is black.

Half the cards are black so the probability of drawing a black card is $1/2$.

iv) The card is a heart.

There are 13 hearts so the probability is $13/52 = 1/4$.

v) The card is a queen.

There are 4 queens so the probability is $4/52 = 1/13$.

vi) The card is a number (2 through 10).

There are $4 \cdot 9 = 36$ number cards so the probability is $36/52 = 9/13$.

vii) The card is the ace of spades.

There is one ace of spades so the probability is $1/52$.

viii) The card is a joker.

The probability is 0. There are no jokers in a standard deck of 52 cards

10.2.3   Urns

Experiment: An urn contains 15 red balls and 10 blue balls. A single ball is drawn.

i) What is the size of the sample space?

There are 25 balls so the size of the sample space is 25. You might want to think of the red balls as numbered from 1 to 15 and the black ones as numbered from 1 to 10.

What is the probability of each of these events?

ii) The ball drawn is red.

There are 15 red balls so the probability is $15/25 = 3/5$.

iii) The ball drawn is blue.

There are 10 blue balls so the probability is $10/25 = 2/5$. Notice that $3/5 + 2/5 = 1$; drawing a red ball and drawing a blue ball are complementary events.

Experiment: An urn contains 15 red balls and 10 blue balls. Three balls are drawn at once.

i) What is the size of the sample space?

The number of possible draws is

$$C(25, 3) = \frac{25 \cdot 24 \cdot 23}{3 \cdot 2 \cdot 1} = 2300.$$

What is the probability of each of these events?

ii) All three balls are red.

There are $C(15, 3) = \frac{15 \cdot 14 \cdot 13}{3 \cdot 2 \cdot 1} = 455$ ways of choosing 3 red balls so the probability is $455/2300 = 91/460$.

iii) Two balls are red and one is blue.

There are $C(15, 2) = \frac{15 \cdot 14}{2 \cdot 1} = 105$ ways of choosing 2 red balls and 10 ways of choosing 1 blue ball so there are $105 \cdot 10 = 1050$ ways of choosing 2 red balls and one blue one. The probability is $1050/2300 = 21/46$.

Experiment: An urn contains 15 red balls and 10 blue balls. Three balls are drawn sequentially and each is returned to the urn before the next ball is drawn.

i) What is the size of the sample space?

There are 25 choices for each of the balls so there are $25^3 = 15625$ possible sequences of three balls (with replacement).

What is the probability of each of these events?

ii) All three balls are red.

There are $15^3 = 3375$ sequences of three red balls (with replacement) so the probability is $\frac{15^3}{25^3} = \frac{3^3}{5^3} = \frac{27}{125}$

iii) Two balls are red and one is blue.

There are 3 positions for the blue ball.

There are 10 balls that can go in this position.

There are $15^2 = 225$ sequences of two red balls for the remaining places.

In all, there are $3 \cdot 10 \cdot 15^2 = 6750$ outcomes with two red balls and one blue ball.

The probability of this event is $\frac{3 \cdot 10 \cdot 15^2}{25^3} = \frac{3 \cdot 2 \cdot 9}{5^3} = \frac{36}{125}$.

10.2.4   Bytes

Experiment: Toss a fair coin 8 times, 1 for heads, 0 for tails to generate a byte.

i) What is the size of the sample space?

There are $2^8 = 256$ bytes.

What is the probability of each of these events?

ii) The byte has exactly four ones.

Each byte with exactly four ones corresponds to a subset of size 4 of the 8 positions in the byte. There are $C(8,4) = \frac{8 \cdot 7 \cdot 6 \cdot 5}{4 \cdot 3 \cdot 2 \cdot 1} = 70$ such subsets. Therefore, the probability of generating a byte with exactly four 1s is $70/256 = 35/128$.

iii) The byte starts and ends with a 1.

The first and last positions in the byte are fixed but the other six places can be anything. The number of such bytes is $2^6 = 64$ and the probability is $\frac{2^6}{2^8} = \frac{1}{4}$.

iv) The byte starts and ends with the same bit.

There are twice as many bytes in the event than in part iii. The probability is $\frac{1}{2}$.

v) The byte contains the substring 111111.

Those strings with exactly 6 ones: $11111100, 01111110, 00111111$
Those strings with exactly 7 ones: $11111110, 11111101, 01111111, 10111111$
and one string with exactly 8 ones: 11111111.
The probability that the byte contains the substring 111111 is $8/256 = 1/64$.

vi) The byte does not contain 2 consecutive ones.

Think of making up the string from the 2-bit blocks, 00, 10, 01 with the constraint that 01 can only be followed by 00 or 01.

1		2		3		4		count
00, 10	$\longrightarrow$	00, 10	$\longrightarrow$	00, 10	$\longrightarrow$	00, 10, 01	$\longleftrightarrow$	$2 \cdot 2 \cdot 2 \cdot 3 = 24$
	$\searrow$		$\searrow$					
				01	$\longrightarrow$	00, 01	$\longleftrightarrow$	$2 \cdot 2 \cdot 1 \cdot 2 = 8$
		01	$\longrightarrow$	00	$\longrightarrow$	00, 10, 01	$\longleftrightarrow$	$2 \cdot 1 \cdot 1 \cdot 3 = 6$
					$\searrow$			
				01	$\longrightarrow$	00, 01	$\longleftrightarrow$	$2 \cdot 1 \cdot 1 \cdot 2 = 4$
01	$\longrightarrow$	00	$\longrightarrow$	00, 10	$\longrightarrow$	00, 10, 01	$\longleftrightarrow$	$1 \cdot 1 \cdot 2 \cdot 3 = 6$
	$\searrow$		$\searrow$					
				01	$\longrightarrow$	00, 01	$\longleftrightarrow$	$1 \cdot 1 \cdot 1 \cdot 2 = 2$
		01	$\longrightarrow$	00	$\longrightarrow$	00, 10, 01	$\longleftrightarrow$	$1 \cdot 1 \cdot 1 \cdot 3 = 3$
					$\searrow$			
				01	$\longrightarrow$	00, 01	$\longleftrightarrow$	$1 \cdot 1 \cdot 1 \cdot 2 = 2$
								total $= 55$

The probability $= 55/256$.

10.3 Conditional Probability and Bayes Theorem

We start with a puzzle—the famous Monty Hall paradox. Suppose you are a contestant in a game show. The host shows you three closed doors. One door leads to a brand new car, and the other two doors each lead to a lemon. If you are able to find the door leading to the car, you get the car! You are asked to select one of the doors but not open it. You go ahead and select one of the doors. At this point, the host opens one of the other two doors that reveals a lemon and asks: "Do you want to stay with your choice or switch?" What should you do? Does it matter?

A priori, without any other information, each of the three doors is equally likely to be the one leading to the car, so at first glance it seems that it does not matter whether you stay or you switch. It turns out, however, that the action of the game show host gives you additional information, so it does matter! Let us first understand this using basic counting; we will then explain this in the context of conditional probability.

Suppose the three doors are labeled A, B, and C. Without loss of generality, we may assume that you selected A as your first choice. There are 3 equally likely possibilities: the car is behind door A, the car is behind door B, or the car is behind door C. Let us consider each of these in turn.

If the car is behind A, then the host can open any one of the other two doors since both lead to lemons. And in this case, your correct response (in hindsight) is to stay.

If the car is behind B, then the host will open door C. In this case, your correct response is to switch.

Similarly, if the car is behind C, then the host will open door B, and your correct response is to switch.

So in 2 out of the 3 equally likely cases, you should switch. This means you are more likely to win the car if you switch!

10.3.1   Conditional Probability

The *conditional probability of an event E_1 given event E_2* is the probability that event E_1 occurs given that event E_2 occurs. It is denoted by $\Pr[E_1|E_2]$ and can be defined as:

$$\Pr[E_1|E_2] = \frac{\Pr[E_1 \cap E_2]}{\Pr[E_2]}.$$

As an example, consider the roll of two fair dice. A priori, the probability that the roll of the first die yields a 5 is 1/6. But if we are told that the sum of the two dice is 9, then the probability of obtaining a 5 in the first roll, given this new information changes.

$$\Pr[\text{the first roll is a 5} \mid \text{the sum is 9}] = \frac{\Pr[\text{the first roll is a 5 AND the sum is 9}]}{\Pr[\text{the sum is 9}]} = \frac{\frac{1}{36}}{\frac{4}{36}} = \frac{1}{4}.$$

10.3.2   Bayes Theorem

Bayes Theorem relates one conditional probability (e.g., the probability of a hypothesis H given an observation E) with its inverse (the probability of an observation given a hypothesis). Bayes Theorem is used heavily in statistics, analysis of data sets, machine learning, information retrieval, and several diverse applications in science and engineering.

To understand Bayes Theorem, it is crucial to note that $\Pr[H|E]$ is quite different from $\Pr[E|H]$. Bayes Theorem states that

$$\Pr[H|E] = \frac{\Pr[E|H] \cdot \Pr[H]}{\Pr[E]}.$$

The theorem directly follows from the definition of conditional probability.

$$\Pr[H|E] = \frac{\Pr[H \cap E]}{\Pr[E]} = \frac{\Pr[E|H] \cdot \Pr[H]}{\Pr[E]}.$$

The above equation can also be easily seen using Venn diagrams.

10.3.3   Explaining Monty Hall paradox using Bayes Theorem

Let us understand the Monty Hall paradox using Bayes Theorem. When the host asks you whether you would like to switch, the calculation you should do is to determine the probability that you will win the prize given the information provided to you.

As before, suppose without loss of generality that the door you select is labeled A. Also, let us label the door that the host opens as B. Now, consider the following calculations.

$$
\Pr[\text{prize behind A} \mid \text{host opens B}] = \frac{\Pr[\text{host opens B} \mid \text{prize behind A}]\Pr[\text{prize behind A}]}{\Pr[\text{host opens B}]}
$$

$$
= \frac{\frac{1}{2} \cdot \frac{1}{3}}{\frac{1}{2}}
$$

$$
= \frac{1}{3}.
$$

$$
\Pr[\text{prize behind B} \mid \text{host opens B}] = \frac{\Pr[\text{host opens B} \mid \text{prize behind B}]\Pr[\text{prize behind B}]}{\Pr[\text{host opens B}]}
$$

$$
= 0.
$$

$$
\Pr[\text{prize behind C} \mid \text{host opens B}] = \frac{\Pr[\text{host opens B} \mid \text{prize behind C}]\Pr[\text{prize behind C}]}{\Pr[\text{host opens B}]}
$$

$$
= \frac{1 \cdot \frac{1}{3}}{\frac{1}{2}}
$$

$$
= \frac{2}{3}.
$$

Thus, you would be better off switching from door A to door C, i.e., from the door you have selected to the other unopened door.

10.3.4   Another Application of Bayes Theorem

Here is an example that illustrates the use of Bayes Theorem in biostatistics. Suppose the a priori probability of you being infected with the H1N1 virus is 10^{-5}. Further suppose that a blood test is 99% accurate and you test positive. How likely is it that you actually have the virus? Let us do the calculations.

$$\Pr[\text{virus}] = 0.00001$$

$$\Pr[\text{no virus}] = 0.99999$$

$$\Pr[\text{positive test} \mid \text{virus}] = 0.99$$

$$\Pr[\text{positive test} \mid \text{no virus}] = 0.01$$

$$\Pr[\text{virus} \mid \text{positive test}] = \frac{\Pr[\text{positive test} \mid \text{virus}] \cdot \Pr[\text{virus}]}{\Pr[\text{positive test}]}$$

$$= \frac{0.99 \cdot 0.00001}{\Pr[\text{positive test}]}$$

$$= \frac{0.0000099}{\Pr[\text{positive test}]}$$

$$\Pr[\text{no virus} \mid \text{positive test}] = \frac{\Pr[\text{positive test} \mid \text{no virus}] \cdot \Pr[\text{no virus}]}{\Pr[\text{positive test}]}$$

$$= \frac{0.01 \cdot 0.99999}{\Pr[\text{positive test}]}$$

$$= \frac{0.0099999}{\Pr[\text{positive test}]}$$

Thus, even after testing positive, you are *1000 times more likely* not to have the virus than have it.

10.4   Markov Chains

Markov chains are often used to model probabilistic systems when the chance of a future event is only dependent on the present and not dependent on the past. Consider the following example. When Prof. Aslam's children were young and the family would go out to dinner, the children often got to choose the restaurant at which they would eat. They had three favorite restaurants: Bertucci's (Italian), Margaritas (Mexican), and Sato (Chinese/Japanese). Over the course of their childhood, Prof. Aslam noticed that his children were much more likely to pick a restaurant that they have eaten at recently than to choose a different restaurant; however, they would eventually tire of eating at the same restaurant repeatedly, and then they would choose a different one. Prof. Aslam also noted that had clear favorites among these restaurants, and this was reflected in how likely they would return to a given restaurant that they had just visited and what restaurants they were likely to visit next if they choose to switch.

This information can be encoded in a Markov chain as follows: There is one *state* for each restaurant and *transition arcs* from state to state, labeled with the probabilities that one will transition from one restaurant to another at any given time. Note that "self transitions" are allowed, corresponding to the chance that one will stay at a given restaurant. Based upon Prof. Aslam's observation of how his children picked the restaurants they wanted to visit, the following Markov chain roughly describes their restaurant choice behavior, where B, M, and S represent Bertucci's, Margaritas, and Sato, respectively:

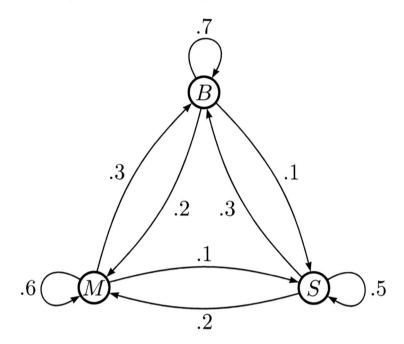

This Markov chain operates as follows. When in some state, say B, the Markov chain will transition to a state in the next round according to the transition arcs outgoing from B. Given the Markov chain above, when in state B, the chance that one will revisit B is 0.7, the chance that one will move to state M is 0.2, and the chance that one will move to state S is 0.1. Note that the probabilities associated with transition arcs are *conditional probabilities*; for example, the arc from B to M is labeled 0.2, and this corresponds to the fact that if one is in state B in round n, then one will be in state M in round $n + 1$ with probability 0.2. If we let X_k be the state of the Markov chain in round k, we then have

$$\Pr[X_{n+1} = M \mid X_n = B] = 0.2.$$

We further note that the sum of the (conditional) probabilities associated with all transition arcs outgoing from a state must be 1.

A useful representation of all the state-to-state Markov chain transition probabilities is a *transition matrix*, typically denoted P, where each entry p_{ij} denotes the conditional probability of transitioning from State i to State j. Assuming that we order the rows and columns of P

alphabetically (Bertucci's first, Margaritas second, Sato third), we have the following transition matrix for our example Markov chain:

$$P = \begin{pmatrix} .7 & .2 & .1 \\ .3 & .6 & .1 \\ .3 & .2 & .5 \end{pmatrix}$$

Note that the sum of each row must be 1, corresponding to the fact that the sum of the (conditional) probabilities associated with all transition arcs outgoing from a state must be 1. Any matrix whose rows sum to 1 and whose elements are values in the range $[0, 1]$ (and thus can be interpreted as probabilities) is said to be *stochastic*. Every stochastic matrix corresponds to a Markov chain and can be interpreted as such.

One can simulate a Markov chain by starting in some state and transitioning from state to state in subsequent rounds according to the transition arcs (and their probabilities) associated with each state. Here is one such simulation lasting 50 rounds and starting at Bertucci's.

BBMMMMMMBBBMBMMBBBBBBBBBBSMSSSSBBBBBMMMMSSSSBBMBBBB

Note that in this sequence of 50 restaurant visits, Bertucci's is visited 26 times, Margaritas is visited 15 times, and Sato is visited 9 times. Thus, the empirical fraction of time that each restaurant is visited is as follows: $B = 0.52$, $M = 0.30$, and $S = 0.18$. Here is another simulation lasting 200 rounds:

BMSMBBBBBBBMMBBMMMMBBBSSBBBSMMBBBBBBBMMMSBBBBBBBBB

MMBBBBMBMBBBBBMMBBBBBBBSBBBBBBBBMMSBBBBBBBBBBBBSSSSBSS

SBMMMSBBMMBSSSSSBBBBBMMMBBMMMSSSSBBSMMMBBBBBBBBBBSMM

MSBBBBBBSSBBMBBMMMMMMMMMMMBBBBBBBBBSSMMMMMSBSBBBBBMM

Here the counts are $B = 108$, $M = 59$, and $S = 33$ corresponding to the empirical fractions $B = 0.540$, $M = 0.295$, and $S = 0.165$.

One natural question that arises in the context of Markov chains is the following: If one were to run a Markov chain for an arbitrarily long amount of time, what fraction of the time would one spend visiting each state? For example, it seems clear from the simulations of the Markov chain given above that one would visit Bertucci's more often than Margaritas, and Margaritas more often than Sato, but can one prove that this is true and determine the exact visit rates?

The set of "long term visit rates" associated with the states of a Markov chain is referred to as the *stationary distribution* of the Markov chain and is typically denoted by a vector $\vec{\pi}$, in our case,

$$\vec{\pi} = \langle \pi_B, \pi_M, \pi_S \rangle$$

where π_B is the long term fraction of time spent visiting Bertucci's, and so on.

How can one solve for these long term visit rates, the stationary distribution of the Markov chain? Consider visits to Bertucci's. Each visit to Bertucci's is preceded by a visit to some restaurant, followed by a transition from that restaurant to Bertucci's. There are three possible restaurants that one could have eaten at preceding the visit to Bertucci's in question: Bertucci's itself, Margaritas, and Sato. The chance that one will eat at Bertucci's (π_B) is the chance that one was at Bertucci's (π_B) and chose to stay there (.7), plus the chance that one was at Margaritas (π_M) and chose to transition to Bertucci's (.3), plus the chance that one was at Sato (π_S) and chose to transition to Bertucci's (.3). Thus, we have the following equation:

$$\pi_B = .7\pi_B + .3\pi_M + .3\pi_S \qquad (10.1)$$

We can similarly derive equations for π_M and π_S:

$$\pi_M = .2\pi_B + .6\pi_M + .2\pi_S \qquad (10.2)$$

$$\pi_S = .1\pi_B + .1\pi_M + .5\pi_S \qquad (10.3)$$

One can compactly express this set of equations using the stationary distribution vector $\vec{\pi}$ and the transition matrix P as follows:

$$\vec{\pi} = \vec{\pi} \cdot P \qquad (10.4)$$

Equations (10.1) through (10.3) are three equations in three unknowns that one could, in principle, solve in the usual way to determine π_B, π_M, and π_S. However, these three equations are not linearly independent: Adding Equation (10.2) to Equation (10.3) yields Equation (10.1). As a consequence, an additional equation is required.[1] Fortunately, we have one additional equation relating π_B, π_M, and π_S: Since $\vec{\pi}$ forms a probability distribution over the possible states, we must have that the sum of π_B, π_M, and π_S is 1.

$$\pi_B + \pi_M + \pi_S = 1 \qquad (10.5)$$

Using two of Equations (10.1) through (10.3) together with Equation 10.5, one can now solve for π_B, π_M, and π_S. For example, rewriting Equations 10.2 and 10.3 to place all variables on

---

[1]The fact that Equations (10.1) through (10.3) are not linearly independent is a consequence of the fact that P is a stochastic matrix, i.e., the rows are constrained to sum to 1. Since this is true for every Markov chain, an additional equation will always be required in order to solve for $\vec{\pi}$.

the left-hand side of the equation, we obtain:

$$.2\pi_B - .4\pi_M + .2\pi_S = 0 \tag{10.6}$$

$$.1\pi_B + .1\pi_M - .5\pi_S = 0 \tag{10.7}$$

Subtracting 5 times Equation 10.6 from Equation 10.5, we obtain that $\pi_M = 1/3$; similarly, subtracting 10 times Equation 10.7 from Equation 10.5, we obtain that $\pi_S = 1/6$. Finally, plugging these values into Equation 10.5, we obtain that $\pi_B = 1/2$ and thus

$$\vec{\pi} = \langle 1/2, 1/3, 1/6 \rangle.$$

Note the similarity of these values to the simulation results we obtained above. If one were to simulate our Markov chain long enough, the average visit rates would converge to the stationary distribution values given in $\vec{\pi}$ above. In the context of our example, over the course of time, Prof. Aslam would expect to spend $1/2$ his time eating at Bertucci's, $1/3$ of his time eating at Margaritas, and $1/6$ of his time eating at Sato.

10.4.1   A Practical Method for Estimating the Stationary Distribution

Not every Markov chain has a stationary distribution, but there are a number of technical conditions (beyond the scope of this book) that guarantee that a Markov chain will have a stationary distribution. When a stationary distribution exists, we have seen one method to solve for that distribution exactly: for an n node Markov chain, create the n equations in n unknowns as described above and solve the system of equations. This works well for small- to moderate-sized Markov chains but can be prohibitively expensive for large Markov chains. For example, solving a system of n equations in n unknowns via standard Gaussian Elimination requires a number of mathematical operations proportional to n^3. For even moderately large n, e.g., a million, n^3 is exceedingly large: one million cubed is a quintillion, $10^{18} = 1,000,000,000,000,000,000$.

We could instead estimate the stationary distribution by simulating the Markov chain, as we showed earlier in this chapter. However, even for our small three-node Markov chain, simulating the Markov chain for 200 rounds yielded estimates of the stationary distribution values that were off by as much as 11.5%. A great number of rounds would be required to get accurate estimates, even for a small Markov chain let alone a very large one.

However, there is another method for estimating the stationary distribution that is quite efficient and accurate, and it is based on Equation 10.4 above which states that the stationary distribution $\vec{\pi}$ must satisfy

$$\vec{\pi} = \vec{\pi} \cdot P.$$

Suppose that we had a guess for $\vec{\pi}$. We could plug it in to the right-hand side of the above equation and check whether it yields our guess, as required. In our example Markov chain above, if we start with the uniform distribution as a guess

$$\vec{\pi}^{(0)} = \langle 1/3, 1/3, 1/3 \rangle$$

and multiply by the transition matrix P, we obtain the result

$$\vec{\pi}^{(1)} = \vec{\pi}^{(0)} \cdot P = \langle 13/30, 1/3, 7/30 \rangle.$$

While this is clearly not correct, since $\langle 13/30, 1/3, 7/30 \rangle$ does not equal our "guess" of $\langle 1/3, 1/3, 1/3 \rangle$, we note that $\langle 13/30, 1/3, 7/30 \rangle$ is *closer* to the correct answer than our original guess: the first value has risen from $1/3$ to $13/30$ (and thus closer to the correct value of $1/2$), the last value has dropped from $1/3$ to $7/30$ (and thus closer to the correct value of $1/6$), while the middle value was and remains correct. In fact, one can show that by repeating this process iteratively, the subsequent estimates will converge to the correct answer, often quite quickly. We can start with the uniform distribution as an initial "estimate" $\vec{\pi}^{(0)}$ and then repeatedly apply the equation

$$\vec{\pi}^{(n)} = \vec{\pi}^{(n-1)} \cdot P \tag{10.8}$$

to obtain subsequent estimates. One can then terminate the procedure once the estimates have converged to the desired accuracy. For example, applying this idea for 10 iterations on our example Markov chain, we obtain:

$$
\begin{aligned}
\vec{\pi}^{(0)} &= \langle 0.3333333333, 0.3333333333, 0.3333333333 \rangle \\
\vec{\pi}^{(1)} &= \langle 0.4333333333, 0.3333333333, 0.2333333333 \rangle \\
\vec{\pi}^{(2)} &= \langle 0.4733333333, 0.3333333333, 0.1933333333 \rangle \\
\vec{\pi}^{(3)} &= \langle 0.4893333333, 0.3333333333, 0.1773333333 \rangle \\
\vec{\pi}^{(4)} &= \langle 0.4957333333, 0.3333333333, 0.1709333333 \rangle \\
\vec{\pi}^{(5)} &= \langle 0.4982933333, 0.3333333333, 0.1683733333 \rangle \\
\vec{\pi}^{(6)} &= \langle 0.4993173333, 0.3333333333, 0.1673493333 \rangle \\
\vec{\pi}^{(7)} &= \langle 0.4997269333, 0.3333333333, 0.1669397333 \rangle \\
\vec{\pi}^{(8)} &= \langle 0.4998907733, 0.3333333333, 0.1667758933 \rangle \\
\vec{\pi}^{(9)} &= \langle 0.4999563093, 0.3333333333, 0.1667103573 \rangle \\
\vec{\pi}^{(10)} &= \langle 0.4999825237, 0.3333333333, 0.1666841429 \rangle
\end{aligned}
$$

Note the rapid convergence of the estimates to their correct values.

10.5   PageRank

In this section, we consider the application of Markov chains to the problem of *web search*. In the early days of information retrieval, search engines typically performed some variant of keyword matching to identify and return relevant documents: documents that contained relatively "large" fractions of the user's search terms were deemed topically "relevant" and returned toward the top of a result list. With the advent of the World Wide Web (WWW), where thousands to millions of web pages may contain the user's search terms, it became increasingly important to determine which of these potentially relevant pages were most "important." To address this problem, Larry Page and Sergey Brin, the founders of Google, developed the *PageRank* algorithm, which we motivate and describe below.

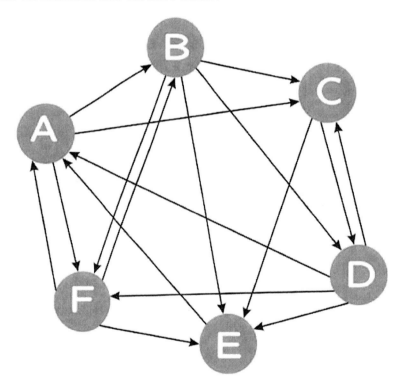

Figure 10.1: Example web graph.

The World Wide Web consists of billions of web pages that point to each other via *hyperlinks*. Consider the example shown in Figure 10.1 which is a graphical representation of six hypothetical web pages and their hyperlink structure. Here we have pages labeled "A" through "F", where page A has hyperlinks to pages B, C, and F; page B has hyperlinks to pages C,

D, E, and F; and so on. How can we determine the "importance" of a web page based on the hyperlink structure of the web? One natural measure is to count *in-links*, i.e., the number of hyperlinks pointing to a page. The reasoning is that the authors of web pages effectively "vote" with their links, creating hyperlinks to pages that they feel are worthy of reference; the more in-links a page has, the more authors have "voted" for that page. However, not all in-links are created equal: for example, an in-link from the *New York Times* would likely carry more weight (and potential web traffic) than an in-link from an obscure and often unread web page. We thus have a recursive definition of importance: the importance of a page is a function of the number and importance of the pages that point to it. How can one calculate such a notion of "importance?" As it turns out, the answer is to calculate the stationary distribution of the Markov chain associated with the web graph.

Consider the following model for measuring the amount of "traffic" that a web page is likely to attract. We will assume a random web surfer who starts at any page, picks an outgoing link at random from that page, follows that link to a new page, and repeats. For example, in the web graph shown in Figure 10.1, the random web surfer might start at page A, choose the outgoing link to page C at random, then choose the outgoing link from C to page E at random, and so on. What is the long-term fraction of web traffic that any page will see from this random web surfer? It is the stationary distribution associated with treating the web graph as a Markov chain, where the transition probabilities correspond to a uniform distribution over all outgoing edges from a page.

We can thus model our notion of "importance" as the stationary distribution of the Markov chain associated with the web graph, and we can use any of the three methods described in the preceding section to calculate that stationary distribution; this is effectively PageRank. Consider page A: If we let $PR(p_i)$ be the PageRank value associated with page p_i, and we equate that value with the stationary distribution of the Markov chain associated with the web graph, then via the arguments that precede Equation 10.1 above we have the following equation for the PageRank value of A.

$$PR(A) = \frac{1}{4} \cdot PR(D) + 1 \cdot PR(E) + \frac{1}{3} \cdot PR(F)$$

Why? To visit page A, one must come from either pages D, E, or F. Thus, the long-term fraction of time a random surfer visits page A is the sum of (1) the long-term fraction of time the surfer visits page D times 1/4, since there is a one-in-four chance that page A will be visited at random from D, plus (2) the long-term fraction of time the surfer visits page E times 1, since page A is the only page that can be visited from E, plus (3) the long-term fraction of time the surfer visits page F times 1/3, since there is a one-in-three chance that page A will be visited at random from F. In general, if we let $M(p_i)$ denote the set of pages that link to page p_i, and if we let $L(p_j)$ denote the number of out-links from page p_j, we have

$$PR(p_i) = \sum_{p_j \in M(p_i)} \frac{PR(p_j)}{L(p_j)}. \tag{10.9}$$

However, note that this is just restating, in PageRank terms, the stationary distribution values of the Markov chain associated with the web graph. Note also that it captures our original notion of "importance": the importance of a page should be a function of the number and importance of the pages that point to it.

The actual PageRank formula is slightly more complicated for two reasons: (1) In the original PageRank formulation, it was assumed that our random web surfer would eventually get bored following links and would eventually start the process over at a new page. This is modeled by a *damping factor d* which is the probability that the random web surfer will, at any time, continue following random links, while with probability $1 - d$, the random web surfer will jump to a new web page entirely, chosen at random from all possible web pages. This is referred to as random surfing with *teleportation*. In most instantiations of PageRank, the damping factor d is set to 0.85. (2) Real-world web graphs can have anomalous structures for which random surfing is ill-defined. Consider page E in our example web graph above. What if the out-link from E to page A did not exist? Then there would be nowhere for the random surfer to go once he or she landed on page E. Such a page is referred to as a *sink*, and the mathematics of PageRank (and the associated Markov chain) break down in the presence of sink pages. To combat this, PageRank assumes that the random surfer *always* teleports to a random page from a sink page; in the associated Markov chain, this is equivalent to assuming that in each sink page there exist virtual out-links to every page in the web graph (including to the page itself). Pulling this all together, we have the following standard formulation of PageRank, where N is the total number of pages in the web graph:

$$PR(p_i) = \frac{1 - d}{N} + d \sum_{p_j \in M(p_i)} \frac{PR(p_j)}{L(p_j)}. \tag{10.10}$$

The interpretation of this formula is as follows: To visit page p_i, (1) there is a $1 - d$ chance that the surfer will choose to teleport and, if so, a $1/N$ chance that the surfer will then teleport to page p_i. (2) There is a d chance that the surfer will choose not to teleport, in which case the basis of Equation 10.9 applies. (Note that we assume, as described above, that all sink pages have virtual out-links to all pages in the web graph.)

Finally, to calculate PageRank at scale, one can apply the iterative procedure described in

Iterative PageRank Algorithm

P is the set of all pages; $|P| = N$
S is the set of sink nodes, i.e., pages that have no out links
$M(p)$ is the set of pages that link to page p
$L(q)$ is the number of out-links from page q
d is the PageRank damping/teleportation factor; $d = 0.85$ is commonly used

foreach page p in P
   $PR(p) = 1/N$ ▷ initial value

while PageRank has not converged do
   sinkPR = 0
   foreach page p in S ▷ calculate total sink PR
     sinkPR = sinkPR + $PR(p)$
   foreach page p in P
     newPR$(p) = (1 - d)/N$ ▷ teleportation
     newPR(p) = newPR$(p) + d \cdot$ sinkPR$/N$ ▷ spread remaining sink PR evenly
     foreach page q in $M(p)$ ▷ pages pointing to p
       newPR(p) = newPR$(p) + d \cdot PR(q)/L(q)$ ▷ add share of PageRank from in-links
   foreach page p
     $PR(p)$ = newPR(p)

return PR

Figure 10.2: An iterative procedure for calculating PageRank.

the preceding section for generating successive approximations to PageRank values until the desired level of convergence is reached. The pseudocode shown in Figure 10.2 accomplishes this, accounting for teleportation and sink pages appropriately.

10.6 Summary

In this chapter we have studied *probability*, the mathematics underlying how one reasons about random events. We have seen how one can leverage counting and basic combinatorics to determine the probability of various events, and we have seen a number of applications of probabilistic reasoning including Bayes Theorem, Markov chains, and PageRank. Another application of probability is in the analysis of computer programs, especially those which are randomized or whose inputs are effectively random. We will begin our study of the analysis of algorithms in the next chapter.

Exercises

Dice

Exercise 10.1

If a pair of fair six-sided dice, one red, one black, are rolled, what is the probability of each of these events?

    a. The total is 4.

    b. The total is 7.

    c. The total is less than 7.

    d. The red die has a higher number than the black die.

    e. The total is even.

Exercise 10.2

If a pair of fair octahedral dice (see Exercise 9.2), one red, one black, are rolled, what is the size of the sample space?

Answer each of the questions in Exercise 10.1, assuming the dice are 8-sided instead of 6-sided.

Exercise 10.3

Assume three fair six-sided dice are rolled.

    a. What is the size of the sample space?

What is the probability of each of these events?

    b. The total is 7.

    c. The total is less than 7.

    d. The total is 15.

    e. The total is even.

Cards

Exercise 10.4

If a single card is drawn from a standard deck of 52 cards, what is the probability of each of these events?

a. The card is a jack.

b. The card is a red face card.

c. The card is an even number.

Exercise 10.5

a. If two cards are dealt from a deck, what is the size of the sample space?

What is the probability of each of the following events?

b. Both cards are face cards.

c. Neither card is a face card.

d. Both cards have the same suit.

e. Both cards are aces.

Exercise 10.6

a. If a poker hand of 5 cards is dealt from a deck, what is the size of the sample space?

What is the probability of each of the following events?

b. The hand contains all 4 aces.

c. The hand is a *royal flush*, ace, king, queen, jack, ten, all in the same suit.

d. The hand is a *full house*, three cards of one rank and two cards of a different rank.

e. The hand is a *pair*, two cards of equal rank and three other cards that do not match these or each other.

Lottery

Exercise 10.7
Ten balls numbered 1 to 10 are in a bag.

a. What is the probability of drawing the ball numbered 8 on a single draw?

b. What is the probability of drawing the ball numbered 8 in three draws if:

  i. The ball drawn is always returned to the bag before the next selection?

  ii. The balls are not returned to the bag before the next selection?

c. What is the probability of drawing the sequence 9, 5, 2 in three draws if:

  i. The ball drawn is always returned to the bag before the next selection?

  ii. The balls are not returned to the bag before the next selection?

d. What is the probability of drawing the numbers 9, 5, 2 in any order in three draws if:

  i. The ball drawn is always returned to the bag before the next selection?

  ii. The balls are not returned to the bag before the next selection?

Part IV

Algorithmic Analysis: Searching and Sorting

CHAPTER 11

Algorithms for Searching and Sorting: Description and Analyses

Searching and sorting are two of the most fundamental and widely encountered problems in computer science. We refer to the tasks of searching and sorting simply as *search* and *sort*. In this chapter, we describe four algorithms to perform search and three algorithms to perform sort.

11.1 Algorithms for Search

Given a collection of objects, the goal of *search* is to find a particular object in this collection or to recognize that the object does not exist in the collection. Often the objects have *key values* on which one searches and *data values* that correspond to the information one wishes to retrieve once an object is found. For example, a telephone book is a collection of *names* (on which one searches) and *telephone numbers* (that correspond to the data being sought). For the purposes of this handout, we shall consider only searching for key values (e.g., names) with the understanding that in reality, one often wants the data associated with these key values.

The collection of objects is often stored in a list or an array. Given a collection of n objects in an array $A[1 \,..\, n]$, the i-th element $A[i]$ corresponds to the key value of the i-th object in the collection. Often, the objects are sorted by key value (e.g., a phone book), but this need not be the case. Different algorithms for search are required depending on whether or not the data is sorted.

The input to a search algorithm is an array of objects A, the number of objects n, and the key value being sought x. In what follows, we describe four algorithms for search.

11.1.1 Unordered Linear Search

Suppose that the given array was not necessarily sorted. This might correspond, for example, to a collection exams that have not yet been sorted alphabetically. If a student wanted to obtain her exam score, how could she do so? She would have to search through the entire collection of exams, one-by-one, until her exam was found. This corresponds to the *unordered linear search* algorithm. Note that in order to determine that an object does not exist in the collection, one needs to search through the *entire* collection.

Now consider the following array:

i	1	2	3	4	5	6	7	8
A	34	16	12	11	54	10	65	37

Consider executing the UNORDERED-LINEAR-SEARCH algorithm on this array while searching for the number 11. The first four elements would need to be examined until the fourth element containing the value 11 is found. In analyzing the performance of search algorithms, we will consider these "examination counts" as a measure of the performance of such algorithms.

Now consider executing the UNORDERED-LINEAR-SEARCH on this array while searching for the number 13. Since 13 does not exist in the array, one must examine all eight of the array elements until one could definitively return "13 not found."

11.1.2 Ordered Linear Search

Now suppose that the given array is sorted. In this case, one need not necessarily search through the entire list to find a particular object or determine that it does not exist in the collection. For example, if the collection of exams were sorted by name, one need not search beyond names starting with "P" to determine that the exam for "Peterson" does or does not exist in the collection. A simple modification of the above algorithm yields the *ordered linear search* algorithm. Note that while scanning the array from left to right (smallest to largest values), a search can now be terminated early if and when it is determined that the number being sought (and as yet not found) is less than the element currently being examined.

Now consider the following array, the sorted version of the array used in our previous example:

i	1	2	3	4	5	6	7	8
A	10	11	12	16	34	37	54	65

Consider executing the ORDERED-LINEAR-SEARCH on this array while searching for the number 11. In this case, the first two elements would need to be examined until the second element containing the value 11 is found.

Now consider executing the ORDERED-LINEAR-SEARCH on this array while searching for the number 13. Note that only the first four elements need be examined until the value 16 is encountered and one can definitively return "13 not found."

11.1.3 Chunk Search

Given an ordered list, one need not (and one typically does not) search through the entire collection one-by-one. Consider searching for a name in a phone book or looking for a particular exam in a sorted pile: one might naturally grab 50 or more pages at a time from the phone book or 10 or more exams at a time from the pile to quickly determine the 50 page (or 10 exam) "chunk" in which the desired data lies. One could then carefully search through this chunk using an ordered linear search. Let c be the chunk size used (e.g., 50 pages or 10 exams). We shall refer to the algorithm encoding the above ideas as *chunk search*.

Again consider the following array:

i	1	2	3	4	5	6	7	8
A	10	11	12	16	34	37	54	65

Consider executing the CHUNK-SEARCH on the above array while searching for the number 34 and using $c = 3$ (i.e., chunks of size 3). To determine if 34 is in the first chunk, the third element (at the end of the first "chunk") with value 12 must be examined. Since $34 > 12$, we next examine the sixth element (at the end of the second "chunk") with value 37. Since $34 < 37$, we conclude that the value 34, if it exists in the array, must be contained in the second chunk. We then simply execute ORDERED-LINEAR-SEARCH on the subarray $A[4 .. 6]$ consisting of the three elements in the second chunk, eventually finding 34 in the fifth position.

Now consider executing CHUNK-SEARCH on the above array while searching for the number 33. CHUNK-SEARCH would behave exactly as described above, except that the call to ORDERED-LINEAR-SEARCH would return "33 not found" when searching the subarray $A[4 .. 6]$.

11.1.4 Binary Search

Now consider the following idea for a search algorithm using our phone book example. Select a page roughly in the middle of the phone book. If the name being sought is on this page, you're done. If the name being sought is occurs alphabetically before this page, repeat the process on the "first half" of the phone book; otherwise, repeat the process on the "second half" of the phone book. Note that in each iteration, the size of the remaining portion of the phone book to be searched is divided in half; the algorithm applying such a strategy is referred to as *binary search*. While this may not seem like the most "natural" algorithm for searching a phone book (or any ordered list), it is provably the fastest. This is true of many algorithms in computer science: the most natural algorithm is not necessarily the best!

Again consider the following array:

i	1	2	3	4	5	6	7	8
A	10	11	12	16	34	37	54	65

Consider executing the BINARY-SEARCH on this array while searching for the number 34. Two determine if 34 is in the first or second half of the array, we split the array in half, considering the fourth element (at the end of the "first half") whose value is 16. Since $34 > 16$, we conclude that the number 34, if it exists in the array, must be contained in the second half, i.e., the subarray $A[5..8]$. We then repeat on the second half of the array, splitting it in half and considering the sixth element whose value is 37. Since $34 < 37$, we continue with the subarray $A[5..6]$, finding the element whose value is 34 in the next iteration.

Now consider executing BINARY-SEARCH on this array while searching for the number 33. BINARY-SEARCH will behave exactly as described above until the last subarray of size 1 containing only the element whose value is 34 is considered. At this point, one can definitively return "33 not found" since there are no subarrays yet to be searched that could possibly contain the number 34.

11.2 Analysis of Algorithms

One of the major goals of computer science is to understand how to solve problems with computers. Developing a solution to some problem typically involves at least four steps: (1) designing an *algorithm* or step-by-step procedure for solving the problem, (2) analyzing the correctness and efficiency of the procedure, (3) implementing the procedure in some programming language, and (4) testing the implementation. One of the goals of CSU200 and CSU211 is to provide you with the tools and techniques necessary to accomplish these steps. In this handout, we consider the problem of analyzing the efficiency of algorithms by first considering the algorithms for search that we developed earlier.

How can one describe the efficiency of a given procedure for solving some problem? Informally, one often speaks of "fast" or "slow" programs, but the absolute execution time of an algorithm depends on many factors:

- the size of the input (searching through a list of length 1,000 takes longer than searching through a list of length 10),

- the algorithm used to solve the problem (UNORDERED-LINEAR-SEARCH is inherently slower than BINARY-SEARCH),

- the programming language used to implement the algorithm (interpreted languages such as Basic are typically slower than compiled languages such as C++),

- the quality of the actual implementation (good, tight code can be much faster than poor, sloppy code), and

- the machine on which the code is run (a supercomputer is faster than a laptop).

In analyzing the efficiency of an algorithm, one typically focuses on the first two of these factors (i.e., the "speed" of the algorithm as a function of the size of the input on which it is run), and one typically determines the number of program steps (or some count of other interesting computer operations) as a function of the input size—the actual "wall clock" time will depend on the programming language used, the quality of the code produced, and the machine on which the code is run.

The latter three factors are important, but they typically induce a constant factor speedup or slowdown in the "wall clock" execution time of an algorithm: a 2GHz PC will be twice as fast as a 1GHz PC, a compiled language may run 10 times faster than an interpreted one, "tight" code may be 30% faster than "sloppy" code, etc. However, a more efficient algorithm may induce a speedup that is proportional to the size of the input itself: the larger the input, the greater the speedup, as compared to an inefficient algorithm.

Finally, when analyzing the efficiency of an algorithm, one often performs a *worst case* and/or an *average case* analysis. A worst case analysis aims to determine the slowest possible execution time for an algorithm. For example, if one were searching through a list, then in the worst case, one might have to go through the entire list to find (or not find) the object in question. A worst case analysis is useful because it tells you that no matter what, the running time of the algorithm cannot be slower than the bound derived. An algorithm with a "good" worst case running time will always be "fast." On the other hand, an average case analysis aims to determine how fast an algorithm is "on average" for a "typical" input. It may be the case that the worst case running time of an algorithm is quite slow, but in reality, for "typical" inputs, the algorithm is much faster: in this case, the average case running time of the algorithm may be much better than the worst case running time, and it may better reflect "typical" performance.

Average case analyses are usually much more difficult than worst case analyses—one must define what are "typical" inputs and then "average" the actual running times over these typical inputs—and in actual practice, the average case running time of an algorithm is usually only a constant factor (often just 2) faster than the worst case running time. Since worst case analyses are (1) interesting in their own right, (2) easier to perform than average case analyses, and (3) often indicative of average case performance, worst case analyses tend to be performed most often.

With this as motivation, we now analyze the efficiency of the various algorithms for search described above.

11.2.1   Linear Search

Consider the UNORDERED-LINEAR-SEARCH algorithm discussed above. This algorithm simply iterates through the array, examining its elements one-by-one. Note that each iteration of this algorithm takes some constant amount of time to execute, dependent on the programming language used, the actual implementation, the machine on which the code is run, etc. Since we do not know this constant, we may simply count how many times the algorithm iterates or how many array elements must be examined; the running time of the algorithm will be proportional to this count. For searching and sorting algorithms, we shall consider the number of array elements that must be examined as an indicator of the performance of the algorithm.

In the worst case, on an input of size n, the number being sought will be compared to each of the n elements in the array for a total of n array examinations. Let $T(n)$ be the function of n that describes the running time of an algorithm. We then have

$$T(n) = n$$

in the worst case. This is a *linear* function—if one were to plot $T(n)$ vs. n, it would be a straight line—and this explains why this algorithm is referred to as a *linear* search algorithm.

Now consider the ORDERED-LINEAR-SEARCH algorithm described above.

In the worst case, on an input of size n, if the number being sought is at least as large as every element in the array A, then each array element must be examined. Thus, we again have

$$T(n) = n$$

in the worst case, which is a linear function.

11.2.2   Chunk Search

Now consider the CHUNK-SEARCH algorithm described above.

One element must be examined for each chunk considered, for a maximum of n/c such examinations on an array of size n using chunks of size c. ORDERED-LINEAR-SEARCH will then be performed on a chunk of size c (at most), engendering c further element examinations in the worst case. We therefore have

$$T(n) = n/c + c. \tag{11.1}$$

Note that the running time of CHUNK-SEARCH depends on both n and c. What does this analysis tell us? We can use this analysis, and specifically Equation 11.1, in order to determine the *optimal* chunk size c; i.e., the chunk size that would *minimize* the overall running time of CHUNK-SEARCH (in the worst case).

Suppose that one were to run CHUNK-SEARCH using a very small value of c. Our chunks would be small, so there would be lots of chunks. Much of the time would be spent trying to find the right chunk, and very little time would be spent searching for the element in question within a chunk. Consider the extreme case of $c = 1$: in the worst case, $n/c = n/1 = n$ element examinations would be spent trying to find the right chunk while only $c = 1$ examinations would be spent searching within a chunk for a total of $n + 1$ examinations (in the worst case). This is worse than UNORDERED-LINEAR-SEARCH or ORDERED-LINEAR-SEARCH (though it is still linear).

Now consider using a very large value of c. Our chunks would be big, so there would be few of them, and very few element examinations would be spent finding the right chunk. However, searching for the element in question within a very large chunk would require many such examinations. Consider the extreme case of $c = n$: in the worst case, $n/c = n/n = 1$ element examinations would be spent "finding" the right chunk (our chunk is the *entire* list) while $c = n$ examinations would be spent searching within a chunk for a total of $n + 1$ examinations (in the worst case). This is again worse than either UNORDERED-LINEAR-SEARCH or ORDERED-LINEAR-SEARCH (though, again, it is still linear).

Is CHUNK-SEARCH doomed to be no faster than linear search? No! One must *optimize* the value of c in order to *minimize* the total number of comparisons, and this can be accomplished by choosing a value of c that *balances* the time (number of examinations) spent *finding* the right chunk and the time spent *searching* within that chunk.

Suppose that we wish to spend precisely *equal* amounts of time searching for the correct chunk and then searching within that chunk; what value of c should we pick? Our goal is then to find a c such that n/c (the time spent searching for a chunk) is equal to c (the time spent searching within a chunk). We thus have

$$
\begin{aligned}
n/c &= c \\
\Leftrightarrow \quad n &= c^2 \\
\Leftrightarrow \quad \sqrt{n} &= c.
\end{aligned}
$$

Thus, the desired chunk size is $c = \sqrt{n}$, and using this chunk size, we have

$$
\begin{aligned}
T(n) &= n/c + c \\
&= n/\sqrt{n} + \sqrt{n} \\
&= \sqrt{n} + \sqrt{n} \\
&= 2\sqrt{n}.
\end{aligned}
$$

Note that for sufficiently large n, this is much faster than a linear search. For example, if $n = 1,000,000$, ORDERED-LINEAR-SEARCH would require 1,000,000 element examinations in the worst case, while CHUNK-SEARCH would require approximately 2,000 examinations in the worst case—CHUNK-SEARCH would be 500 times faster (in the worst case).

Do even better values of c exist? No. One can show through the use of calculus that $c = \sqrt{n}$ is optimal. We essentially have a function $(n/c + c)$ that we wish to minimize with respect to c. Taking the derivative with respect to c, setting this derivative to zero, and solving for c yields $c = \sqrt{n}$.

11.2.3   Binary Search

Finally, consider the BINARY-SEARCH algorithm discussed above. In each iteration of binary search, one element is examined and the procedure either returns (if the number being sought is found or the subarray being considered cannot further be cut in half) or the (sub)array being considered is cut in half. The question now becomes, "How many times can one cut an array of size n in half until there is only one element left?" This is the maximum number of array elements that will be examined. Consider: Cutting an array of size n in half yields $n/2$. Cutting this array in half again yields $(n/2)/2 = n/2^2 = n/4$. Cutting the array in half a third time yields $((n/2)/2)/2 = (n/2^2)/2 = n/2^3 = n/8$. In general, cutting an array in half k times yields an array of size $n/2^k$. How large can k be until $n/2^k$ is one? We have

$$
\begin{aligned}
n/2^k &= 1 \\
\Leftrightarrow \qquad n &= 2^k \\
\Leftrightarrow \qquad \log_2 n &= k.
\end{aligned}
$$

Therefore, at most $\log_2 n$ iterations will be performed until the array can no longer be cut in half, and thus the worst case running time of BINARY-SEARCH is

$$
T(n) = \log_2 n.
$$

This is faster still than even CHUNK-SEARCH: on an array of size 1,000,000 BINARY-SEARCH would perform 20 comparisons (in the worst case), as compared to 2,000 for CHUNK-SEARCH and 1,000,000 for ORDERED-LINEAR-SEARCH! This is the power of fast algorithms.

11.2.4 Comparison of Search Algorithms

The table below compares the worst times for the search methods we has discussed..

Name	WorstTime	Comment	$n = 1000$
Linear Search	n	$key \geq last$	1000
Chunk Search	$\sqrt{n}$	when $c = n/c$	32
Binary Search	$\log_2 n$		10

11.3 Algorithms for Sorting

ORDERED-LINEAR-SEARCH, CHUNK-SEARCH, and BINARY-SEARCH each assume that the underlying array or list that is being searched is already in sorted order. How can one take an unordered array or list and sort it? Algorithms for sorting are fundamental to computer science and dozens have been developed. In this section, we shall consider three such algorithms: INSERTION-SORT, SELECTION-SORT, and MERGE-SORT.

11.3.1 Insertion Sort

INSERTION-SORT corresponds to the method that many people use to sort cards as they are being dealt to them. The first card is placed in one's hand, the second card is compared to the first and placed either before or after it, and so on. In general, one has some i cards, in sorted order, in one's hand, and the $i + 1$st card is compared to successive cards (starting from the left or right) until the proper location to "insert" the card is found.

Now consider the following array:

i	1	2	3	4	5	6	7	8
A	34	16	12	11	54	10	65	37

Let us consider how to sort this array using INSERTION-SORT. Imagine the numbers 34, 16, 12, ..., being "dealt" to you, in this order, like cards. You would start with the number 34, a trivially sorted list. Then the number 16 would be inserted into this list, producing the sorted list "16 34." The number 12 would then be inserted into this list, producing "12 16 34," and so on. In general, in phase k of the algorithm, the kth element of the array is inserted into the sorted list formed from the first $k - 1$ elements of the array. The process of insertion sort is shown below, where a diamond $\diamond$ is used to separate the processed and sorted array elements from the as yet unprocessed array elements.

Phase	Processed					$\diamond$	Unprocessed		
0	$\diamond$ 34	16	12	11	54	10	65	37	
1	34 $\diamond$	16	12	11	54	10	65	37	
2	16 34 $\diamond$	12	11	54	10	65	37		
3	12 16 34 $\diamond$	11	54	10	65	37			
4	11 12 16 34 $\diamond$	54	10	65	37				
5	11 12 16 34 54 $\diamond$	10	65	37					
6	10 11 12 16 34 54 $\diamond$	65	37						
7	10 11 12 16 34 54 65 $\diamond$	37							
8	10 11 12 16 34 37 54 65 $\diamond$								

Analysis: What is the running time of INSERTION-SORT on an array containing n elements? In phase 1 of the algorithm, the first array element must be examined. In phase 2 of the algorithm, the second element must be examined and compared to the first (which must therefore be examined). In general, in the kth phase of INSERTION-SORT, the kth element must be examined, and in the worst case, it may be compared to each of the previously processed $k-1$ elements, resulting in k total elements being examined. Thus, the total number of elements examined (in the worst case) is given by

$$1 + 2 + 3 + \cdots + (n-2) + (n-1) + n.$$

We shall consider mathematical techniques for determining the size of such sums in Chapter 12.

11.3.2   Selection Sort

While INSERTION-SORT can be used to process cards as they are being dealt, the next algorithm we shall consider cannot proceed until all the cards have been dealt. However, in sorting a list or array of elements that are all given in advance, both algorithms are equally applicable.

SELECTION-SORT begins by examining the list of elements, "selecting" the smallest one, and "swapping" it with the first element of the list. In phase 2, SELECTION-SORT selects the smallest element from the remaining $n-1$ elements and swaps it with the element in position 2. In general, in the kth phase, SELECTION-SORT selects the smallest element from the remaining $n-k+1$ elements and swaps it with the element in position k. The process of selection sort is shown below.

Phase	Processed							◇	Unprocessed
0	◇	34	16	12	11	54	10	65	37
1	10	◇	16	12	11	54	34	65	37
2	10	11	◇	12	16	54	34	65	37
3	10	11	12	◇	16	54	34	65	37
4	10	11	12	16	◇	54	34	65	37
5	10	11	12	16	34	◇	54	65	37
6	10	11	12	16	34	37	◇	65	54
7	10	11	12	16	34	37	54	◇	65
8	10	11	12	16	34	37	54	65	◇

Analysis: What is the running time of SELECTION-SORT on an array containing n elements? In phase 1 of the algorithm, all n elements must be examined in order to find the smallest element. In phase 2 of the algorithm, the $n-1$ remaining elements must all be examined to find the second smallest element. In general, in phase k of the algorithm, the remaining $n-k+1$ elements must all be examined to determine the kth smallest element. Thus, the total number of elements examined is given by

$$n + (n-1) + (n-2) + \cdots + 3 + 2 + 1.$$

Note that this is the same sum as given by the analysis of INSERTION-SORT, only written in reverse order. Again, we shall consider mathematical techniques for determining the size of such sums in Chapter 12.

11.3.3   Merge Sort

MERGE-SORT is a divide-and conquer algorithm. This is how it works:
   Start with an unsorted list of n elements.

1. If $n = 1$, STOP. The list is sorted.

2. Break the list into two approximately equal pieces and apply MERGE-SORT to each piece.

3. MERGE the two sorted sublists to produce the sorted list.

   MERGE takes two sorted lists and combines them by repeatedly comparing the two lowest elements and sending the smaller one off to be the next element in the combined list.

Example 11.1

Original List					19	3	12	5	7	22	18	4			
Two Parts			19	3	12	5				7	22	18	4		
Four Parts		19	3		12	5				7	22		18	4	
Eight Parts	19		3		12		5		7		22		18		4
MERGE to Four Parts		3	19		5	12				7	22		4	18	
MERGE to Two Parts			3	5	12	19				4	7	18	22		
MERGE to Sorted List					3	4	5	7	12	18	19	22			

In Chapter 14 we analyze MERGE-SORT, whose implementation is inherently recursive and whose analysis depends on the mathematical technique of *recurrences*. MERGE-SORT is provably faster than either INSERTION-SORT or SELECTION-SORT in the worst case.

11.3.4   Comparison of Sorting Algorithms

There is a table comparing many sorting algorithms in this article, Wikipedia on Sorting Algorithms. The table below is just about the sorts we are looking at this semester.

Name	Best	Average	Worst	Average $n = 1000$
Insertion sort	n	n^2	n^2	10^6
Selection sort	n^2	n^2	n^2	10^6
Merge sort	$n \log n$	$n \log n$	$n \log n$	9966
Quicksort	$n \log n$	$n \log n$	n^2	9966

11.4   Summary

In this chapter, we have studied a number of algorithms for searching and sorting. Algorithms are fundamental building blocks of computer programs, and the efficiency of these algorithms directly impact the speed of executed code. We have performed rudimentary analyses of various algorithms, and we have seen that different algorithms for solving the same problem can have vastly different efficiencies. In the next chapter, we will study the mathematics underlying the analysis of most iterative algorithms (such as INSERTION-SORT), and in a subsequent chapter we will study the mathematics underlying the analysis of recursive algorithms (such as MERGE-SORT).

Exercises

In the problems that follow, you will consider three of the algorithms for search that we discussed in class: ORDERED-LINEAR-SEARCH, CHUNK-SEARCH, and BINARY SEARCH. Let $T_1(n)$, $T_2(n)$, and $T_3(n)$, respectively, be the number of element examinations[1] required by these algorithms when run on a list whose length is n. We have

$$
\begin{aligned}
T_1(n) &= n \\
T_2(n) &= \sqrt{n} \\
T_3(n) &= \log_2(n).
\end{aligned}
$$

In the problems that follow, you will compare and contrast the growth rates of these functions.

Exercise 11.1

On a *single* sheet of graph paper, plot the number of element examinations required for each of the three algorithms when run on lists of length $n = 1, 2, 4, 8$, and 16. For each algorithm, connect the plot points with a smooth, hand-drawn curve. See the plots given in the "Exponentials and Logs" handout for examples of what you should do. You may print a piece of graph paper from the PDF located at the following URL:

http://www.printfreegraphpaper.com/gp/c-i-14.pdf

(If you view this assignment online, you may simply click on the above hyperlink.)

Exercise 11.2

i. Suppose that you were given a budget of 20 element examinations. For each of the three algorithms, determine the largest array length such that the number of examinations made is guaranteed to be at most 20.

ii. How many times larger is the array that BINARY-SEARCH can handle, as compared to the arrays that CHUNK-SEARCH and ORDERED-LINEAR-SEARCH can handle? How many times larger is the array that CHUNK-SEARCH can handle, as compared to the array that ORDERED-LINEAR-SEARCH can handle?

Exercise 11.3

Moe, Larry, and Curly have just purchased three new computers. Moe's computer is 10 times

---
[1] worst-case...

faster than Larry's and 50 times faster than Curly's.[2] However, Moe runs ORDERED-LINEAR-SEARCH on his computer, while Larry and Curly run CHUNK-SEARCH and BINARY-SEARCH, respectively. Moe, Larry, and Curly begin to perform searches over various data stored on their computers.

i. How large must n (the size of the array) be so that Curly's computer begins to outperform Moe's?

ii. How large must n be so that Larry's computer begins to outperform Moe's?

iii. How large must n be so that Curly's computer begins to outperform Larry's?

Hint: For parts of this problem, you will have to solve an equation that involves n (or $\sqrt{n}$) and $\log_2 n$. Such equations typically cannot be solved *analytically*, i.e., by applying the rules of algebra to obtain a formula for n. Such equations are often solved *numerically* by using... binary search! Consider the equation

$$10 \log_2 n = n.$$

First, find two initial values of n, one of which causes the left-hand side of the equation to exceed the right and the other of which causes the right-hand side of the equation to exceed the left. The solution to the equation lies somewhere between these two values. For example, when $n = 2$, the left-hand side of the equation is 10 while the right-hand side is 2. Conversely, when $n = 128$, the left-hand side is 70 while the right-hand side is 128. The solution to this equation lies somewhere between $n = 2$ and $n = 128$. One could then apply binary search in this range to find the solution in question. (Think about which half of the interval one should search and why.)

Exercise 11.4
Consider the setup described in the problem above.

i. Moe and Curly both run a search on the same data set. Despite the fact that Curly's machine is 50 times slower than Moe's, Curly's machine performs the search 100 times faster than Moe's machine. How large is the data set?

ii. Suppose that Moe switches to CHUNK-SEARCH. On this same data set, will Moe's machine now outperform Curly's? Explain.

Hint: Again, for part of this problem, you will need to solve an equation using binary search.

---

[2]In other words, Moe's computer can perform 50 operations (such as an element examination) in the time it takes Curly's computer to perform one operation, and Moe's computer can perform 10 operations in the time it takes Larry's computer to perform one operation.

CHAPTER 12

Sequences, Sums, and Series

Sequences $a_1, a_2, \ldots, a_n$ are used to represent ordered lists of objects. When we analyzed search algorithms in the last chapter, we saw sequences of running times corresponding to input array sizes and we found formulas to describe the correspondence mathematically. In this chapter we will look at some particular types of sequences that often occur in discrete structures.

When we study algorithms for sorting, we'll see that we have to make several passes through our input and we'll have sequences of running times for these passes. We will have to sum up the terms of the sequence to find the total running time. We will develop the notation for these sums and techniques to arrive at formulas for their values.

12.1 Sequences

A *sequence* is a function t from a subset of the integers (usually N or Z^+) to a set S. In this discussion, the set S will be a set of numbers but we could have a sequence of colors, musical notes, or even computer programs.

We often write $a_n = t(n)$. Each a_n is a *term* of the sequence. The sequence $a_1, a_2, a_3, \ldots$ may be denoted by $\{a_n\}$ or $\{a_n\}_{n=1\cdots\infty}$. The numbers $1, 2, 3, \ldots$ are the term indices and $a_1, a_2, a_3, \ldots$ are the term values

Cover the right-hand side of the page below and see if you can give the next term of each sequence and the function $t(n)$ that defines the sequence. Assume the first term is a_1.

Example 12.1

$1, 1/2, 1/3, 1/4, 1/5, 1/6, \ldots$
next term $= 1/7$, $t(n) = 1/n$.

Example 12.2

$2, 4, 6, 8, 10, 12, \ldots$ next term $= 14$, $t(n) = 2n$.

Example 12.3

$2, 4, 8, 16, 32, 64, \ldots$ next term $= 128$, $t(n) = 2^n$.

Example 12.4

$7, 8, 9, 10, 11, 12, \ldots$ next term $= 13$, $t(n) = n + 6$.

Example 12.5

$1/2, 1, 2, 4, 8, 16, \ldots$ next term $= 32$, $t(n) = 2^{n-2} = \frac{2^n}{4}$.

Example 12.6

$1, 3, 6, 10, 15, 21, \ldots$ next term $= 28$, $t(n) = (n^2 + n)/2$.

Example 12.7

$1, 1, 1, 1, 1, 1, 1, \ldots$ next term $= 1$, $t(n) = 1$.

Example 12.8

$1, 1, 2, 3, 5, 8, \ldots$ next term $= 13$, $t(n) = \begin{cases} 1 & n = 1, 2 \\ t(n-1) + t(n-2) & n > 2 \end{cases}$

Example 12.9

$1/2, -2/3, 3/4, -4/5, 5/6, -6/7, \ldots$ next term $= 7/8$, $t(n) = (-1)^{(n-1)} n/(n+1)$.

Example 12.10

$2, 3, 5, 7, 11, 13, \ldots$ next term $= 17$, $t(n) = n$-th prime number.

These examples include several different types of sequences. For some it is easy to find the next term and the function that describes the general term while for others the formulas may seem to come out of nowhere. In the next section, we will discuss some special types of sequences that will cover many, but not all, of the sequences above.

12.1.1   Arithmetic Sequences

An *arithmetic sequence* is a sequence in which each term equals the preceding term plus a constant. A general arithmetic sequence looks like this $a, a + d, a + 2d, a + 3d, \ldots$. The first term is a and the constant difference between terms is d. The n-th term of the sequence $a, a + d, a + 2d, a + 3d, \ldots$ is given by $t(n) = a + (n - 1)d$.

The following examples are arithmetic sequences. For each example, find a, d, the next term, and the n-th term, $t(n)$.

Example 12.11

$4, 7, 10, 13, 16, 19, \ldots$ $a = 4$, $d = 3$, next term $= 22$, $t(n) = 4 + 3(n - 1) = 3n + 1$.

Example 12.12

$-7, -1, 5, 11, 17, 23, \ldots$ $\qquad a = -7$, $d = 6$, next term $= 29$, $t(n) = -7 + 6(n-1) = 6n - 13$.

Example 12.13

$30, 25, 20, 15, 10, 5, \ldots$ $\qquad a = 30$, $d = -5$, next term $= 0$, $t(n) = 30 - 5(n-1) = -5n + 35$.

12.1.2 Geometric Sequences

A *geometric sequence* is a sequence in which each term equals the preceding term times a constant. A general geometric sequence looks like this $a, ar, ar^2, ar^3, ar^4, \ldots$ the first term is a and the constant ratio between successive terms is r. The n-th term of the sequence $a, ar, ar^2, ar^3, ar^4, \ldots$ is given by $t(n) = a \cdot r^{(n-1)}$.

The following examples are geometric sequences. For each example, find a, r, the next term, and the n-th term, $t(n)$.

Example 12.14

$2, 6, 18, 54, 162, \ldots$ $\qquad a = 2$, $r = 3$, next term $= 486$, $t(n) = 2 \cdot 3^{(n-1)}$.

Example 12.15

$1, -4, 16, -64, 256, \ldots$ $\qquad a = 1$, $r = -4$, next term $= -1024$, $t(n) = (-4)^{(n-1)}$.

12.1.3 Quadratic Sequences

A *quadratic sequence* is a sequence whose n-th term is given by a quadratic function,

$$a_n = an^2 + bn + c.$$

Here are some quadratic sequences and the quadratic function that generates each one.

Example 12.16

$1, 4, 9, 16, 25, 36, \ldots$ $\qquad\qquad\qquad\qquad\qquad\qquad\qquad a_n = n^2$.

Example 12.17

$6, 15, 28, 45, 66, 91, \ldots$ $\qquad\qquad\qquad\qquad\qquad\qquad a_n = 2n^2 + 3n + 1$.

An arithmetic sequence is given by a linear function and the difference between successive terms is a constant. In a quadratic sequence the differences between successive terms are given by a linear function and the second differences are constant.

Example 12.18

sequence		6	15	28	45	66	91	$\cdots$
differences			9	13	17	21	25	$\cdots$
second differences				4	4	4	4	$\cdots$

You can check whether a sequence of number can be given by a quadratic function by finding the second differences. Once you know that a sequence is quadratic, to find the coefficients a, b, and c, plug in the values you have and solve for a, b, and c. The system of three equations in three unknowns that you get will be particularly easy to solve. The method shown in the example below should always work.

For the sequence $6, 15, 28, 45, 66, 91, \ldots$,

$$a \cdot 1^2 + b \cdot 1 + c = a + b + c = 6$$
$$a \cdot 2^2 + b \cdot 2 + c = 4a + 2b + c = 15$$
$$a \cdot 3^2 + b \cdot 3 + c = 9a + 3b + c = 28$$

Subtract the first equation from the second and the second from the third to get:

$$3a + b = 9$$
$$5a + b = 13$$

Now subtract the first of these equations from the second to get:

$$2a = 4 \text{ Or } a = 2.$$

Use the value $a = 2$ to find b: $3a + b = 6 + b = 9$ so $b = 3$. Finally, use the values of $a = 2$ and $b = 3$ to find c: $a + b + c = 2 + 3 + c = 6$ so c $= 1$ and $a_n = 2n^2 + 3n + 1$.

12.2   Series and Partial Sums

A *series* is a sum of the terms of a sequence. Since a sequence has infinitely many terms, a series is the sum of infinitely many terms. We often sum only the first n terms of a sequence. The sum of the first n terms is called the n-th partial sum. The following is a sum of an infinite number of terms.

$$\sum_{k=1}^{\infty} a_k = a_1 + a_2 + a_3 + \cdots$$

Below is the sum of the first n terms. This is the n-th *partial sum*. k is the *index of summation*; 1 is the *lower limit*; n is the *upper limit*.

$$\sum_{k=1}^{n} a_k = a_1 + a_2 + a_3 + \cdots + a_n$$

This is also a partial sum. j is the index of summation; m is the lower limit; n is the upper limit.

$$\sum_{j=m}^{n} a_j = a_m + a_{m+1} + a_{m+2} + \cdots + a_n$$

12.2.1 Arithmetic Sums

An *arithmetic sum* is a sum of the terms of an arithmetic sequence.

$$\sum_{k=0}^{n} a + kd = a + (a + d) + (a + 2d) + (a + 3d) + \cdots + (a + nd)$$

We shall refer to the method for computing the value of such a sum as *Gauss's Trick*, as it is related to a (possibly apocryphal) story about Carl Friedrich Gauss, one of the greatest mathematicians in history. In a common version of the story,[1] Carl Friedrich Gauss, at the age of eight, was the youngest student in a mathematics class. One day, to keep his students busy, the schoolmaster asked each student in the class to sum up all the integers from 1 to 100. The young Carl immediately placed his slate on the schoolmaster's table with the answer 5050. When all the other students had finished their sums, the slates were turned over and only Carl's was correct. How did Carl get the correct answer so quickly? Here is the method. Let S be the sum of the first 100 integers, in increasing order:

$$S = 1 + 2 + 3 + \cdots + 100.$$

We could equivalently write the sum in decreasing order:

$$S = 100 + 99 + 98 + \cdots + 1.$$

Now consider taking the sum of these two equations. On the left-hand side, we obtain $2S$. On the right-hand side, compute the sum term-by-term: the sum of the first terms is $1 + 101 = 101$; the sum of the second terms is $2 + 99 = 101$; the sum of the third terms is $3 + 98 = 101$; and the sum of the last terms is $100 + 1 = 101$. Each successive set of terms adds to the same value, 101, which is simply the sum of the first and last terms in the original sum. As such, we obtain:

$$2S = 101 + 101 + 101 + \cdots + 101$$

---

[1] For more versions of this tale, see "Gauss's Day of Reckoning" by Brian Hayes.

where we have 100 total terms on the right-hand side. Thus, we have

$$2S = 100 \cdot 101$$

or

$$S = \frac{100 \cdot 101}{2} = 50 \cdot 101 = 5050.$$

We can generalize Gauss's Trick to arbitrary arithmetic sums. Consider the sum

$$S = 2 + 5 + 8 + \cdots + 29.$$

This is a sum corresponding to an arithmetic sequence starting at 2 where each successive term is 3 larger than the previous term. To apply Gauss's Trick, we also write the sum in decreasing order

$$S = 29 + 26 + 23 + \cdots + 2$$

and sum both equations, obtaining

$$2S = 31 + 31 + \cdots + 31.$$

Each term on the right-hand side is 31, the sum of the first and last terms in the original sum, and we now only need to compute the number of terms on the right-hand side.

To compute the number of terms in the sum $2 + 5 + 8 + \cdots + 29$, we note that the *range* of the terms is $29 - 2 = 27$ and the *gap* between consecutive terms is 3. If we divide the *range* by the *gap size*, we obtain the number of gaps: $27/3 = 9$. The number of terms is just the number of gaps, plus 1. (One gap would correspond to two terms; two gaps would correspond to three terms; and so on.) Thus, we have 10 total terms, each of size 31, and the value of the arithmetic sum is therefore

$$S = \frac{10 \cdot 31}{2} = 5 \cdot 31 = 155.$$

In general, for any arithmetic sum, we have

$$S = \frac{\#\text{terms} \cdot (\text{first-term} + \text{last-term})}{2}$$

where

$$\#\text{terms} = \frac{\text{range}}{\text{gap-size}} + 1.$$

Example 12.19

$1 + 2 + \cdots + 100 = \frac{100 \cdot (1 + 100)}{2} = 5050$

Example 12.20

$1 + 2 + 3 + \cdots + n = \frac{n \cdot (n+1)}{2}$

Example 12.21

$-11 - 5 + 1 + 7 + 13 + \cdots + 67 = \frac{\left(\frac{67-(-11)}{6}+1\right) \cdot \left(-11+67\right)}{2} = \frac{\left(\frac{78}{6}+1\right) \cdot 56}{2} = \frac{14 \cdot 56}{2} = 392.$

12.2.2   Geometric Sums and Series

A *geometric sum* is a sum of terms of a geometric sequence.

$$\sum_{k=1}^{n} ar^k = ar + ar^2 + ar^3 + \cdots + ar^n$$

or, summing from 0

$$\sum_{k=0}^{n} ar^k = a + ar + ar^2 + ar^3 + \cdots + ar^n$$

With geometric sequences, summing the infinite sequence may be meaningful. Infinite sums are called *series*.

$$\sum_{k=0}^{\infty} ar^k = a + ar + ar^2 + ar^3 + \cdots$$

Let's find a formula for the n-th partial sum $\sum_{k=0}^{n} ar^k = a + ar + ar^2 + ar^3 + \cdots + ar^n$. You should find it more useful to learn the method below than to memorize any particular formula it leads to.

Let $S = \sum_{k=0}^{n} ar^k = a + ar + ar^2 + ar^3 + \cdots + ar^n$.

Then $rS = \sum_{k=0}^{n} ar^{k+1} = ar + ar^2 + ar^3 + ar^4 + \cdots + ar^n + ar^{n+1}$.

$S - rS = a - ar^{n+1}$ as all the other terms cancel out when we subtract rS from S.

So $S = \frac{a - ar^{n+1}}{1-r} = \frac{a(1-r^{n+1})}{1-r}$. When $r > 1$, we usually compute $rS - S$ instead of $S - rS$ so we don't have to work with negative numbers. See the second example below.

Example 12.22

$\sum_{k=0}^{6} \frac{1}{3^k} = 1 + \frac{1}{3} + \frac{1}{3^2} + \frac{1}{3^3} + \frac{1}{3^4} + \frac{1}{3^5} + \frac{1}{3^6} = \frac{1\left(1-\frac{1}{3^7}\right)}{1-\frac{1}{3}} = \frac{3^7-1}{3^7-3^6} = \frac{2187-1}{2197-729} = \frac{2186}{1458} \approx 1.499.$

Using the method rather than the formula, set

$$S = \sum_{k=0}^{6} \frac{1}{3^k} = \frac{1}{1} + \frac{1}{3} + \frac{1}{3^2} + \frac{1}{3^3} + \frac{1}{3^4} + \frac{1}{3^5} + \frac{1}{3^6}$$

The ratio, $r = \frac{1}{3}$.

$$\frac{1}{3}S = \sum_{k=0}^{6} \frac{1}{3^{k+1}} = \frac{1}{3} + \frac{1}{3^2} + \frac{1}{3^3} + \frac{1}{3^4} + \frac{1}{3^5} + \frac{1}{3^6} + \frac{1}{3^7}$$

$$\frac{2}{3}S = S - \frac{1}{3}S = 1 - \frac{1}{3^7} \qquad \text{so } S = \frac{3}{2}\left(1 - \frac{1}{3^7}\right) = 1.5 \cdot \left(1 - \frac{1}{2187}\right) \approx 1.499$$

Example 12.23

$\sum_{k=0}^{6} 3^k = 1 + 3 + 3^2 + 3^3 + 3^4 + 3^5 + 3^6 = \frac{1(1-3^7)}{1-3} = \frac{2^7-1}{2} = \frac{2186}{2} = 1093.$

Using the method rather than the formula, set

$$S = \sum_{k=0}^{6} 3^k = 1 + 3 + 3^2 + 3^3 + 3^4 + 3^5 + 3^6$$

The ratio, $r = 3$.

$$3S = \sum_{k=1}^{7} 3^k = 3 + 3^2 + 3^3 + 3^4 + 3^5 + 3^6 + 3^7$$

$$2S = 3S - S = 3^7 - 1 \qquad \text{so } S = \frac{3^7 - 1}{2} = \frac{2186}{2} = 1093.$$

Example 12.24

$\sum_{k=0}^{6} \frac{1}{2^k} = 1 + \frac{1}{2} + \frac{1}{2^2} + \frac{1}{2^3} + \frac{1}{2^4} + \frac{1}{2^5} + \frac{1}{2^6} = \frac{1\left(1-\frac{1}{2^7}\right)}{1-\frac{1}{2}} = \frac{2^7-1}{2^7-2^6} = \frac{128-1}{128-64} = \frac{127}{64} \approx 1.984.$

Example 12.25

$\sum_{k=0}^{n} \frac{1}{2^k} = \frac{1\left(1-\frac{1}{2^{n+1}}\right)}{1-\frac{1}{2}} = \frac{1-\frac{1}{2^{n+1}}}{\frac{1}{2}} = 2 - \frac{1}{2^n}.$ What happens when n gets very large?

Example 12.26

$\sum_{k=0}^{\infty} \frac{1}{2^k} = ?$

12.2.3   Some Special Sums

The following two sums are neither arithmetic nor geometric but they frequently appear in applications so we include them here.

$\sum_{k=1}^{n} k^2 = \frac{n(n+1)(2n+1)}{6}.$

$\sum_{k=1}^{n} k^3 = \frac{n^2(n+1)^2}{4}.$

12.3 Summary

In this chapter we discussed *sequences* in general and found ways to express the n-th term of *arithmetic*, *geometric*, and *quadratic* sequences. We used summation notation to describe partial (or infinite) sums of the terms of a sequence. Gauss's trick gives us a simple way to find partial sums of arithmetic series, [(first term + last term) $\times$ (number of terms)]/2. For partial sums of geometric series, we set S to the sum and then saw that $S - rS$ where r is the ratio has only two terms so we can easily solve for S to get a closed for for the sum.

Exercises

Arithmetic Sequences

Exercise 12.1

The following series are all arithmetic. In each case, tell the next term, give a formula for the nth term assuming that $n = 1$ for the first term, and give a formula for the kth term assuming that $k = 0$ for the first term.

    a. $6, 8, 10, 12, 1416, \ldots$

    b. $16, 14, 12, 10, 8, 6, \ldots$

    c. $-16, -14, -12, -10, -8, -6, \ldots$

    d. $-6, -8, -10, -12, -14 - 16, \ldots$

    e. $-6, -3, 0, 3, 6, 9, \ldots$

    f. $0, 5, 10, 15, 20, 25, \ldots$

    g. $5, 10, 15, 20, 25, 30, \ldots$

    h. $0, \frac{1}{2}, 1, \frac{3}{2}, 2, \frac{5}{2}, \ldots$

    i. $1.1, 2.2, 3.3, 4.4, 5.5, 6.6, \ldots$

    j. $-72, -60, -48, -36, -24, -12, \ldots$

Geometric Sequences

Exercise 12.2

The following series are all geometric. In each case, tell the next term, give a formula for the nth term assuming that $n = 1$ for the first term, and give a formula for the kth term assuming that $k = 0$ for the first term.

a. $4, 16, 64, 256, 1024, \ldots$

b. $-4, -16, -64, -256, -1024, \ldots$

c. $4, -16, 64, -256, 1024, \ldots$

d. $\frac{1}{3}, \frac{1}{9}, \frac{1}{27}, \frac{1}{81}, \frac{1}{243}, \ldots$

e. $81, 27, 9, 3, 1, \ldots$

f. $\frac{1}{2}, -\frac{1}{4}, \frac{1}{8}, -\frac{1}{16}, \frac{1}{32}, \ldots$

g. $6, -6, 6, -6, 6, \ldots$

h. $1, .5, .25, .125, .625, \ldots$

i. $2, 6, 18, 54, 162, \ldots$

j. $7, -14, 28, -56, 112, \ldots$

Quadratic Sequences

Exercise 12.3

The following series are all quadratic. In each case, tell the next term, show the sequence of first differences, show the constant second difference, give a formula for the nth term assuming that $n = 1$ for the first term, and give a formula for the kth term assuming that $k = 0$ for the first term.

a. $1, 3, 7, 13, 21, \ldots$

b. $1, 2, 5, 10, 17, \ldots$

c. $-2, -1, 2, 7, 14, \ldots$

d. $-1, -.5, .5, 2, 4, \ldots$

e. $10, 9, 7, 4, 0, \ldots$

f. $-1, -5, -10, -16, -23, \ldots$

g. $2, 5, 6, 5, 2, \ldots$

h. $4, 8, 11, 13, 14, \ldots$

i. $15, 6, 0, -3, -3, \ldots$

j. $4, 0, 0, 4, 12, \ldots$

Miscellaneous Sequences

Exercise 12.4

Some of the following series are arithmetic, some are geometric, some are quadratic, and some are none of the above. In each case, tell the type of series, the next term, and, unless otherwise indicated, give a formula for the kth term assuming that $k = 0$ for the first term.

a. $7, 5, 3, 1, -1, \ldots$

b. $3, 3, 5, 9, 15, \ldots$

c. $5, 10, 20, 40, 80, \ldots$

d. $3, 1.5, 0.75, 0.375, 0.1875, \ldots$

e. $2, 4, 10, 28, 82, \ldots$

f. $-8, -3, 2, 7, 12, \ldots$

g. $-6, 1, 22, 57, 106, \ldots$

h. $-1, 1, 0, 1, 1, 2, 3, \ldots$ - no formula

i. $3, 4, 7, 11, 18, \ldots$ - no formula

j. $4, 14, 23, 34, 42, \ldots$ - no formula

Summation Notation

Exercise 12.5

Expand the following sums to show the individual terms, and evaluate the sums e.g.

$$\sum_{n=1}^{n=4} n^2 = 1^2 + 2^2 + 3^2 + 4^2 = 1 + 4 + 9 + 16 = 30.$$

a. $\displaystyle\sum_{k=1}^{6} 3k$ b. $\displaystyle\sum_{k=0}^{5} 2k+3$ c. $\displaystyle\sum_{k=1}^{6} \frac{1}{k}$

d. $\displaystyle\sum_{k=1}^{7} 6$ e. $\displaystyle\sum_{m=2}^{10} \frac{m}{2}$ f. $\displaystyle\sum_{n=5}^{10} n^3$

g. $\displaystyle\sum_{j=-3}^{3} j^2$ h. $\displaystyle\sum_{i=-3}^{3} i^3$ i. $\displaystyle\sum_{k=1}^{5} k^2 - k + 1$

Exercise 12.6

Write each of the following sums using summation notation. Try to make you answers as simple as possible.

a. $7 + 12 + 17 + 22 + \cdots + 177$

b. $4 + 7 + 10 + 13 + \cdots + 304$

c. $1 + 11 + 21 + 31 + \cdots + 251$

d. $1 + 2 + 4 + 8 + ... + \cdots + 1,073,741,824$

e. $2 + 6 + 18 + 54 + \cdots + 2,324,522,934$

f. $\frac{1}{5} - \frac{1}{25} + \frac{1}{125} - \frac{1}{625} + \cdots + \frac{1}{30,517,578,125}$

Arithmetic Sums

Exercise 12.7

Apply Gauss's trick to evaluate each of the following sums.

a. $7 + 12 + 17 + 22 + \cdots + 177$

b. $4 + 7 + 10 + 13 + \cdots + 304$

c. $1 + 11 + 21 + 31 + \cdots + 251$

d. $1 + 2 + 3 + 4 + \cdots + 1000$

e. $1 + 3 + 5 + 7 + \cdots + 1001$

f. $15 + 22 + 29 + 36 + \cdots + 715$

Exercise 12.8

Apply Gauss's trick to evaluate each of the following sums.

a. $\displaystyle\sum_{k=1}^{200} 3k$ b. $\displaystyle\sum_{k=1}^{300} 2k$ c. $\displaystyle\sum_{k=1}^{50} 9k$

d. $\displaystyle\sum_{k=1}^{200} 6$ e. $\displaystyle\sum_{k=1}^{37} 7k$ f. $\displaystyle\sum_{k=1}^{1000} 8k$

g. $\displaystyle\sum_{k=7}^{83} 3k$ h. $\displaystyle\sum_{k=11}^{255} 2k$ i. $\displaystyle\sum_{k=43}^{450} 9k$

Exercise 12.9

Consider the arithmetic series

$$5 + 8 + 11 + 14 + \cdots + 125.$$

a. How many terms are in this series? Explain.

b. Apply Gauss's trick to evaluate this sum. Show your work. You *must* give an answer in the form
$$\frac{x \cdot y}{2}$$
for some x and y, and you may then use a calculator to evaluate this expression.

c. Write this series as a summation in the form
$$\sum_{k=1}^{n}(a \cdot k + b)$$
for some a, b, and n.

d. Rewrite this summation in the form
$$a \cdot \sum_{k=1}^{n} k + \sum_{k=1}^{n} b.$$

What is the value of
$$\sum_{k=1}^{n} b$$

for your values of n and b? Apply the standard arithmetic summation formula to evaluate

$$\sum_{k=1}^{n} k$$

for your value of n. Finally, evaluate the original expression by using the values of these summations and your value of a. Show your work. You should obtain the same value as in part ii above, of course.

Geometric Sums

Exercise 12.10

Use the method described in Section 12.1.2 to evaluate the following geometric sums.

a. $1 + 2 + 4 + 8 + \cdots + 1024$

b. $1 + 2 + 4 + 8 + \cdots + 2^n$ where n is an integer greater than 1

c. $1 + \frac{1}{2} + \frac{1}{4} + \frac{1}{8} + \cdots + \frac{1}{1024}$

d. $1 + \frac{1}{2} + \frac{1}{4} + \frac{1}{8} + \cdots + \frac{1}{2^n}$ where n is an integer greater than 1

e. $1 + \frac{1}{3} + \frac{1}{9} + \frac{1}{27} + \cdots + \frac{1}{59,049}$

f. $1 + \frac{1}{3} + \frac{1}{9} + \frac{1}{27} + \cdots + \frac{1}{3^n}$ where n is an integer greater than 1

g. $5^{10} + 5^9 + 5^8 + \cdots + 1 + \frac{1}{5} + \cdots + \frac{1}{5^{10}}$

Exercise 12.11

Use the method described in Section 12.1.2 to find closed forms for the following geometric sums. You may include exponents like 3^{489} or r^N in your answers.

a. $\displaystyle\sum_{k=1}^{200} 3^k$ b. $\displaystyle\sum_{k=1}^{300} 2^k$ c. $\displaystyle\sum_{k=1}^{50} 2 \cdot 5^{-k}$

d. $\displaystyle\sum_{k=1}^{200} \frac{5}{2^{-k}}$ e. $\displaystyle\sum_{k=1}^{37} 7^k$ f. $\displaystyle\sum_{k=1}^{1000} r^k$ where r is a real number greater than 0.

g. $\displaystyle\sum_{k=1}^{N} 3^k$ h. $\displaystyle\sum_{k=11}^{255} 2^k$ i. $\displaystyle\sum_{k=1}^{2N} 10^k$

Miscellaneous Sums

Exercise 12.12

A *telescoping series* is a series of the form

$$\sum_{k=1}^{n}(a_k - a_{k+1})$$

for some sequence $a_1, a_2, a_3, \ldots$

a. Show that $\sum_{k=1}^{n}(a_k - a_{k+1}) = a_1 - a_{n+1}$.

b. Show that $\sum_{k=1}^{n}\frac{1}{k(k+1)}$ is a telescoping series. What is the form of a_k for any k?

   Hint: Factor the ratio $\frac{1}{k(k+1)}$ into terms involving $\frac{1}{k}$ and $\frac{1}{k+1}$.

c. Using parts i and ii above, show that

$$\sum_{k=1}^{n}\frac{1}{k(k+1)} = 1 - \frac{1}{n+1}.$$

   Explain.

CHAPTER 13

Mathematical Induction

Mathematical induction is a technique used to prove specific statements about the natural numbers very directly, and it can be applied in a wide variety of circumstances. In this chapter we introduce some variations on mathematical induction with examples to lay the groundwork for its use in studying recurrences later.

13.1   The Principle of Mathematical Induction

Mathematical induction is a proof technique. We often find ourselves with statements about the natural numbers that begin "for all integers n, where $n \geq 0$, ...". We have already seen several such statements; for example Gauss's trick from Chapter 12:

$$\text{For all } n \geq 0, \ \sum_{i=0}^{n} i = \frac{n(n+1)}{2}$$

When we first saw this equation, we verified its truth by noticing a pattern in the sums of the first and last elements. That proof is essentially creative, because it requires you to have seen the pattern and determined its importance.

The use of mathematical induction is considerably less creative but still quite powerful. For this formula, we can apply induction to convince ourselves that the statement is true in a predictable, formulaic way. The rough idea is to first show that the statement in question is true for $n = 0$, and also show that if it is true for some arbitrary $n = k$ it must also be true for $n = k + 1$. The principle of mathematical induction says that this is enough to establish truth everywhere.

The Principle of Mathematical Induction   *If $P \subseteq \mathbb{N}$ is some set of natural numbers, and*

1. (Base case) $0 \in P$.

2. (Inductive step) Whenever $k \in P$, also $k + 1 \in P$.

then P encompasses the whole set of natural numbers: $P = \mathbb{N}$.

This principle is deceptively simple. It only says that if you've got a set that contains 0, and also if you know $k + 1$ is in the set for every k in the set, then your set is really all of the natural numbers. Because, first 0 is in the set because of the base case. And because of the inductive step as well as the fact that you have 0, you must also have $0 + 1 = 1$. And since you have 1 and the inductive step you must also have 2. And since you have 2 you must also have 3. And so on; in this way you can accumulate all the numbers into P.

If you're thinking this is obvious or clearly uninteresting, your instinct is right. This property of $\mathbb{N}$ is so fundamental that it is often taken as an axiom when studying the natural numbers. It is, very deeply, one of the core ideas makes the natural numbers what they are.

13.2   A First Example

Returning to the idea that we can use induction as a formulaic way to prove things about numbers, consider how we would use this to show that $\sum_{i=0}^{n} i = n(n + 1)/2$. If we take P to be "the set of values n for which this equation is true" and establish conditions 1 and 2, then we will have shown that this equation is true for all n. The power here is that in the course of doing this, we will only have had to verify the theorem in one real case (for 0). So,

1. First we must show that this equation is true for $n = 0$. So plugging in 0 for n,

$$\sum_{i=0}^{n} i = \sum_{i=0}^{0} i = 0 = \frac{0 \cdot (0 + 1)}{2} = \frac{n(n + 1)}{2}$$

we see clearly that this equation is true for $n = 0$.

2. Now, we want to show that whenever this equation is true for $n = k$, it is also true for $n = k + 1$. So we *assume* that it is true for $n = k$ and use that to prove that it is true for $n = k + 1$. Notice this usage of the inductive step as we proceed to the second line. This

assumption baked into our proof is typically called the *induction hypothesis*.

$$\sum_{i=0}^{n} i = \sum_{i=0}^{k+1} i = \left(\sum_{i=0}^{k} i\right) + (k+1)$$

$$= \frac{k(k+1)}{2} + (k+1)$$

$$= \frac{k(k+1)}{2} + \frac{2 \cdot (k+1)}{2}$$

$$= \frac{(k+1)((k+1)+1)}{2} = \frac{n(n+1)}{2}$$

And that's all there is to it; the preceding two demonstrations, together with the principle of mathematical induction, proves the equation. Often these proofs give the impression that not much has really been demonstrated, but so long as you have the basic structure in which you show that 0 is OK and that $k+1$ is OK (assuming k is), then you have a proof by induction.

13.3   More Examples

Example 13.1

Prove *Bernoulli's Inequality*: if $x \in \mathbb{R}$ and $x > -1$, and n is any natural number, then

$$(1+x)^n \geq 1 + nx$$

First, we establish the base case, $n = 0$.

$$(1+x)^n = (1+x)^0 = 1 \geq 1 + 0 \cdot x = 1 + nx$$

Then, the induction step. Assume the inequality for $n = k$. Then, when $n = k+1$,

$$(1+x)^n = (1+x)^{k+1} = (1+x)^k(1+x)$$
$$\geq (1+kx)(1+x)$$
$$= 1 + kx + x + kx^2$$
$$= 1 + (k+1)x + kx^2$$
$$\geq 1 + (k+1)x = 1 + nx$$

Notice that as we proceed to the second line we've used the induction hypothesis, and also note that $kx^2 \geq 0$ for all the permissible values of k and x.

Example 13.2

Prove that for any natural number n, $n^3 - n$ is divisible by 3.

First the base case: if $n = 0$, $n^3 - n = 0$, and 0 is divisible by 3. Now suppose that $k^3 - k$ is divisible by 3; then for $n = k + 1$,

$$
\begin{aligned}
n^3 - n = (k+1)^3 - (k+1) &= (k^3 + 3k^2 + 3k + 1) - (k+1) \\
&= (k^3 - k) + 3(k^2 + k)
\end{aligned}
$$

And notice that the final form is the sum of two values known to be divisible by 3, $k^3 - k$ (by the induction hypothesis) and $3(k^2 + k)$ (since it is a multiple of 3). Therefore the sum itself, $n^3 - n$ is also divisible by 3.

13.4   Variations of Mathematical Induction

Although one frequently encounters the need to prove statements for all natural numbers, mathematical induction is also useful when you don't need to go quite that far.

It's possible, and straightforward, to use mathematical induction when you have some other infinite subsets of the natural numbers. For instance, consider this statement: for all $n \geq 5$, $n^2 < 2^n$. This is true, but the $n \geq 5$ part is important since the inequality is false at $n = 4$ for instance. We can prove it by using a variation of mathematical induction where the base case is $n = 5$ instead of $n = 0$.

So, for the base case, when $n = 5$,

$$
n^2 = 5^2 = 25 < 32 = 2^5 = 2^n
$$

And if we assume that $n^2 < 2^n$ for $n = k$, then for $n = k + 1$,

$$
n^2 = (k+1)^2 = k^2 + 2k + 1 < 2^k + 2k + 1 < 2^k + 2^k = 2 \cdot 2^k = 2^{k+1} = 2^n
$$

The first inequality is true by the induction hypothesis. The second inequality is true if $2k+1 < 2^k$, which is left as an exercise for the reader. Given that, we have shown the induction step is true, and therefore our statement, $n^2 < 2^n$ is true whenever $n \geq 5$.

One justification for the validity of this variation of mathematical induction is that the theorem in question can be viewed as a theorem beginning at $n = 0$ when written in terms of $n + 5$, or in this case $(n + 5)^2 < 2^{n+5}$.

We can also vary the induction step to prove statements about all even numbers, for instance. In such a proof we would need to show that $n = 0$ is true, and that whenever $n = k$ is true then

$n = k + 2$ is true. Just as in the base case variation, you could consider such a proof as normal induction where the theorem is written in terms of $2 \cdot n$. Similarly you could prove a theorem about all negative integers by using a base case of $n = -1$ and an induction step in which you use the $n = k$ case to demonstrate the $n = k - 1$ case.

13.5   Summary

In this chapter, we introduced *mathematical induction*, a technique formally used to prove statements about the natural numbers. The use of induction is central to the analysis of algorithms, both in terms of their correctness and often their efficiency. In the next chapter, we will study *recurrences* which are used in the analysis of recursive algorithms (such as MERGE-SORT), and we shall see that induction plays a central role in such analyses.

Exercises

Exercise 13.1

a. Consider the series

$$1 \cdot 2 + 2 \cdot 3 + 3 \cdot 4 + \cdots + n \cdot (n + 1) = \sum_{k=1}^{n} k(k + 1).$$

Show that

$$\sum_{k=1}^{n} k(k + 1) = \frac{n(n + 1)(n + 2)}{3}$$

by induction.

b. Now consider the series

$$\frac{1}{1 \cdot 2} + \frac{1}{2 \cdot 3} + \frac{1}{3 \cdot 4} + \cdots + \frac{1}{n \cdot (n + 1)} = \sum_{k=1}^{n} \frac{1}{k(k + 1)}.$$

Show that

$$\sum_{k=1}^{n} \frac{1}{k(k + 1)} = 1 - \frac{1}{n + 1}$$

by induction.

CHAPTER 14

Recurrences

The running times of most inherently recursive procedures, such as MERGE-SORT, lend themselves to specification and analysis via *recurrences*. In this chapter, we discuss how one specifies recurrences and how one solves such recurrences.

14.1   Specifying Recurrences

A recurrence is simply a mathematical formula that specifies the running time of the algorithm on n elements, $T(n)$, as a function of the running time on some smaller number of elements (e.g., $T(n/2)$) plus some amount of overhead. For example, consider MERGE-SORT. In order to MERGE-SORT n elements, one must

1. recursively call MERGE-SORT on the first and second halves of the n elements and then

2. merge the sorted subgroups returned by the recursive calls.

So, what is the running time of MERGE-SORT? If we let $T(n)$ represent the total running time of MERGE-SORT on n elements, then in Step 1 above, $T(n/2)$ must be the running time of MERGE-SORT on each of the first and second halves of those n elements. In Step 2, on the order of n operations is required to merge two sorted groups whose total size is n. Therefore, the total running time of MERGE-SORT, $T(n)$, is twice $T(n/2)$ (for the recursive calls) plus on the order of n work to perform the merge. Pulling this all together, we have

$$T(n) = 2\,T(n/2) + n. \qquad (14.1)$$

There are a few subtleties in the above description that we have glossed over:

1. What if n is not even so that $n/2$ is not an integer? If n were 27, how could one recursively call MERGE-SORT on 13 1/2 elements?

2. What does "on the order of n operations" mean, anyway?

3. What happens when n gets small? The recursion eventually has to stop, right?

To answer the first question, we note that in reality MERGE-SORT splits the set of n elements as evenly as possible, and this is specified in the code for MERGE-SORT itself: one recursive call is on $\lfloor n/2 \rfloor$ elements and the other recursive call is on $\lceil n/2 \rceil$ elements. If n is even, we do have two recursive calls on exactly $n/2$ elements each; if n is odd, we have recursive call on $(n-1)/2$ and $(n+1)/2$ elements, respectively. So in reality, our recurrence is more precisely

$$T(n) = T(\lfloor n/2 \rfloor) + T(\lceil n/2 \rceil) + n. \tag{14.2}$$

However, one can show that for the class of recurrences corresponding to the overwhelming majority of real recursive procedures and programs, the floors and ceilings do not affect the analysis in any significant way. In other words, Recurrence 14.2 "behaves" just like Recurrence 14.1.

To answer the second question, one must specify precisely what "effort" one is counting. The merge operation in MERGE-SORT, for example, involves comparing elements, copying elements, incrementing counters, etc. Should we count compares? Compares and copies? Program lines executed? Microseconds of wall-clock time? The answer is to count all and none of them.

The merge operation entails somewhere between $\lfloor n/2 \rfloor$ and n compares and exactly n copies. Each compare or copy is associated with a few lines of program code plus some constant overhead. Each line of code may be executed in some number of microseconds, etc. So, depending on what "effort" one is counting, we might assess the merge as requiring n, $2n$, $15n + 6$, or some similar amount of "effort." However, each of these accountings is effectively the same, they're just in different *units: n compares, 2n counts and compares, 15n + 6 program lines*, and so on. It's analogous to seconds vs. minutes vs. hours.

What's important is the fact that *all* of these accountings grow *linearly* in n (as opposed to, say, n^2). In algorithmic analysis, one cares about the *asymptotic growth rate* (i.e., the function of n, say n vs. n^2) and not constant factors, lower order terms, or specific "units" of accounting. Furthermore, one can show that for the class of recurrences corresponding to the overwhelming majority of real recursive procedures and programs, dropping the constant factors (e.g., the "15" in $15n + 6$) and lower order terms (e.g., the "6" in $15n + 6$) does not affect the asymptotic analysis in any way. Thus, while our recurrence may precisely be

$$T(n) = T(\lfloor n/2 \rfloor) + T(\lceil n/2 \rceil) + 15n + 6, \tag{14.3}$$

(as measured in units of program lines), Recurrence 14.3 "behaves" (asymptotically) just like Recurrence 14.1.

Dropping constant factors and lower order terms yields what is referred to as "order notation" indexorder notation for example, "$15n + 6$" is said to be "on the order of n." Order notation is used so often in mathematics and computer science that a special notation has been developed for it: one would write $15n + 6 = \Theta(n)$, where Θ is the Greek capital letter "theta." Variants on this notation include O (big-oh) and Ω (big-omega) which roughly correspond to "at most on the order of" (big-oh) and "at least on the order of" (big-omega). Θ, O, and Ω are the asymptotic analogues of $=$, $\leq$, and $\geq$.

Finally, to answer the third question, we note that recursive procedures do eventually terminate when some base condition is met. In the case of MERGE-SORT, a one item list need not be recursive split in order to be sorted: it is already (trivially) sorted. Thus, MERGE-SORT returns in (on the order of) one unit of time when called on a list of length one. Thus, $T(1) = 1$. This is a *base case* of the recurrence. Our recurrence is therefore more precisely

$$T(n) = \begin{cases} 1 & \text{if } n = 1 \\ 2\,T(n/2) + n & \text{if } n > 1. \end{cases} \tag{14.4}$$

A recurrence may have more than one base case (for instance, a recursive procedure may specify different termination actions when $n = 1$, $n = 2$, and $n = 3$). However, for all recurrences corresponding to the overwhelming majority of real recursive procedures and programs, the base case(s) take some small, constant amount of "effort" and are thus "on the order of" 1. So, a recurrence of the form given by Recurrence 14.1 is *implicitly* assumed to be of the form given by Recurrence 14.4, unless the base case(s) are given *explicitly*. So, after all those subtleties, we are back where we started:

$$T(n) = 2\,T(n/2) + n.$$

How can one solve such recurrences?

14.2   Solving Recurrences

Consider our recurrence $T(n) = 2T(n/2) + n$. In order to solve the recurrence, it is good practice to first rewrite the recurrence with the recursive component *last* and to use a generic parameter not to be confused with n. We may think of the following equation as our general pattern, which holds for any value of $\square$.

$$T(\square) = \square + 2\,T(\square/2) \tag{14.5}$$

Since our pattern (Equation 14.5) is valid for any value of □, we may use it to "iterate" the recurrence as follows.

$$
\begin{aligned}
T(n) &= n + 2\,T(n/2) \\
&= n + 2\left(n/2 + 2\,T(n/2^2)\right) \\
&= n + n + 2^2\,T(n/2^2) \quad\quad\quad\quad\quad\quad (14.6) \\
&= 2n + 2^2\,T(n/2^2) \quad\quad\quad\quad\quad\quad\;\; (14.7)
\end{aligned}
$$

Always simplify the expression, eliminating parentheses and combining terms as in Equations 14.6 and 14.7, before expanding further. Continuing...

$$
\begin{aligned}
T(n) &= 2n + 2^2\left(n/2^2 + 2\,T(n/2^3)\right) \\
&= 2n + n + 2^3\,T(n/2^3) \\
&= 3n + 2^3\,T(n/2^3) \\
&= 3n + 2^3\left(n/2^3 + 2\,T(n/2^4)\right) \\
&= 3n + n + 2^4\,T(n/2^4) \\
&= 4n + 2^4\,T(n/2^4)
\end{aligned}
$$

Notice the pattern that has been developed:

$$
T(n) = n + 2\,T(n/2) = 2n + 2^2\,T(n/2^2) = 3n + 2^3\,T(n/2^3) = 4n + 2^4\,T(n/2^4).
$$

Thus, we expect that for any k, we would have

$$
T(n) = k \cdot n + 2^k\,T(n/2^k).
$$

Formally, one must *prove* that this pattern is, indeed, correct (and we shall do so later in this chapter), but *assuming* that it is correct, we may continue as follows.

Given that $T(n) = k \cdot n + 2^k\,T(n/2^k)$ for all k, we next choose a value of k that causes our recurrence to reach a known base case, e.g., $T(1)$. For what value of k does $n/2^k = 1$? We must solve for k in this equation...

$$
\begin{aligned}
n/2^k &= 1 \\
\Leftrightarrow \qquad n &= 2^k \\
\Leftrightarrow \qquad \log_2 n &= k
\end{aligned}
$$

Since $n/2^k = 1$ when $k = \log_2 n$ and $T(1) = 1$, we have

$$
\begin{aligned}
T(n) &= k \cdot n + 2^k \, T(n/2^k) \\
&= \log_2(n) \cdot n + 2^{\log_2 n} \, T(1) \\
&= n \log_2 n + n \cdot 1 \\
&= n \log_2 n + n
\end{aligned}
$$

Dropping the lower order term, we have that $T(n)$ is on the order of $n \log_2 n$, and we would write

$$
T(n) = \Theta(n \log_2 n).
$$

Thus, MERGE-SORT is not quite as fast as linear search, which is $\Theta(n)$, but it is faster than INSERTION-SORT, which is $\Theta(n^2)$.

To complete our analysis, we next prove that the pattern we used was indeed correct.

Claim 1 *For all $k \geq 1$, if we iterate the equation $T(n) = 2\,T(n/2) + n$ a total of k times, we obtain $T(n) = k \cdot n + 2^k \, T(n/2^k)$.*

Note that we are making a claim about the *iterative pattern* one obtains by "unfolding" the recurrence equation k times, rather than a claim about the actual solution to the recurrence. For the actual recurrence, our iterative pattern only makes sense when $k \leq \log_2 n$, as we then reach a base case as shown above. Our proof about the form of the iterative pattern is by induction.

Proof: The proof is by induction on k. The base case, $k = 1$, is trivially true since the result matches the original recurrence equation. For the inductive step, assume that the statement is true for $k - 1$; i.e.,

$$
T(n) = (k - 1) \cdot n + 2^{k-1} \, T(n/2^{k-1}).
$$

Our task is then to show that the statement is true for k. This may be accomplished by starting with this *inductive hypothesis* and applying the given recurrence equation, as follows.

$$
\begin{aligned}
T(n) &= (k-1) \cdot n + 2^{k-1} \, T(n/2^{k-1}) \\
&= (k-1) \cdot n + 2^{k-1} \left(n/2^{k-1} + 2 \, T(n/2^k) \right) \\
&= (k-1) \cdot n + n + 2^k \, T(n/2^k) \\
&= k \cdot n + 2^k \, T(n/2^k)
\end{aligned}
$$

$\square$

14.3   Summary

In this chapter, we have seen how recurrences can be used to model the running time of recursive algorithms such as MERGE-SORT, and we have demonstrated one method for solving recurrences via *iteration*. Not all recurrences lend themselves easily to analysis via iteration, but many of those that naturally arise in the context of analyzing the running time of algorithms do. Other techniques exist for solving recurrences, and any text on *Algorithms* would be a good resource to learn such techniques.

Exercises

Exercise 14.1

Solve the following recurrences via iteration. Assume a base case of $T(1) = 1$. As part of your solution, you will need to establish a pattern for what the recurrence looks like after the k-th iteration. You need *not* formally prove that your patterns are correct. Your solutions may involve n raised to a power and/or logarithms of n. For example, a solution of the form $9^{\log_3 n}$ is unacceptable; this should be simplified as $n^{\log_3 9} = n^2$.

   i. $T(n) = 4 \, T(n/2) + n.$

   ii. $T(n) = 4 \, T(n/2) + n^2.$

CHAPTER 15

Growth of Functions

In previous chapters, we have encountered the functions n, $\sqrt{n}$, and $\log_2(n)$ with respect to algorithms for search, and the functions $n \log_2 n$ and n^2 with respect to algorithms for sorting. What difference is there among algorithms whose running times correspond to these functions?

Let's assume that your computer can perform 10,000 operations (e.g., data structure manipulations, database inserts, etc.) per second. Given algorithms that require $\lg n$, $n^{1/2}$, n, $n \lg n$, n^2, n^3, n^4, n^6, 2^n, and $n!$ operations to perform a given task on n items, here's how long it would take to process 10, 50, 100, and 1,000 items.

			n	
	10	50	100	1,000
$\lg n$	0.0003 sec	0.0006 sec	0.0007 sec	0.0010 sec
$n^{1/2}$	0.0003 sec	0.0007 sec	0.0010 sec	0.0032 sec
n	0.0010 sec	0.0050 sec	0.0100 sec	0.1000 sec
$n \lg n$	0.0033 sec	0.0282 sec	0.0664 sec	0.9966 sec
n^2	0.0100 sec	0.2500 sec	1.0000 sec	100.00 sec
n^3	0.1000 sec	12.500 sec	100.00 sec	1.1574 day
n^4	1.0000 sec	10.427 min	2.7778 hrs	3.1710 yrs
n^6	1.6667 min	18.102 day	3.1710 yrs	3171.0 cen
2^n	0.1024 sec	35.702 cen	4×10^{16} cen	1×10^{166} cen
$n!$	362.88 sec	1×10^{51} cen	3×10^{144} cen	1×10^{2554} cen

Table 15.1: Time required to process n items at a speed of 10,000 operations/sec using ten different algorithms. *Note:* The units above are seconds (sec), minutes (min), hours (hrs), days (day), years (yrs), and centuries (cen)!

Note the explosive growth of the exponential and factorial algorithms, rendering them nearly useless for all practical purposes. The explosive growth of the exponential and factorial functions is explored in more detail in the tables that follow.

n						
15	20	25	30	35	40	45
3.28 sec	1.75 min	55.9 min	1.24 days	39.8 days	3.48 yrs	1.12 cen

Table 15.2: Time required to process n items at a speed of 10,000 operations/sec using a 2^n algorithm.

n						
11	12	13	14	15	16	17
1.11 hrs	13.3 hrs	7.20 days	101 days	4.15 yrs	66.3 yrs	11.3 cen

Table 15.3: Time required to process n items at a speed of 10,000 operations/sec using an $n!$ algorithm.

Algorithms whose running times are slower than n^3 (e.g., the n^4, n^6, 2^n, and $n!$ algorithms in the tables above) are generally too slow to be useful on meaningfully large data sets, and 2^n and $n!$ algorithms are effectively useless on all but trivially small data sets. One of the goals of a course in algorithms is to provide the techniques for developing fast and practical polynomial-time algorithms; unfortunately, the theory of NP-completeness that one typically studies in a theory of computation course dictates that there are large classes of interesting computer science problems that in all likelihood cannot be solved faster than exponential (e.g., 2^n) time.

A plot of the functions $\lg n$, $\sqrt{n}$, n, $n \lg n$, and n^2 is shown in Figure 15.1. Note that $\lg n$ and $\sqrt{n}$ are nearly identical in the range $[1, 10]$ shown, though $\lg n$ grows much more slowly than $\sqrt{n}$ for larger values of n. Further note the large disparity in the values of the functions n, $n \lg n$, and n^2 even over this limited range; these differences become even more dramatic as n becomes larger, thus emphasizing the importance of asymptotic efficiency in algorithm design.

15.1   Summary

In this chapter, we have investigated the impact of various asymptotic running times on the practical utility of algorithms exhibiting those running times. The study of *Algorithms* is largely devoted to developing provably correct and *efficient* solutions to various problems, i.e., those solutions whose running times render them practicable, as described above.

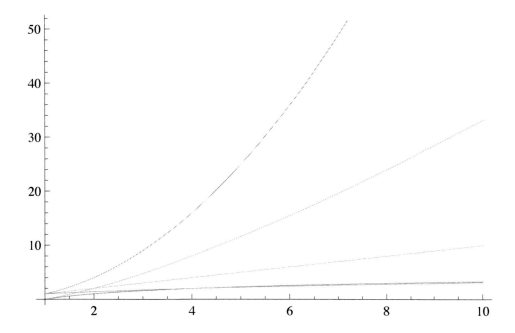

Figure 15.1: A plot of the functions $\lg n$, $\sqrt{n}$, n, $n \lg n$, and n^2 over the range $n \in [1, 10]$.

PCR

PCR stands for **polymerase chain reaction**. PCR is a technique to generate millions of copies of a particular DNA sequence from a single piece of DNA. The words chain reaction accurately capture the essence of the technique. In a nuclear chain reaction one nucleus splits emitting particles that then cause two other nuclei to split which in turn cause four and then eight and then sixteen setting off an exponential explosion, literally. Similarly PCR creates an explosion of copies. Polymerase is an enzyme that enables the chain reaction and we will explain its role in greater detail in what follows. At its heart PCR is actually an *algorithm*. And it is possible to understand how PCR works without understanding all the deep biology and chemistry underlying it. [6]

16.1 Why is PCR Such a Major Breakthrough?

PCR is such a major breakthrough that biochemists and molecular biologists refer to biology as essentially consisting of two epochs before PCR and after PCR. Before PCR was invented creating copies of DNA sequences involved painstaking and back-breaking lab work. Numerous hours had to be spent with reagents in test tubes to splice longer sequences and then separate the desired portion using centrifuges and mass spectrometers. But all this work resulted in a very low yield

PCR was invented (demonstrated) by Kary Mullis on 16 December 1983 while working as a chemist at (the now defunct) Cetus Corp. PCR is now so commonplace that it is considered as indispensable and ordinary as the test tube. It is utilized for a wide variety of applications. These include DNA cloning for sequencing, DNA-based phylogeny, or functional analysis of genes; the diagnosis of hereditary diseases; the identification of genetic fingerprints (used in forensic sciences and paternity testing); and the detection and diagnosis of infectious diseases. When detectives on *CSI* nail a suspect by lifting his DNA prints from a drinking glass that's PCR in action.

In 1993, Mullis was awarded the Nobel Prize in Chemistry (along with Michael Smith) for his work on PCR.

16.2   Why is PCR Controversial?

Almost as soon as news of the discovery of PCR hit the scientific establishment, controversy erupted. According to Mullis it was in the spring of 1983 while driving on the highway late one night with his girlfriend that he got the idea for PCR. Cetus awarded him $10,000 for the patent filing. A spate of lawsuits followed with Du Pont ultimately losing out to Roche which acquired Cetus for three hundred million dollars. Academics pointed out that a 1968 paper of Hargobind Khorana (another Nobel Prize winner) and Kjell Kleppe had foreseen many of the central points of the discovery. Senate committees were convened to debate whether PCR was really a discovery at all and whether a patent was justified for something in which no new biology or chemistry was invented.

The main reason for all the controversy was the enormous amount of money at stake. Another factor in the controversy was the personality of Kary Mullis, which is/was quirky to say the least. After his PhD from Berkeley he quit science to pursue a career as a sci-fi writer before returning to Cetus as a biochemist. He has openly promoted fields such as astrology in addition to being an AIDS denialist and a climate change denialist. He has claimed to talk to extraterrestrials. He has decried establishment science and lab work claiming that he did his best work while surfing or driving.

16.3   Basic Biology

We need to know just a minimal amount of biology to follow PCR. In particular we need to know about DNA. Deoxyribonucleic acid (DNA) is a nucleic acid containing the genetic instructions used in the development and functioning of most known living organisms. The DNA segments carrying this genetic information are called genes. DNA consists of two long polymers of simple units called nucleotides. These two strands run in opposite directions to each other. Each nucleotide contains one of four types of molecules called bases (or nucleobases or nucleic acids). These four bases are denoted: A (adenine), T (thymine), C (cytosine) and G (guanine). (It is the sequence of these four bases along the backbone that encodes information. This information is read using the genetic code, which specifies the sequence of the amino acids within proteins.

The code is read by copying stretches of DNA into the related nucleic acid RNA in a process called transcription.)

For our purposes we can think of a strand of DNA as consisting of a directed sequence of bases:

$$A \rightarrow T \rightarrow T \rightarrow C \rightarrow A \rightarrow G \rightarrow T$$

Within cells DNA is organized into long structures called chromosomes characterized by the now-legendary Watson-Crick double-helix structure comprised of two anti-parallel strands with the weak bonds: $A - T$ and $C - G$. The above single strand is part of the following double-stranded DNA:

$$
\begin{array}{ccccccccccccc}
A & \rightarrow & T & \rightarrow & T & \rightarrow & C & \rightarrow & A & \rightarrow & G & \rightarrow & T \\
| & & | & & | & & | & & | & & | & & | \\
T & \leftarrow & A & \leftarrow & A & \leftarrow & G & \leftarrow & T & \leftarrow & C & \leftarrow & A
\end{array}
$$

16.4 Elementary Transformations

Rather than present Mullis discovery right away we are going to present the basic operations on DNA that were well-known at the time of the discovery.

First, when a test tube of double stranded DNA is heated (in a controlled fashion) then it breaks up into two constituent and complementary single strands:

$$
\begin{array}{ccccccccccccc}
A & \rightarrow & T & \rightarrow & T & \rightarrow & C & \rightarrow & A & \rightarrow & G & \rightarrow & T \\
| & & | & & | & & | & & | & & | & & | \\
T & \leftarrow & A & \leftarrow & A & \leftarrow & G & \leftarrow & T & \leftarrow & C & \leftarrow & A
\end{array}
$$

breaks into

$$A \rightarrow T \rightarrow T \rightarrow C \rightarrow A \rightarrow G \rightarrow T$$

and

$$T \leftarrow A \leftarrow A \leftarrow G \leftarrow T \leftarrow C \leftarrow A$$

Second when single strands of DNA are cooled then complementary copies (if sufficient in proportion) will rejoin and form the complete double stranded DNA. This is the reverse of heating.

Third, when a single strand of DNA is cooled in a test tube with an abundant supply of bases along with polymerase the polymerase will create a complementary strand by moving along the given strand and adding bases one by one. Thus for example, polymerase could start adding to the strand as follows:

$$A \rightarrow T \rightarrow T \rightarrow C \rightarrow A \rightarrow G \rightarrow T$$

becomes

$$
\begin{array}{ccccccccccccc}
A & \rightarrow & T & \rightarrow & T & \rightarrow & C & \rightarrow & A & \rightarrow & G & \rightarrow & T \\
& & & & & & & & & & | & & | \\
& & & & & & & & & & C & \leftarrow & A
\end{array}
$$

Note that polymerase will only add in the complementary direction to the given strand; in other words, if polymerase started adding in the middle then it could not complete the initial part:

$$
\begin{array}{ccccccccccccc}
A & \rightarrow & T & \rightarrow & T & \rightarrow & C & \rightarrow & A & \rightarrow & G & \rightarrow & T \\
| & & | & & | & & & & & & & & \\
T & \leftarrow & A & \leftarrow & A & & & & & & & &
\end{array}
$$

Further, note that complementary strands started by polymerase are not stable until they are many (tens of) bases long. This means that the addition of polymerase will only rarely result in a complementary strand that starts at the beginning and goes all the way to the end. More typically it would start somewhere in the middle and continue to the end.

Lastly, it is possible to get quantities of short DNA strands (tens of bases) called **primers** through conventional (pre-PCR) techniques.

16.5   The PCR Algorithm

So here is the problem: given a small quantity of DNA containing a DNA (sub)sequence of interest, create a large number of copies of the DNA sequence.

And at this point, knowing about DNA, heating, cooling, polymerase and primers you know everything that Kary Mullis knew at the time of his revolutionary discovery.

Here is the solution to the problem. Let the given double strand be

$$
\begin{array}{ccccccc}
\cdots & \rightarrow & o & \rightarrow & \cdots & \rightarrow & \omega & \rightarrow & \cdots \\
& & | & & & & | & & \\
\cdots & \leftarrow & \acute{o} & \leftarrow & \cdots & \leftarrow & \acute{\omega} & \leftarrow & \cdots
\end{array}
$$

and let the sequence of interest be bracketed between o and ω, i.e. $o \rightarrow \cdots \rightarrow \omega$.

Mullis brilliant idea was to add enough primers o and $\acute{\omega}$ and then to heat and cool repeatedly in cycles. Observe what happens after the first heating:

$$
\begin{array}{ccccccc}
\cdots & \rightarrow & o & \rightarrow & \cdots & \rightarrow & \omega & \rightarrow & \cdots \\
\cdots & \leftarrow & \acute{o} & \leftarrow & \cdots & \leftarrow & \acute{\omega} & \leftarrow & \cdots
\end{array}
$$

Now comes the magic of polymerase with the primers, and we get:

$$\cdots \quad \to \quad \mathrm{o} \quad \to \quad \cdots \quad \to \quad \omega \quad \to \quad \cdots$$
$$| \qquad\qquad\qquad |$$
$$\cdots \quad \leftarrow \quad \acute{\mathrm{o}} \quad \leftarrow \quad \cdots \quad \leftarrow \quad \acute{\omega} \quad \leftarrow$$

and

$$\to \quad \mathrm{o} \quad \to \quad \cdots \quad \to \quad \omega \quad \to \quad \cdots$$
$$| \qquad\qquad\qquad |$$
$$\cdots \quad \leftarrow \quad \acute{\mathrm{o}} \quad \leftarrow \quad \cdots \quad \leftarrow \quad \acute{\omega} \quad \leftarrow \quad \cdots$$

After the second heating:

$$\cdots \quad \to \quad \mathrm{o} \quad \to \quad \cdots \quad \to \quad \omega \quad \to \quad \cdots$$

and

$$\cdots \quad \leftarrow \quad \acute{\mathrm{o}} \quad \leftarrow \quad \cdots \quad \leftarrow \quad \acute{\omega} \quad \leftarrow$$

and

$$\to \quad \mathrm{o} \quad \to \quad \cdots \quad \to \quad \omega \quad \to \quad \cdots$$

and

$$\cdots \quad \leftarrow \quad \acute{\mathrm{o}} \quad \leftarrow \quad \cdots \quad \leftarrow \quad \acute{\omega} \quad \leftarrow \quad \cdots$$

So far we are getting more than our desired sequence (or its complement) we are getting extensions of our desired sequence (or its complement). Let us denote the desired sequence or its complement by D. Let us denote a sequence that extends the desired sequence (or its complement) on both ends by _D_ and let us denote a sequence that extends the desired (or its complement) on only one end by D_. In other words we use _D_ to denote both:

$$\cdots \quad \to \quad \mathrm{o} \quad \to \quad \cdots \quad \to \quad \omega \quad \to \quad \cdots$$

and

$$\cdots \quad \leftarrow \quad \acute{\mathrm{o}} \quad \leftarrow \quad \cdots \quad \leftarrow \quad \acute{\omega} \quad \leftarrow \quad \cdots$$

We use D_ to denote (both):

$$\cdots \quad \leftarrow \quad \acute{\mathrm{o}} \quad \leftarrow \quad \cdots \quad \leftarrow \quad \acute{\omega} \quad \leftarrow$$

and

$$\to \quad \mathrm{o} \quad \to \quad \cdots \quad \to \quad \omega \quad \to \quad \cdots$$

We use D to denote:

$$\acute{\mathrm{o}} \quad \leftarrow \quad \cdots \quad \leftarrow \quad \acute{\omega}$$

and

$$\mathrm{o} \quad \to \quad \cdots \quad \to \quad \omega$$

Observe that after the first heating we have 2 _D_s. After two heatings we have 2 _D_s and 2 D_s. Once again we see the magic of polymerase with the primers: after the third heating we get 2 _D_s, 4 D_s and 2 D so we have two copies (or complements) of the desired sequence.

If we have 2 _D_s to start, we will always have just 2 _D_s. Each of these will yield a new D_ with each heating while the D_s will each yield a D_ and a D. After n heating cycles, we have 2 _D_s and $2(n-1)$ D_s as there were none after the first heating but we then added 2 with each cycle. Each existing D_ will yield a D and each existing D will yield 2 Ds with the next heating cycle. The number of Ds after n cycles is $2^n - 2n$.

If we create a table of tallies of the three kinds of sequences we get:

Heating Cycle	_D_	D_	D
1	2	0	0
2	2	2	0
3	2	4	2
4	2	6	8
5	2	8	22
n	2	$2(n-1)$	$2^n - 2n$

Observe that each row totals to 2^n as it should. Observe also that the number of _D_s is constant while the number of D_s grows linearly and the number of the desired sequence D grows exponentially.

Below we plot a tally of the three kinds of sequences to get a sense for why exponential growth is so explosive.

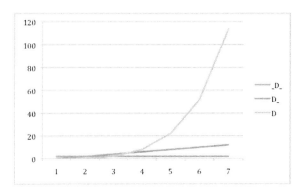

Figure 16.1: Exponential (D) vs. Linear (D_) vs. Constant (_D_)

16.6   Summary

In this chapter, we have investigated the PCR technique, providing an analysis of how PCR behaves over time. We showed that the number of desired sequences grows exponentially while other sequences grow only linearly or remain constant. As our discussion in the previous chapter indicates, the desired sequences whose numbers grow exponentially will quite quickly overwhelm those sequences which only grow linearly (or remain constant), thus emphasizing the importance of the relative growth of functions in this context. For additional reading on the PCR technique, see Wikipedia: Polymerase chain reaction [9].

Part V

Networks: Graphs and Trees

CHAPTER 17

Graphs

We use graphs to model networks such as computer, airline, phone, or social networks. They can also be used to model such diverse things as connections between data in a database or molecular structure.

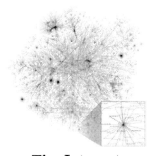

High School Dating Patterns
Mark Newman's Gallery of Network Images

The Internet
Bill Cheswick's Internet Mapping Project

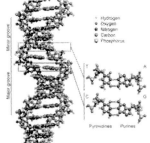

Boston Subway
MBTA Maps and Schedules

DNA
Santa Monica College - animated image

Figure 17.1: Samples of Graphs: Dating, the Internet, MBTA, DNA

217

17.1 Simple Graphs

A *simple graph*[1] $G = (V, E)$ is a set of *vertices* V connected by *edges* E.

An *edge* in a simple graph is just an unordered pair of vertices, i.e. a set containing two vertices. The two vertices of an edge are said to be *adjacent*. We talk about going along an edge to get to one vertex from another. In a simple graph, each edge is like a two-way street. When an edge e connects two vertices u and v, we write $e = \{u, v\}$ or $e = \{v, u\}$[2]. An edge cannot go from a vertex to itself.

Example 17.1

This graph has six vertices and seven edges.

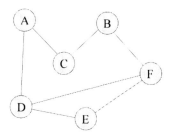

$V = \{A, B, C, D, E, F\}$
$E = \{\{A, C\}, \{A, D\}\{D, F\}, \{D, E\}, \{C, B\}, \{B, F\}, \{F, E\}\}$
Vertices D and F are adjacent.
Vertices C and E are not adjacent.

We say an edge $e = \{v, u\}$ is *incident* to the vertices u and v. The *degree*, $deg(v)$ of a vertex is the number of edges that are incident to it.

Example 17.2

In the graph of example 17.1 vertices A, B, C, and E have degree 2. Vertices D and F have degree 3.

If u and v are vertices in a graph $G = (V, E)$, a *path* of *length* n from u to v is a sequence of vertices $\langle v_0, v_1, \cdots, v_n \rangle$ in V such that $u = v_0$, $v = v_n$, and such that $\{v_k, v_{k+1}\} \in E$ for $0 \le k \le n - 1$. That is, each successive pair of vertices is connected by an edge. We say that

---

[1]also called an *undirected graph*
[2]Graph theorists often write (u, v) for a bidirectional edge even though it really is a set as the ordering doesn't matter. We will stick with $\{v, u\}$ to emphasize this fact.

the path *contains* the vertices $v_0, v_1, \cdots, v_n$ and the edges $\{v_k, v_{k+1}\}$, $0 \le k \le n-1$. Note that the *length of a path* is the number of edges in the path. The path $\langle u \rangle$ is a path of length 0 from u to itself.

A vertex v is *reachable* from a vertex u if there is a path from u to v. We also say that u and v are *path connected* if there is a path from u to v. The *connected component* of a vertex u is the set of all vertices v such that v is reachable from u.

Example 17.3

Here are some paths in the graph of example 17.1:

$\langle A, C, B, F \rangle$ is a path from vertex A to vertex F.

$\langle F, E, D \rangle$ is a path from vertex F to vertex D.

$\langle D, E, F \rangle$ is a path from vertex D to vertex F.

$\langle D, F \rangle$ is also a path from vertex D to vertex F.

$\langle D, A, C, B, F \rangle$ is another path from vertex D to vertex F.

$\langle D, A, C, B, F, D, E, F, D, E, F \rangle$ is a long path from vertex D to vertex F.

Example 17.4

This graph has eight vertices and eight edges.

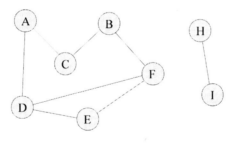

$V = \{A, B, C, D, E, F, H, I\}$

$E = \{\{A, C\}, \{A, D\}, \{D, F\}, \{D, E\}, \{C, B\}, \{B, F\}, \{F, E\}, \{H, I\}\}$

All the paths in example 17.3 are paths in this graph too.

$\langle HI \rangle$ is a path from H to I.

There is no path from vertex D to vertex I. Vertex I is not reachable from the vertex D.

The vertices A, B, C, D, E, and F are all path connected to each other.

The connected component of C is $\{A, B, C, D, E, F\}$.

The connected component of H is $\{H, I\}$.

A *simple path* is a path that has no repeated vertices. If you follow a simple path, you will never go through that same vertex twice.

Example 17.5

The paths $\langle D, E, F \rangle$, $\langle D, F \rangle$, and $\langle D, A, C, B, F \rangle$ are all simple paths from vertex D to vertex F in the graph of example 17.4 . The path $\langle D, A, C, B, F, D, E, F, D, E, F \rangle$ is not a simple path from vertex D to vertex F as it goes through each of the vertices D, E, and F multiple times.

A *cycle* is a path $\langle v_0, v_1, \cdots, v_n \rangle$ such that the vertices $\langle v_1, \cdots, v_n \rangle$ are distinct and $v_0 = v_n$. A cycle is just a closed path or loop that has no repeated vertices except for ending up where it started.

Example 17.6

This is the graph of example 17.4.

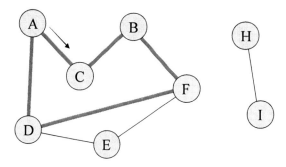

The path $\langle A, C, B, F, D, A \rangle$ is shown in blue. The path starts at vertex A and proceeds in the direction of the arrow. These paths $\langle D, E, F, D \rangle$ and $\langle F, E, D, F \rangle$ are also cycles in the graph.

The paths $\langle D, E, F, D, E, F, D \rangle$ and $\langle D, E, F, D, A \rangle$ are not cycles.

17.2 Weighted Graphs

In the graphs we have looked at so far, all edges were treated as equal. If the graph is a model of a highway system with the edges representing roads and the vertices representing cities, then each edge will have a distance associated with it. If a graph represents a computer network, each edge might have a bandwidth. For an airline network, the edges would have prices of tickets. A *weighted graph* $G = (V, E, w)$ is a simple graph with a *weight* associated with each edge that is given by a function $w : E \to \mathbb{R}$. When we draw a weighted graph, we put the weights on or next to the edges. In the graph below, $w(\{A, B\}) = 7$ and $w(\{H, N\}) = 3$. The *weight of a path* is the sum of the weights of its edges.

Example 17.7

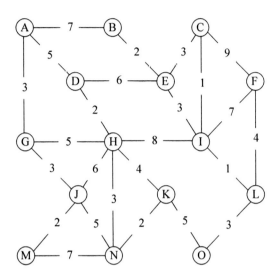

In this weighted graph, the edge $\{H, N\}$ has weight 3.

The weight of the path $\langle A, D, H, K, O \rangle = 5 + 2 + 4 + 5 = 16$.

The paths $\langle E, D, H, K \rangle$ and $\langle E, C, F, L, O, K \rangle$ are both paths from E to K. The weight of $\langle E, D, H, K \rangle = 6 + 2 + 4 = 12$ and the weight of $\langle E, C, F, L, O, K \rangle = 3 + 9 + 4 + 3 + 5 = 24$.

17.3   Graph Data Structures

There are many operations we need to do with graph structures. When you look for a flight on Travelocity, its computer must find a path between the cities you name. When it finds the cheapest flight, it is actually finding the path with the lowest weight. Before we can write programs to do these searches, we must have a way of representing graphs that our programs can understand. We could just keep a list of the vertices and a list of the edges, but it is time consuming to search through such lists to find paths. There are two standard representations of graphs that are used in computer programs: *adjacency lists* and *adjacency matrices*.

17.3.1   Adjacency List

The *adjacency list* of a graph $G = (V, E)$ is an array of the vertices and a list, for each vertex, of the vertices adjacent to it, i.e all the vertices $u \in V$ such that $\{v, u\} \in E$. With an adjacency list, it is easy to find all the vertices that are adjacent to a given vertex which is the same as finding all the edges incident to that vertex.

Example 17.8

Here is a simple graph and its adjacency list.

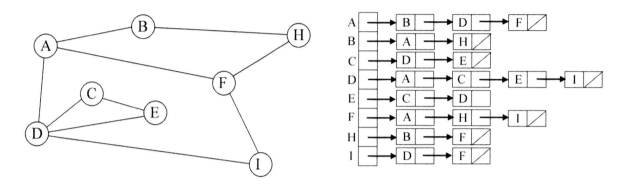

For a weighted graph, we need a way to store the weights as well as the vertices and edges. We store these weights in the adjacency lists right next to the names of the adjacent vertices.

Example 17.9

Here is a weighted graph and its adjacency list.

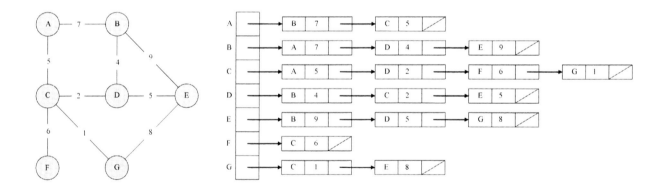

17.3.2 Matrices

A *matrix* is just a two-dimensional array of numbers. Matrices are very important in mathematics as they provide a concise and algebraically useful way of representing linear functions on *n*-dimensional spaces. In computer science, you will see them used for such diverse things as solving systems of linear equations and representing rotations in computer graphics. Here, we use them to represent simple graphs.

Formally, an $n \times m$ matrix A has n rows and m columns. We write $A = (a_{ij})$ where (a_{ij}) is the number in row i and column j. The numbers (a_{ij}) are called the *elements* of A.

Example 17.10

The matrix A below is a 3×4 matrix. $a_{13} = 6$, $a_{31} = 0$, $a_{24} = 8$, and there is no a_{42}.

$$A = \begin{bmatrix} 3 & 0 & 6 & 7 \\ 5 & 2 & 9 & 8 \\ 0 & 1 & 7 & 4 \end{bmatrix}$$

17.3.3   Adjacency Matrix

Given the simple graph $G = (V, E)$, assume $V = \{v_1, v_2, \cdots, v_n\}$ where $n = |V|$. Recall that $|V|$ is the cardinality of V which is just the number of vertices in the graph. The *adjacency matrix* of $G = (V, E)$ is a $|V| \times |V|$ matrix, $adj = (a_{ij})$ where

$$a_{ij} = \begin{cases} 1 & \text{if there is an edge}\{v_i, v_j\} \in E. \\ 0 & \text{otherwise} \end{cases}$$

Example 17.11

Here is the same simple graph as in example 17.8, this time with its adjacency matrix.

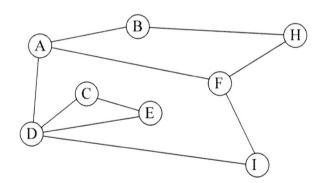

$$\begin{array}{c} \\ A \\ B \\ C \\ D \\ E \\ F \\ H \\ I \end{array} \begin{array}{cccccccc} A & B & C & D & E & F & H & I \\ \begin{bmatrix} 0 & 1 & 0 & 1 & 0 & 1 & 0 & 0 \\ 1 & 0 & 0 & 0 & 0 & 0 & 1 & 0 \\ 0 & 0 & 0 & 1 & 1 & 0 & 0 & 0 \\ 1 & 0 & 1 & 0 & 1 & 0 & 0 & 1 \\ 0 & 0 & 1 & 1 & 0 & 0 & 0 & 0 \\ 1 & 0 & 0 & 0 & 0 & 0 & 1 & 1 \\ 0 & 1 & 0 & 0 & 0 & 1 & 0 & 0 \\ 0 & 0 & 0 & 1 & 0 & 1 & 0 & 0 \end{bmatrix} \end{array}$$

Notice that the elements of *adj* along the main diagonal, a_{ii}, $i = 1 \ldots n$, are all 0. That's because there are no edges from a vertex to itself. Also notice that the matrix is symmetric about its main diagonal, $a_{ij} = a_{ji}$ for $i, j = 1 \ldots n$. That is because any edge $\{u, v\}$ is an edge from u to v and an edge from v to u.

For a weighted graph, we put the weight of the edge in the matrix instead of a 1. The adjacency matrix of a weighted graph $G = (V, E, w)$ is a $|V| \times |V|$ matrix, $adj = (a_{ij})$ where

$$a_{ij} = \begin{cases} w(\{v_i, v_j\}) & \text{if there is an edge} \{v_i, v_j\} \in E \\ 0 & \text{otherwise} \end{cases}$$

Example 17.12

Here is the weighted graph of example 17.9 with its adjacency matrix.

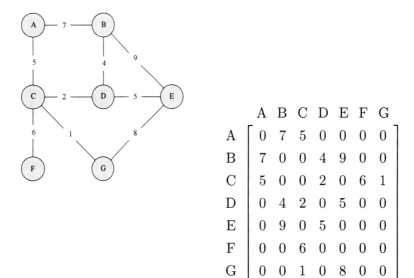

$$\begin{array}{c} \\ A \\ B \\ C \\ D \\ E \\ F \\ G \end{array} \begin{array}{ccccccc} A & B & C & D & E & F & G \\ \begin{bmatrix} 0 & 7 & 5 & 0 & 0 & 0 & 0 \\ 7 & 0 & 0 & 4 & 9 & 0 & 0 \\ 5 & 0 & 0 & 2 & 0 & 6 & 1 \\ 0 & 4 & 2 & 0 & 5 & 0 & 0 \\ 0 & 9 & 0 & 5 & 0 & 0 & 0 \\ 0 & 0 & 6 & 0 & 0 & 0 & 0 \\ 0 & 0 & 1 & 0 & 8 & 0 & 0 \end{bmatrix} \end{array}$$

17.4   Graph Problems

We will now introduce some problems involving graphs that we solve with computers in order to manage networks or to study properties of any phenomena that are modeled by graphs. We present these problems informally and without detailed methods or proofs. You will meet these problems again in your programming courses where you will implement solutions and in analysis of algorithms where you will see formal solutions and proofs.

17.4.1   Graph Traversal

To *traverse* a graph, you must visit all the vertices of the graph by following edges. We want to be able to do this in a systematic and efficient way. A solution to this problem would allow an airline inspector to fly to every airport a company flies to, a subway aficionado to take the train to every stop in a city, or a network administrator to send a message to every computer on a network.

Can you start at any vertex and visit all the other vertices by following edges? Not in general; in the graph of example 17.4 you cannot start at vertex A and visit vertex H. You can only visit the vertices in the connected component of the starting vertex. To visit all the vertices, every vertex must be reachable from every other vertex. In this case, we say the graph is *connected*. We will look at two methods for traversing a connected graph. Both of these search methods can be used for traversals or for finding paths between two vertices.

Depth-first Search

The idea of *depth-first search* is to move forward from the starting vertex as far as you can go without repeating a vertex, then go back up one edge and look for another vertex to visit, again using a depth-first search. As you can see the process is recursive.

Example 17.13

We'll show a depth-first traversal of the graph of example 17.8 and use its adjacency list to guide the search. Note that the vertices in the adjacency lists are in alphabetical order so it is easy to remember which comes next.

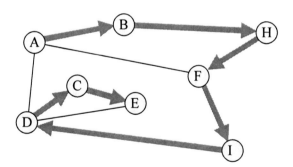

This traversal starts at vertex A and proceeds to the first vertex on A's adjacency list B and then to the only vertex on B's list H. The first vertex on H's list is B which has already been visited so the traversal proceeds to the next vertex in H's list, F, then I, then D. The first vertex on D's list is A which has already been visited so the traversal goes on to C and then to E. There is no place left to go from E so the traversal is complete. The vertices are visited in this order: A, B, H, F, I, D, C, E.

Example 17.14

This time we start from vertex B.

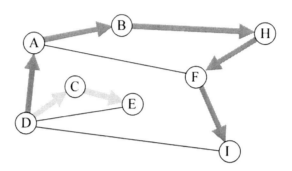

This traversal proceeds A and continues from there as in example 17.13 until it reaches vertex I. There is nowhere to go from I that has not already been visited so it goes back until it reaches a vertex whose adjacency list contains an unvisited vertex. It has to go all the way back to vertex D and then goes on to the first unvisited vertex C in D's list. From there it goes to C and with no place left to visit, the traversal is complete. The vertices are visited in this order: D, A, B, H, F, I, C, E.

Example 17.15

Now let's start with a slightly different graph, shown on the left. A depth-first traversal starting from A is shown on the right. The vertices are visited in this order: A, B, H, F, I, D, C, E.

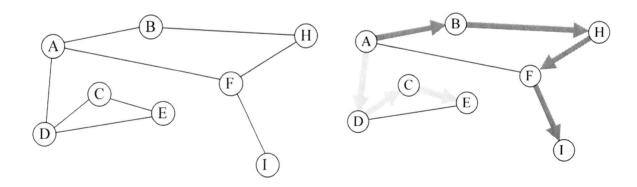

Breadth-first Search

In *breadth-first search* you visit all the vertices adjacent to the starting vertex and then do a breadth-first search from each of those vertices.

Example 17.16

Here is a breadth-first traversal of the graph of example 17.8 using its adjacency list to guide the search.

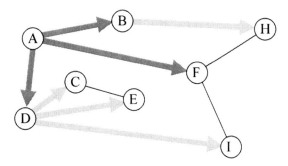

Starting from A, we first visit all of A's neighbors in the order they appear on A's adjacency list, i.e. B, D, F. We then visit the neighbors of B that have not yet been visited; that's just vertex H. Then the unvisited neighbors of D in the order they appear on D's list, C, E, I. At this point, all the vertices have been visited and the traversal is complete. The vertices are visited in this order: A, B, D, F, H, C, E, I.

Example 17.17

This figure shows a breadth-first traversal starting from vertex F.

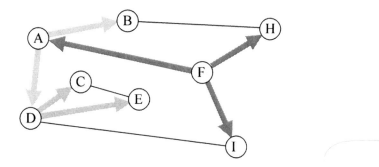

After F, we visit F's neighbors, A, H, I, then the unvisited neighbors of A, i.e. B and D. At that point all the neighbors of H and I are visited so we visit the remaining neighbors of D, the vertices C and E. The vertices are visited in this order: F, A, H, I, B, D, C, E.

17.4.2   Any Path

Sometimes, we are given two vertices in a graph and we need to find *any path* that connects them. This is like answering the question, "Can you show me any route to drive from Worcester, Massachusetts to Logan airport?" I might show you a nice direct route or I might show you a route via Hartford, Connecticut. Either will do in this case.

We start a depth-first or breadth-first search at one of our two vertices and follow the search until we reach the second vertex. Then we know a path exists but we won't know what the path is. A slight modification of either search will give us the path too. Instead of just marking a vertex as having been visited, mark it with the name of the vertex you just came from. This is like leaving a trail of bread crumbs. We can follow the trail back to reconstruct the path.

If the graph is not connected, the search might never get to the second vertex. This is a case of, "You can't get there from here."

Example 17.18

This is the graph and search of example 17.14 with labels added to the vertices to show how we got there. The arrow points to vertex D where the search started.

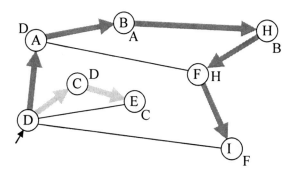

If we want a path from D to F, we start the search at D and when we arrive at F, we can read the labels to create a path $\langle F, H, B, A, D \rangle$ from F to D, or writing in reverse, a path $\langle D, A, B, H, F \rangle$ from D to F.

17.4.3   Shortest Path

The *shortest path* problem is to find the path with the smallest number of edges that connects two given vertices in a graph. When you ask Orbitz for a flight between Madison, Wisconsin and Manhattan, Kansas with as few stops as possible, you are actually asking the Orbitz program to solve a shortest path problem. To find the shortest path in a graph from vertex u to vertex

v, just do what we suggested for "any path" but use a breadth-first search. The path you find will be a shortest path!

Example 17.19

On the left is the graph of example 17.8 showing a breadth-first search from vertex F with labels added showing where you came from to get to each vertex. On the right is the same graph (without the labels) rearranged to show how far away each vertex is from the starting vertex. breadth-first search first visits all the vertices you can get to by one edge, then all those you can get to by two edges but not by one edge, and so on. You always get to a vertex by a path with as few edges as possible.

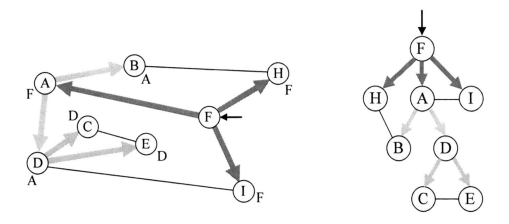

17.4.4   Cheapest Path

Given a weighted graph, $G = (V, E, w)$ and two vertices, $u, v \in V$, the *cheapest path* problem is to find a path connecting u to v that has the lowest weight among all paths connecting u and v. A cheapest path may also be a shortest path but this is not always true. When I buy an airline ticket, I generally look for the cheapest one I can find even if it means an extra stop, i.e. a longer route. The flight finder program must solve a cheapest path problem to offer me a route.

The cheapest path problem is the same as the shortest path problem if all the weights are 1 so the two problems are often grouped together and just called the "shortest path problem." We have treated them separately because the "all the weights are 1" problem is pretty easy to solve just using breadth-first search. Dijkstra's Shortest Path Algorithm solves the more difficult problem with arbitrary weights. You will learn this algorithm in your programming and algorithms courses.

Example 17.20

In the graph of example 17.9, the shortest path from A to E is $\langle A, B, E \rangle$ which has length 2 and weight 16. The cheapest path from A to E is $\langle A, C, D, E \rangle$ which has length 3 and weight 12.

17.4.5   Spanning Tree

Given a simple graph $G = (V, E)$ a *spanning tree* is a connected graph $T = (V, E')$ with $E' \subseteq E$ such that T is a tree; that is a graph with no cycles. The size of the spanning tree is the number of edges $|E'|$.

For a weighted graph, the edges in E' keep the same weights they had in T. The *weight* of the spanning tree is the sum of the weights of all the edges in E'.

We look for a spanning tree of minimal weight to find a set of highways with minimal total distance that connect a group of major cities.

You will study Kruskal's and Prim's algorithms for finding minimal spanning trees in your programming and algorithms courses.

Example 17.21

Each of the images below shows, in thickened edges, a spanning tree for the weighted graph of example 17.9. The one on the left has weight 40 and the one on the right has weight 23.

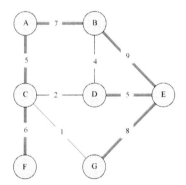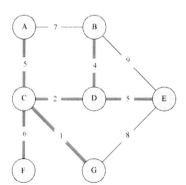

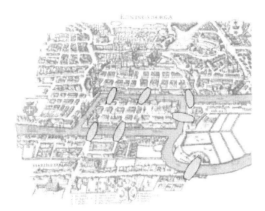

Figure 17.2: The Seven Bridges of Königsberg - the actual map modified by Bogdan Giuşcă

17.5   Graph Theory

Graph Theory is a field of pure mathematics devoted to the study of graphs for their own sake. The theorems that come out of this theoretical study often have applications to computer science. Euler's solution of the Königsberg bridge problem is considered to be the first theorem of graph theory. It all started with seven real bridges in the city of Königsberg.

Is it possible to take a walk that crosses each bridge exactly once and return to your starting point? In 1736, Leonhard Euler proved that is impossible. He used a graph with four vertices to represent the four land masses and seven edges to represent the seven bridges. He proved:

Theorem 12 *You can traverse a connected simple graph, following each edge exactly once and returning to the starting point, if and only if there are no vertices of odd degree.*

Recall that the degree of a vertex $deg(v)$ is the number of edges incident to that vertex. The graph representing the Bridges of Königsberg has one vertex of degree 5 and three of degree 3.

There are many theorems about graphs that involve the vertex degree. This theorem relates the vertex degrees to the number of edges in a graph.

Theorem 13 *Given a simple graph $G = (V, E)$, the sum of the degrees of the vertices is twice the number of edges.*

$$\sum_{v \in V} deg(v) = 2|E|$$

Proof: Each edge contributes to the degree of two vertices that is it adds 2 to the sum on the left.   □

17.6 Directed Graphs

In the graphs we have looked at in this chapter the edges are undirected like two way streets. Clearly we cannot model real highway systems or wireless networks with transmitters and receivers with such graphs. *Directed graphs* are just the structure we need to model these problems. You will work with directed graphs in your algorithms course so we will only introduce them here. Much of our discussion of simple graphs applies to these graphs too with just minor changes.

A *directed graph* $G = (V, E)$ is a set of vertices V connected by edges E. What distinguishes a directed graph from a simple graph is that the edges are one-way. An edge $e \in E$ is an ordered pair of vertices, $e = (u, v)$. The edge $e = (u, v)$ goes from u to v.

Example 17.22

Here is a directed graph and its adjacency list.

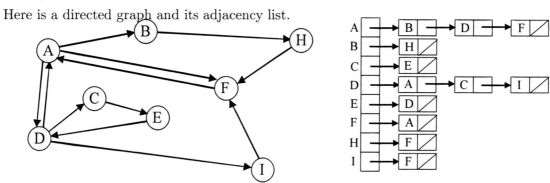

17.7 Summary

In this chapter, we introduced mathematical graphs to model computer networks and other structures where items are linked to each other. An *simple* or *undirected graph* $G = (V, E)$ is a set of *vertices* V connected by *edges* E. If u and v are vertices in a graph $G = (V, E)$, a *path* of *length* n from u to v is a sequence of vertices $\langle v_0, v_1, \cdots, v_n \rangle$ in V such that $u = v_0$, $v = v_n$, and such that $\{v_k, v_{k+1}\} \in E$ for $0 \leq k \leq n - 1$. We also discussed weighted graphs where each edge has a weight, e.g. a length or cost associated with it. We saw two data structures for representing graphs, *adjacency lists* and *adjacency matrices*. Traversing a graph means visiting every vertex in it by using the data structure to follow edges. We saw two algorithms for graph traversal, *Depth-first Search* and *Breadth-first Search*. We applied each of these methods to find a path between two given vertices in a graph if there is, in fact, a path connecting them. We discussed three other graph problems, finding a *shortest path*, a *cheapest path*, and a *minimal spanning tree*. We ended with a bit of graph theory and a quick look at directed graphs.

Credits

Figure 17.1 (top left): Copyright © 2004 by Mark Newman. Reprinted with permission.

Figure 17.1 (top right): Copyright © 2006 by The Opte Project, (CC BY 2.5)
at https://commons.wikimedia.org/wiki/File:Internet_map_1024_-_transparent,_inverted.
png.

Figure 17.1 (bottom left): Copyright © 2013 by Michael Kvrivishvili, (CC by 2.0) at
https://commons.wikimedia.org/wiki/File%3A2013_unofficial_MBTA_subway_map_by_Michael_
Kvrivishvili.png.

Figure 17.1 (bottom right): Copyright © 2011 by Zephyris / Wikimedia Commons, (CC BY-
SA 3.0)
at https://commons.wikimedia.org/wiki/File%3ADNA_Structure%2BKey%2BLabelled.pn_
NoBB.png.

Figure 17.2: Copyright © 2005 by Bogdan Giuc, (CC BY-SA 3.0)
at https://en.wikipedia.org/wiki/File:Konigsberg_bridges.png.

Exercises

Simple Graph Basics

Exercise 17.1
Refer to the graph of example 17.1 for the following questions.

  a. List all the paths with no repeated vertices from vertex F to vertex C.

  b. Give the degree of each vertex.

  c. What is the length of the longest cycle in this graph?

  d. What is the length of the shortest cycle in this graph?

Exercise 17.2
Answer the questions of Exercise 17.1 using the graph of example 17.8.

  Does this graph have a cycle that goes through all the vertices?

Weighted Graphs

Exercise 17.3
Refer to the graph of example 17.7 for the following questions.

  a. What is the weight of the path $\langle A, D, H, K, O \rangle$?

b. How many paths of length 3 or less are there from vertex A to vertex J? What is the weight of each of these paths?

c. Find simple paths from vertex H to vertex N of length 1, 2, 3, 4, and 5. What is the weight of each of these paths?

d. What is the length of the longest path from vertex A to vertex N? Is there more than one path of this length?

e. What is the shortest path from vertex F to vertex I? Which path from vertex F to vertex I has the lowest weight?

Adjacency Lists

Exercise 17.4

Give the adjacency list for the graph of example 17.4.

Exercise 17.5

Draw the graphs described by each of these adjacency lists.

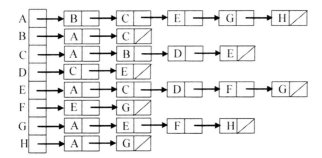

a.

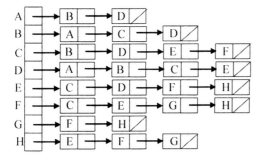

b.

Adjacency Matrices
Exercise 17.6

a. Give the adjacency matrix for the graph of example 17.4.

b. Give the adjacency matrix for the graph described by an adjacency list in part a of Exercise 17.5.

c. Give the adjacency matrix for the graph described by an adjacency list in part b of Exercise 17.5.

Depth-first Search

Exercise 17.7
Give the order in which the vertices are visited for each of these searches.

a. Use the graph and adjacency list of example 17.8 to do a depth-first search from vertex I.

b. Using the same graph and adjacency list, do a depth-first search from vertex E.

c. Use the adjacency list and corresponding graph of Exercise 17.5.a to do a depth from vertex A.

d. Use the adjacency list and corresponding graph of Exercise 17.5.b to do a depth from vertex A.

Breadth-first Search

Exercise 17.8

Repeat Exercise 17.7 using breadth-first search instead of depth-first search.

Any Path

Exercise 17.9

For each of the following, give the path that you find from the first vertex to the second vertex using the graph, adjacency list, and search indicated.

- **a.** Graph and adjacency list of example 17.8, depth-first search, vertex I to vertex A. (see Exercise 17.7.a.

- **b.** Graph and adjacency list of example 17.8, depth-first search, vertex E to vertex A. (see Exercise 17.7.b.

- **c.** Graph and adjacency list of example 17.8, breadth-first search, vertex I to vertex A. (see Exercise 17.8.a.

- **d.** Graph and adjacency list of example 17.8, breadth-first search, vertex E to vertex A. (see Exercise 17.8.b.

- **e.** What happens when you try to use a depth-first or breadth-first search to find a path from vertex A to vertex H in the graph of example17.4?

Shortest Path

Exercise 17.10

In this exercise, *shortest path* means the path with the smallest number of edges.

- **a.** Use the breadth-first search you did in Exercise 17.8.a to redraw the graph in a manner similar to the graph shown on the right in example 17.19 but with vertex I at the top.

- **b.** Use part a to give a shortest path from vertex I to each of the other vertices in the graph, A, B, C, D, E, F, and H.

- **c.** Use the breadth-first search you did in Exercise 17.8.b to redraw the graph in a manner similar to the graph shown on the right in example 17.19 but with vertex E at the top.

- **d.** Use part c to give a shortest path from vertex E to each of the other vertices in the graph, A, B, C, D, F, H, and I.

Cheapest Path
Exercise 17.11
Refer to the graph of example 17.7.

   a. Find a cheapest path from vertex M to vertex C. (We haven't given you a method for doing this but it is a small enough graph that you can probably find a solution anyway.)

   b. Find two examples in this graph where the cheapest path is not the shortest path.

Spanning Tree
Exercise 17.12

   a. Find a spanning tree for the graph of example 17.7.

   b. Find the weight of your spanning tree.

   c. Can you find a spanning tree with a lower weight? Compare your solution with those of your classmates to see who has the lowest weight spanning tree.

Exercise 17.13
Find all the spanning trees for this graph.

Graph Theory
Exercise 17.14
What is the longest possible length of a simple path in a connected simple graph with n vertices? Justify your result.

Exercise 17.15
For each of the following, give an example of a simple graph G with the indicated properties.

   a. G is connected and has exactly one vertex of degree 5 and 5 vertices of degree 3.

   b. G has 8 vertices, 3 connected components, exactly 7 vertices of degree 2 and one of degree 0.

   c. G is connected and has 8 vertices, exactly two vertices of degree 3 and 6 vertices of degree 2.

Part VI

Relations: Properties and Applications

Relations

If Susan is the mother of Tim and Jill, Susan is related to Tim by the *relation* "mother of." Susan is also related to Jill by the *relation* "mother of." We can also say that Tim is related to Susan by the relation "son of" but we cannot say the same about Jill and Susan. Tim is a student at Northeastern University. Tim is related to Northeastern University by the relation "student at." Seven is less than twelve. Seven is related to twelve by the relation "less than" and usually, we use the symbol $<$ to denote this relation, i.e we write $7 < 12$.

Relations are ubiquitous in computing and we will soon look at many examples. First, let us formalize what we mean by a relation. We see from the above examples that a relation might be between two things of similar type, e.g. two people or two numbers, or between things of different type, e.g. a person and a university. A relation expresses a connection between the objects of two sets where the two sets may be the same.

> A *relation from set A to set B* is a set of ordered pairs (a, b) where $a \in A$ and $b \in B$.[1]
>
> When A and B are the same, we just say a *relation on A*.

This definition means that a relation from A to B is just a subset of the Cartesian product $A \times B$. Think about that next time you go to a family reunion. Let's look at some relations that arise in computing.

---

[1] Really, this is a *binary relation*; that is, it relates two objects. Mathematicians talk about more general relations that relate n objects. These are represented by $n-$tuples, or subsets of cross product of n sets where n is an integer greater than 1.

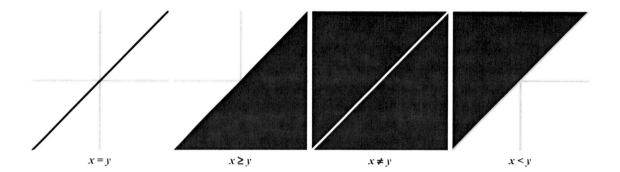

$x = y$ $x \geq y$ $x \neq y$ $x < y$

Figure 18.1: The black in each image (graph) shows the subset of $\mathbb{R} \times \mathbb{R}$ that corresponds to the relation indicated. From left to right and top to bottom: "=" is the single line of points $y = x$; "$\geq$" is the entire region below and including the line $y = x$; "$\neq$" is everything but the line of points $y = x$; "$<$" is everything above but not including the line $y = x$.

18.1   Examples

18.1.1   Equality and Inequality

We regularly define conditional expressions by using the relations $<, >, \leq, \geq, \neq$, and $=$ $\mathbb{R}$ to $\mathbb{R}$ (or from $\mathbb{N}$ to $\mathbb{N}$). Figure 18.1 shows these relations as subsets of $\mathbb{R} \times \mathbb{R}$. As with functions, these drawings are called *graphs* of the relations.

18.1.2   Divides

In our study of integers and division, we have already used the relations $|$ (*divides*) and $\nmid$ (*does not divide*) and their reverse relations *multiple of* and *not multiple of*. These relations can be defined between any two sets of integers, e.g. $\mathbb{Z}$ to $\mathbb{Z}$ or $\{primes\}$ to $\mathbb{N}$. Figure 18.2 shows a graph of the relation *divides* on $\mathbb{N} \times \mathbb{N}$.

18.1.3   Set Relations

When we work with sets, we often ask whether one set is a subset of another. The relations $\subset$ (subset of) and $\subsetneq$ (proper subset of) are defined on sets. If $S = \{1, 2\}$, the relation $\subsetneq$ on 2^S includes these ordered pairs: $(\emptyset, \{1\}), (\emptyset, \{2\}), (\emptyset, \{1, 2\}), (\{1\}, \{1, 2\}), (\{2\}, \{1, 2\})$. Note that this relation is a subset of the Cartesian product $2^S \times 2^S$.

We say a set A *intersects* a set B if $A \cap B \neq \emptyset$. The relation *intersects* on 2^S includes the ordered pairs $(\{1\}, \{1\}), (\{2\}, \{2\}), (\{1\}, \{1, 2\}), (\{2\}, \{1, 2\}), (\{1, 2\}, \{1, 2\})$.

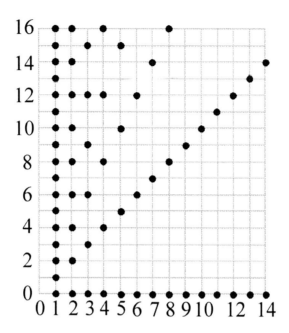

Figure 18.2: Graph of the relation **divides**

18.1.4   **Congruence** mod n

Arithmetic mod n gives us an important relation on the integers. If a and b are integers, we say *a is congruent modulo n to b* if $(a - b)$ mod $n = 0$. We write this as

$$a \equiv b \pmod{n}$$

Remember that $(a - b)$ mod $n = 0$ means that $n \mid (a - b)$. This is equivalent saying that a mod $n = b$ mod n which means that a and b give the same remainder when you divide by n. For example, $0 \equiv 21 \pmod{7}$, $322 \equiv 91 \pmod{3}$, and $26 \equiv -9 \pmod{5}$.

Figure 18.3 a graph of the relation $\equiv \pmod{5}$ on $\mathbb{Z}$ to $\mathbb{Z}$.

18.1.5   **Triangles**

In high school geometry, you studied two relations on the set of all triangles, *congruence* and *similarity*

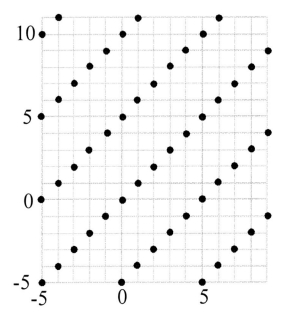

Figure 18.3: Graph of the relation $\equiv$ (mod5) on $\mathbb{Z}$ to $\mathbb{Z}$

18.1.6   People to People

When we talk of relations to people outside of discrete structures class, we are usually talking about mothers, fathers, siblings aunts, uncles, cousins, inlaws, etc. Indeed, each of these can be thought of as a mathematical relation on the set of people, e.g. "is the father of," "is a sibling of," or "is a first-cousin once removed of." Genealogy software models these relations in code to allow users to generate family trees.

Relations between people are also very important in the business place. Consider the set of all people at Northeastern University. Relations that are important in this setting include "is a student of," "is a roommate of," "is in the same major as," "is the secretary of," "is in the same coop sequence as," "is a teammate of." Some of these relations are important to the educational aspect of the university, some to social connections, others to the business operation. They must all be modeled in the varied database programs that are used to keep track of life at Northeastern.

18.1.7   People to Things

We often need to talk about relations between people and things. At a university, there are many relations from {students} to {courses}, e.g, "is registered for," "has credit for," "flunked," "owes tuition for," or "received an'A' in."

In a business, there are relations from {employees} to {banks} and from {employees} to {insurance plans} and in a hospital from {patients} to {medications}. An employee probably has her paycheck sent to only one bank and probably subscribes to only one medical plan so these relations are actually functions. A patient, however, is likely to have more than one medication so we need a relation in this situation.

18.1.8   Programming Languages

$$\{\text{strings}\} \rightarrow \{\text{programming languages}\}$$

is a reserved word in

is a syntactically valid program in

18.1.9   Functions

Any function $f : A \rightarrow B$ defines a relation from A to B by $x \in A$ is related to $y \in B$ if $y = f(x)$. The graph of the function is a subset of $A \times B$ and is the same as the graph of the relation. If $y = \sqrt{x}$ then x *"is the positive square root of"* y is a relation on $\mathbb{R}$.

There is another relation that arises from a function. If $f : A \rightarrow B$ is a function, then

$$\{(a_1, a_2) | f(a_1) = f(a_2)\}$$

is a relation on A. That is, two elements of A are related it they have the same function value.

If $f(x) = x^2$, $x \in \mathbb{R}$ then a and $-a$ are related for every $a \in \mathbb{R}$.

We often use latitude $(0 \le \varphi \le \pi)$ and longitude $(0 \le \theta \le 2\pi)$ to represent places on earth. If $h(\varphi, \theta) = $ the height above sealevel[2] at (φ, θ) then two places are related if they are at the same altitude. Level curves on a map go through points that are related under this relation.

18.1.10   Partitions

A *partition* is a subdivision of a set into disjoint subsets. A partition on S defines a relation on S by x is related to y if x and y are in the same subset of the partition. For example, I can define a partition on CSU200 students by grouping students according to their grades on the

---

[2]negative if below sealevel

last exam. Groups will correspond to grades of less than 60, 61 to 80, and 81 to 100. There is no overlap in these groups so they define a partition of CSU200 students. One student is related to another if their grades are in the same group.

We have seen that congruence mod n defines a relation on the integers. Modular arithmetic also defines a partition of the integers. The disjoint sets are

$$\{k \in \mathbb{Z} | k \bmod n = 0\}, \{k \in \mathbb{Z} | k \bmod n = 1\}, \ldots, \{k \in \mathbb{Z} | k \bmod n = n - 1\}.$$

and if a and b are integers, then $a \equiv b \pmod{n}$ if and only if $a \bmod n = b \bmod n$.

18.1.11   Networks and Graphs

Networks are commonly modeled by graphs consisting of a collection of vertices (or nodes) and a collection of edges. Sometimes we specify that the edges are directed, like a flight between two cities. Sometimes the edges are undirected to indicate, e.g. that data or cars can move in both directions. Sometimes we add weights (or costs) to the edges, like the price of a plane ticket or the length of the edge. There are relations that naturally arise on the vertices of a graph. One relation answers the question, "Can you get there from here?" Vertex a is related to vertex b if there is a path in the graph from a to b. In the graph below, the vertices a, e, f, g, and h are all related to each other under this relation as are the vertices b, c, and d.

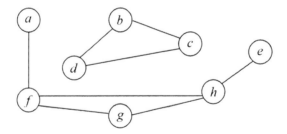

We can define a relation on the nodes of a graph based on any property the nodes may have. For example, when you book a flight online, you may be asked whether nearby airports are ok. Beneath this is a graph algorithm that says one node is related to another if the airports they represent are closer than 50 miles.

18.2   Properties of Relations

When we talk about general properties that functions may have, we usually give names to our functions like f, g, h, f_6, and so on. We can then make and prove statements like If $f(x) < g(x)$ and $h(x) < k(x)$ for all $x \in \mathbb{R}$ then $f(x) = h(x) < g(x) + k(x)$ for all $x \in \mathbb{R}$.

For relations, we usually use names like R, R_1, R_2 and so on. The expression xRy is read as "x R y" and means x is related to y by the relation R. If x and y are numbers, then R might mean $<$ or *divides* or *is the square of*. If x and y are people, the R might mean *is a niece of* or *plays tennis with*. We can talk about a relation R without having a particular relation in mind.

There are three important properties that a relation may or may not have. A relation may be *reflexive*, *symmetric*, and/or *transitive*. We will define these properties and reconsider many of the examples above with respect to these properties.

18.2.1   Reflexive

A relation R on S is *reflexive* if xRx for every $x \in S$.

The relation $=$ (is equal to) is a reflexive relation on any set. Anything is equal to itself. The relation $\leq$ on $\mathbb{Z}$ is also a reflexive relation as $n \leq n$ for any $n \in \mathbb{Z}$. However, the relation $<$ is not reflexive on $\mathbb{Z}$.

Two other numerical relations discussed above are reflexive on $\mathbb{Z}$: $\mid$ (divides) and $\equiv$ (mod n). For any $n \in \mathbb{Z}$, $n \mid n$ and $n \equiv n(\mathrm{mod} n)$.

A relation is reflexive if and only if its graph contains the line $y = x$.

18.2.2   Symmetric

A relation R on S is *symmetric* if xRy implies yRx for every $x, y \in S$.

The relation $=$ is symmetric on any set as if $x = y$ then $y = x$ is a basic property of equality. The relation $\leq$ on $\mathbb{Z}$ is not symmetric as $3 \leq 6$ but $6 \nleq 3$. Similarly, the relation $\mid$ (divides) is not symmetric on $\mathbb{Z}$. The relation $\equiv$ (mod n) is symmetric on $\mathbb{Z}$ as $n \mid (a-b)$ implies $n \mid (b-a)$.

The relations "is a sibling of," "is married to," and "is a roommate of" are symmetric relations on people.

A relation is symmetric if and only if its graph is symmetric about the line $y = x$.

18.2.3   Transitive

A relation R on S is *transitive* if xRy and yRz implies xRz for every $x, y, z \in S$.

The relation $=$ is transitive on any set as if $x = y$ and $y = z$ then $x = z$ is a basic property of equality. The relations $<$, $\leq$, $>$, and $\geq$ are all transitive on $\mathbb{Z}$ or $\mathbb{R}$. The relations $\mid$ (divides) and $\equiv$ (mod n) are both transitive on $\mathbb{Z}$.

18.3   Equivalence Relations

An *equivalence relation* is a relation that is reflexive, symmetric, and transitive.

The most obvious equivalence relation is the relation $=$ on any set. From the comments above, we see that the relation $\equiv \pmod{n}$ is an equivalence relation on $\mathbb{Z}$. Congruence and similarity are equivalence relations on the set of triangles.

A relation on a set that is derived from a partition of that set is always an equivalence relation. Actually, there is a correspondence between the equivalence relations on a set and the partitions of that set (see the theorem below). This is an important fact. When we partition a set, we are usually grouping elements of the set together that we want to identify because they have some common property. For some application, we might want to treat students as equivalent if they have the same major (ignore the possibility of double majors). We might identify days of the year that fall on the same day of the week for Tuesday night potluck dinners or Friday night beer parties. This is really just identifying (or relating) days of the year modulo 7.

Theorem: Every equivalence relation on a set S defines a partition of S and conversely, every partition of S defines an equivalence relation on S.

Proof: First assume that we have an equivalence relation $\sim$ on a set S. For each $a \in S$ let

$$E_a = \{b \in S \mid a \sim b\}.$$

The set E_a is called the *equivalence class of a*. The collection of equivalence classes forms a partition of S. From the definition of an equivalence class and the fact that an equivalence relation is reflexive we know that every element of S is in the equivalence class E_a. We must show that the classes are disjoint to prove that we have a partition. To prove the classes are disjoint, we show that if two classes intersect then they are equal to each other. Suppose, as in the figure below, that $c \in E_a \cap E_b$.

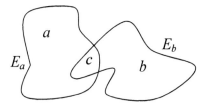

Since $c \in E_a$ and $c \in E_b$, we know that $a \sim c$ and that $b \sim c$. Since the relation $\sim$ is symmetric, $b \sim c$ implies that $c \sim b$. Since $\sim$ is transitive, $a \sim c$ and $c \sim b$ implies that $a \sim b$ so b is in E_a. Then, if d is any element of E_b, $b \sim d$ and that along with $a \sim b$ and transitivity implies that

d is any element of E_a. This means that $E_b \subseteq E_a$. Similarly, $E_a \subseteq E_b$ so the two sets must be equal. The collection of equivalence classes form a partition of S.

Now assume that we have a partition of the set S. We already know how to define a relation based on this partition. We leave it to the reader to prove that this relation is an equivalence relation.

The relation "is connected to" on the nodes of an undirected graph is an equivalence relation. The equivalence classes are the connected components of the graph. Here is another kind of graph equivalence relation.

A company might represent the internal email traffic by a directed graph with a weighted edge (how many emails) from each person (node) to each other person. The graph below shows the email traffic at Acme Designs on June 5, 2006. A number next to an edge indicates how many emails were sent while an edge without a number indicates a single email.

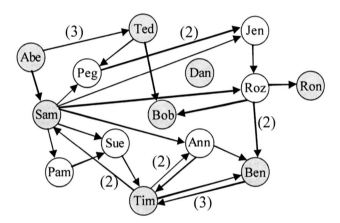

Notice that some nodes are white (female employees) while others are cyan (male employees). Gender creates a partition of the nodes and hence a relation (actually an equivalence relation as we'll see below). The sets of males and females are equivalence classes of the relation "has the same gender as." We can group together the members of each class to get a graph that shows the flow of email between genders.

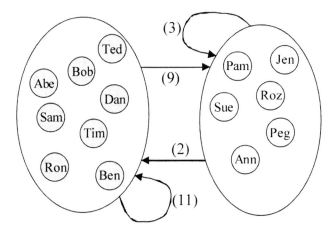

18.4 Summary

In this chapter, we have seen how the notion of "relation" like that of a parent to a child is similar to relations like < or ≥ between numbers. We generalized this idea to express a connection between objects of two sets, or objects in the same set. We presented examples from many other domains, e.g set relations, partitions, modular arithmetic, geometry, programming languages, and networks. We introduced three properties, *reflexive*, *symmetric*, *transitive*, that a relation may or may not have, A relation that has all three of these properties is called an *equivalence relation*. Equivalence relations are important in mathematical group theory. The last example in this chapter 18.3, shows how equivalence relations can be important in working with graphs and networks. In computer theory, you will see them applied to minimizing the number of states in deterministic finite automata.

Part VII

Appendices

Variables and Expressions

A *variable* is a letter (or identifier) that stands an unspecified value from a set. The set of possible values for the variable is called the *domain* of the variable.

An *expression* is a combination of variables, constants, and operators (and parentheses if necessary) that represents a number. To *evaluate* an expression, you must substitute a number for each variable.

Example 1.1

Evaluate $x^2 + 3x - 17$ at $x = 2$.

$$x^2 + 3x - 17 = 2^2 + 3 \times 2 - 17 = -7$$

Example 1.2

Evaluate $x^2 + y^3 - xy + 2$ at $x = 3$ and $y = 5$.

$$x^2 + y^3 - xy + 2 = 3^2 + 5^3 - 3 \times 5 + 2 = 3 \times 3 + 5 \times 5 \times 5 - 3 \times 5 + 2 = 9 + 125 - 15 + 2 = 121$$

We often use a center dot $\cdot$ in place of $\times$ to indicate multiplication so $5 \times 5 \times 5 = 5 \cdot 5 \cdot 5$. In computer programs, we use $*$ to indicate multiplication so we would write $5 * 5 * 5$ instead of $5 \times 5 \times 5$. When we write an expression with products of variables or numbers and variables, we usually omit the multiplication symbol altogether as in xy or $5z$.

253

The expressions above use the exponentiation operation as well as $+$ and ?. Here are some operations we commonly use on real numbers.

Subtraction: $\quad x - y$ means $x + (-y)$

$\quad\quad\quad\quad\quad\quad\quad\quad$ where $-y$ is the unique number such $y + (-y) = 0$.

Division: $\quad\quad x/y$ means $x \times (1/y)$

$\quad\quad\quad\quad\quad\quad\quad\quad$ where $1/y$ is the unique number such that $y \times (1/y) = 1$.

Exponentiation: $\quad x^n$ means x times itself n times.

When we evaluate an arithmetic expression, we adhere to the following sequence of operations:

1. Evaluate anything in parentheses first.

2. Perform all exponentiation next.

3. Do all multiplication and division from left to right.

4. Do all addition and subtraction from left to right.

A.1 Further Reading

This material is based on Sections 1–3 of "Algebra and Trigonometry: Functions and Applications" by Paul A. Foerster [3].

Exercises

Variables and Expressions

Exercise 1.1

Reduce the following expressions to their simplest form.

$\quad$ **a.** $\;3x^2 - 5x + 7$ when $x = 5$ $\quad\quad$ **b.** $\;3x^2 - 5x + 7$ when $x = -5$

$\quad$ **c.** $\;x^3 - x^2 + x + 1$ when $x = 2$ $\quad$ **d.** $\;x^3 - x^2 + x + 1$ when $x = -2$

$\quad$ **e.** $\;\left(\frac{4x^4 y^3}{12x^{-5} y^6}\right)^2$ $\quad\quad\quad\quad\quad\quad$ **f.** $\;\left(\frac{15x^{-2} y^{25}}{5x^{-5} y^{26}}\right)^3$

$\quad$ **g.** $\;(a^7 b^3 c^{-2})(a^{-5} b^6 c^{-1})(a^2 bc^3)$ $\quad$ **h.** $\;(p^{2m} q^n r^{m^2})(p^m q^{-n} r^{-m})$

Composite Expressions

A mathematical function has one *independent* variable and one or more *dependent* variable(s). For example, if

$$y = f(x) = x^3$$

then x is the independent variable and y is the dependent variable. Once we choose a value for x, the value of y is determined. A function may have more than one independent variable; for example, if

$$z = G(u, v) = \frac{3u^2}{1 + v^2}$$

then z is the independent variable and u and v are the dependent variables.

Often, the "independent" variable(s) actually depends on other variable(s). The cost C of a 100 mile car trip depends on the number of gallons of gas consumed N and the cost of a gallon of gas g.

$$C = N \times g.$$

But N in turn depends on miles per gallon, mpg.

$$C = N \times g = \frac{100}{mpg} g.$$

We might also observe that the number of miles per gallon mpg is inversely proportional to the wind resistance r which is directly proportional to the square of the speed s of the car.

$$mpg = \frac{K_1}{r} = \frac{K_1}{K_2 \times s^2} = \frac{K}{s^2},$$

where K_1 and K_2 are constants and $K = \frac{K_1}{K_2}$. So

$$C = N \times g = \frac{100}{mpg} \times g = \frac{100}{\frac{K}{s^2}} \times g = \frac{100 s^2 g}{K}.$$

We also know that cost of a gallon of gas is dependent on events in Iraq and New Orleans but these dependencies are difficult to express mathematically. [1].

Now, let's return to the mathematical functions we introduced above. With our first function, $y = x^3$, we might have $x = 2t + 1$. Then

$$y = x^3 = (2t + 1)^3 = 8t^3 + 12t^2 + 6t + 1.$$

When $x = 2$,

$$y = x^3 = 2^3 = 8.$$

When $t = 2$,

$$y = (2t + 1)^3 = (2 \times 2 + 1)^3 = 5^3 = 125.$$

Similarly for our second function, $z = G(u, v) = \frac{3u^2}{1+v^2}$, the variables u and v might each depend on other variables. If $u = r^5$ and $v = s^3$ then

$$z = \frac{3u^2}{1 + v^2} = \frac{3(r^5)^2}{1 + (s^3)^2} = \frac{3r^{10}}{1 + s^6}.$$

It is also possible that u and v both depend on the same variable; for example, they might both vary with a time variable t. If $u = t - 1$ and $v = 1/t$ then

$$z = \frac{3u^2}{1 + v^2} = \frac{2(t-1)^2}{1 + (1/t)^2} = \frac{3(t^2 - 2t + 1)t^2}{t^2 + 1} = \frac{3(t^4 - 2t^3 + t^2)}{t^2 + 1}$$

We can now think of z as a function of u and v or as a function of r and s or as a function of a single variable t.

When $u = 2$ and $V = 3$,

$$z = \frac{3u^2}{1 + v^2} = \frac{3 \times 2^2}{1 + 3^2} = \frac{12}{10} = \frac{6}{5}.$$

---

[1]Paul A. Foerster, Algebra and Trigonometry: Functions and Applications [3, Exercise 9, page 242]

When $r = 2$ and $s = 3$,

$$z = \frac{3r^{10}}{1 + s^6} = \frac{3 \times 2^{10}}{1 + 3^6} = \frac{300}{1 + 729} = \frac{300}{730} = \frac{30}{73}.$$

When $t = 2$,

$$z = \frac{3(t^4 - 2t^3 + t^2)}{t^2 + 1} = \frac{3(2^4 - 2 \times 2^3 + 2^2)}{2^2 + 1} = \frac{3(16 - 16 + 4)}{5} = \frac{12}{5}.$$

Exercises

Composite Expressions

Exercise 2.1

Evaluate each of the following.

a. $3x^2 - 5x + 7$ when $x = 2t - 1$ and $t = 3$

b. $3x^2 - 5x + 7$ when $x = 2t + 1$ and $t = 3$

c. $z = \frac{3u^2}{1+v^2}$ when $u = 3$ and $v = 2$

d. $z = \frac{3u^2}{1+v^2}$ when $u = v = 2$

e. $z = \frac{3u^2}{1+v^2}$ when $u = r^5$, $v = s^3$, $r = 3$, and $s = 2$

f. $z = \frac{3u^2}{1+v^2}$ when $u = t - 1$, $v = 1/t$, $u = 3$, and $v = 2$

g. $z = \frac{3u^2}{1+v^2}$ when $u = t - 1$, $v = 1/t$, and $t = 3$

Exponentials and Logarithms

C.1   Exponential Functions

An *exponential function* has an equation of the form

$$y = a \cdot b^x \qquad b > 0$$

where a is the constant of proportionality and b is the base. Exponential functions are defined for all real x. Let's look at the example, $y = 2^x$, before we state the general rules. (You have probably seen the function $y = (10)^x$ in high school and $y = e^x$ if you did AP calculus, but $y = 2^x$ is very important in computer science.) It is easy to define 2^x for integer values of x.

$$2^x = \begin{cases} \underbrace{2 \cdot 2 \cdots 2}_{x \ times} & \text{if } x \text{ is a positive integer} \\ 1 & \text{if } x = 0 \\ \frac{1}{2^{-x}} & \text{if } x \text{ is a negative integer} \end{cases}$$

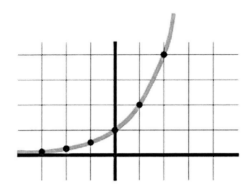

Figure C.1: $y = 2^x$ plotted at integer values of x, $-3 \le x \le 2$ and extended smoothly. Grid lines are at integer values.

We define $y = 2^x$ at all rational values of x as follows. Set $x = \frac{m}{n}$ where m and n are integers and n is positive, so the sign of x is the same as the sign of m.

$$y = (\sqrt[n]{2})^m$$

This agrees with the definition above when x is an integer. These values fit along the graph we have already drawn.

Values of $y = 2^x$ can be defined rigorously at irrational values of x using limits of values at rational approximations to x. We won't be that rigorous here (that is material for a mathematical analysis course) but if we want to compute $y = 2^\pi$, for example, we know that we could approximate is as closely as we like by computing

$$2^3, \ 2^{3.1}, \ 2^{3.14}, \ 2^{3.142}, \ 2^{3.1416}, \ 2^{3.14159}, \ \text{and so on.}$$

If b is a positive real number and n is a positive integer then, as for $b = 2$ above, we define

$$b^x = \underbrace{b \cdot b \cdots b}_{x \ times}.$$

Note: Later this semester, you will learn about recursion in your programming course and in this course. We can define b^n recursively for positive integers n by

$$b^n = \begin{cases} b & \text{if } n = 1 \\ b \cdot b^{n-1} & \text{if } n > 1 \end{cases} \tag{C.1}$$

Then, if n is a negative integer, define $b^n = \frac{1}{b^n}$.

C.1.1   Properties of Exponentiation

Product of two powers with the same base

$$b^x \cdot b^y = b^{x+y}$$

To multiply powers of the same base, add the exponents.

Quotient of two powers with the same base

$$\frac{b^x}{b^y} = b^{x-y}$$

To divide powers of the same base, subtract the exponent of the numerator from the exponent of the denominator.

Power of a Power

$$(b^x)^y = b^{xy}$$

To raise a power to a power, multiply the exponents.

Power of a Product

$$(ab)^x = a^x b^x$$

To raise a product to a power, raise each factor to that power.

Power of a Quotient

$$\left(\frac{a}{b}\right)^x = \frac{a^x}{b^x}$$

To raise a quotient to a power, raise the numerator and denominator to that power.

C.2   Logarithms

The logarithm *base b* is defined by

$$y = \log_b x \quad if \quad b^y = x.$$

The functions $\log_b x$ and b^x are *inverse functions* which means: If $y = b^x$, then $\log_b y = x$. If $y = \log_b x$, then $b^y = x$.

C.2.1   Properties of Logarithms

Logarithm of a product

$$\log_b(xy) = \log_b x + \log_b y$$

To compute the logarithm of a product, add the logarithms of the factors.

Logarithm of a quotient

$$\log_b \frac{x}{y} = \log_b x - \log_b y$$

To compute the logarithm of a quotient, subtract the logarithm of the denominator from the logarithm of the numerator.

Logarithm of a Power
$$\log_b(x^c) = c(\log_b x)$$
To compute the logarithm of a power multiply the logarithm of the base of the argument by the exponent of the argument. (x^c is the argument.)

C.3   Further Reading

The authors referred to Foerster [3] when writing this but that book is out of print. Paul A. Foerster has published many excellent high school and beginning college mathematics texts; see `http://www.keypress.com/x2511.xml`. For further reading on exponential and logarithmic functions, we suggest Foerster [4, Chapter 7] or Hein [5, pages 85-87].

Exercises

Exponents and Exponential Functions

Exercise 3.1

Assume that b is a positive real number and n is a positive integer. Try to prove these facts about exponents using only the definition C.1 and the five properties of exponentiation above.

   a. $b^0 = 1$

   b. $b^{-n} = \frac{1}{b^n}$

   c. $b^{\frac{1}{n}} = \sqrt[n]{b}$

   d. $b^{\frac{m}{n}} = \left(\sqrt[n]{b} \right)^m$

Logarithms and Logarithmic Functions

Exercise 3.2

Evaluate the following without a calculator.

   a. $\log_2(1)$ **b.** $\log_2(2)$ **c.** $\log_2(4)$

   d. $\log_2(32)$ **e.** $\log_2(256)$ **f.** $\log_2(1024)$

   g. $\log_2(.5)$ **h.** $\frac{\log_2(9)}{\log_2(\frac{1}{9})}$ **i.** $\log_2(1024^{1024})$

Special Functions

We define here some functions of numbers that you will frequently use in computing practice and theory. The Scheme examples are from "The Scheme Programming Language, Second Edition" [1], http://www.scheme.com/tspl2d/.

D.1 Factorial Function

If n is a positive integer, the *factorial* function $n!$ is defined to be

$$n! = n(n-1)\cdots 2 \cdot 1$$

So, for example

$$3! = 3 \cdot 2 \cdot 1 = 6$$
$$6! = 6 \cdot 5 \cdot 4 \cdot 3 \cdot 2 \cdot 1 = 720$$

We also define

$$0! = 1$$

This fits with the combinatorial formulas we will derive later in the semester. We can define the factorial function recursively by:

$$n! = \begin{cases} 1 & n = 0 \\ n \cdot (n-1)! & n > 0 \end{cases}$$

263

This recursion can be expressed in Scheme by:

```
(define factorial
   (lambda (n)
      (let fact ((i n))
         (if (= i 0)
             1
             (* i (fact (- i 1)))))))))
```

D.2   Floor and Ceiling

The functions *floor* and *ceiling* (or *ceil*) are functions that take real arguments and give integer values.

$$floor(x) = \lfloor x \rfloor = \text{the greatest integer less than or equal to } x.$$

$$ceiling(x) = \lceil x \rceil = \text{the smallest integer greater than or equal to } x.$$

The following definitions and examples are from "The Scheme Programming Language, Second Edition" [1], http://www.scheme.com/tspl2d/.

procedure: (floor real)
returns: the integer closest to real toward $-\infty$
(floor 19) $\Rightarrow$ 19
(floor 2/3) $\Rightarrow$ 0
(floor -2/3) $\Rightarrow$ -1
(floor 17.3) $\Rightarrow$ 17.0
(floor -17/2) $\Rightarrow$ -9

procedure: (ceiling real)
returns: the integer closest to real toward $+\infty$
(ceiling 19) $\Rightarrow$ 19
(ceiling 2/3) $\Rightarrow$ 1
(ceiling -2/3) $\Rightarrow$ 0
(ceiling 17.3) $\Rightarrow$ 18.0
(ceiling -17/2) $\Rightarrow$ -8

D.3   Truncate and Round

The functions *truncate* (or *trunc*) and *round* are also functions that take real arguments and give integer values. You probably learned about round back in elementary school but the *round* implemented in Scheme and other programming languages is slightly different if a real is exactly between two integers, the closest **even** integer is returned.

The following definitions and examples are from "The Scheme Programming Language, Second Edition" [1], http://www.scheme.com/tspl2d/.

procedure: (round real)   procedure: (truncate real)

returns: the integer closest to real   returns: the integer closest to real toward zero

If real is exactly between two integers,

the closest even integer is returned.

(round 19) ⇒ 19   (truncate 19) ⇒ 19

(round 2/3) ⇒ 1   (truncate 2/3) ⇒ 0

(round -2/3) ⇒ -1   (truncate -2/3) ⇒ 0

(round 17.3) ⇒ 17.0   (truncate 17.3) ⇒ 17.0

(round -17/2) ⇒ -8   (truncate -17/2) ⇒ -8

(round 2.5) ⇒ 2.0

(round 3.5) ⇒ 4.0

D.4   Absolute Value

The *absolute value* of a real number is defined by

$$abs(x) = |x| = \begin{cases} x & \text{if } x \geq 0 \\ -x & \text{if } x < 0 \end{cases}$$

The following definition and these examples are from "The Scheme Programming Language, Second Edition" [1], http://www.scheme.com/tspl2d/.

procedure: (abs real)

returns: the absolute value of real

abs is equivalent to

```
(lambda (x) (if (< x 0) (- x) x)).
```

abs and magnitude are identical for real inputs.

(abs 1) ⇒ 1

(abs -3/4) ⇒ 3/4

(abs 1.83) ⇒ 1.83

(abs -0.093) ⇒ 0.093

Exercises

Special Functions

Exercise 4.1

Carefully sketch a graph of each of these functions for $-3 \leq x \leq 3$. Use ∘ to show an endpoint that is not in the graph and • to show an endpoint that is in the graph. For example, here is a graph of *ceiling*(*x*) for $-3 \le x \le 3$.

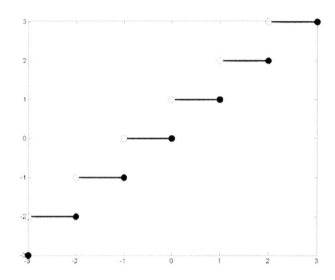

a. *floor*(*x*)

b. *ceiling*(2*x*)

c. *round*(*x*)

d. *truncate*(*x*)

e. |*x*|

f. (⌊|*x*|⌋)!

Solutions to Selected Exercises

Chapter 1 Solutions

Changing Bases

Exercise 1.1
You can convert from binary to decimal by adding the appropriate powers of 2, e.g.

$$10110110_2 = 1\cdot 2^7 + 0\cdot 2^6 + 1\cdot 2^5 + 1\cdot 2^4 + 0\cdot 2^3 + 1\cdot 2^2 + 1\cdot 2^1 + 0\cdot 2^0 = 128+32+16+4+2 = 182.$$

    a. $1010_2 = 10_{10}$ **b.** $10100_2 = 20_{10}$ **c.** $10101_2 = 21_{10}$ **d.** $10110_2 = 22_{10}$

    e. $11101110_2 = 238_{10}$ **f.** $10101011_2 = 171_{10}$ **g.** $11111_2 = 31_{10}$ **h.** $10000_2 = 16_{10}$

    i. $11100111_2 = 231_{10}$ **j.** $11111111_2 = 255_{10}$ **k.** $10000001_2 = 129_{10}$ **l.** $10111111_2 = 191_{10}$

Exercise 1.2
These are small integers so you can easily calculate the binary representation of each N by finding the largest power of 2 less than or equal to N, say 2^k, and then finding the binary representation of $N - 2^k$.

    a. $17_{10} = 2^4 + 2^0 = 10001_2$ **b.** $19_{10} = 2^4 + 2^1 + 2^0 = 10011_2$

    c. $24_{10} = 2^4 + 2^3 = 11000_2$ **d.** $29_{10} = 2^4 + 2^3 + 2^2 + 2^0 = 11101_2$

    e. $35_{10} = 2^5 + 2^1 + 2^0 = 100011_2$ **f.** $42_{10} = 2^5 + 2^3 + 2^1 = 101010_2$

    g. $56_{10} == 2^5 + 2^4 + 2^3 = 111000_2$ **h.** $61_{10} = 2^5 + 2^4 + 2^3 + 2^2 + 2^0 = 111101_2$

    i. $73_{10} = 2^6 + 2^3 + 2^0 = 1001001_2$ **k.** $99_{10} = 2^6 + 2^5 + 2^1 + 2^0 = 1100011_2$

    k. $115_{10} = 2^6 + 2^5 + 2^4 + 2^1 + 2^0 = 1110011_2$ **k.** $143_{10} = 2^7 + 2^3 + 2^2 + 2^1 + 2^0 = 10001111_2$

Exercise 1.3

a.

$$
\begin{aligned}
34092 &= 17046 \cdot 2 + \mathbf{0} \\
17046 &= 8523 \cdot 2 + \mathbf{0} \\
8523 &= 4261 \cdot 2 + \mathbf{1} \\
4261 &= 2130 \cdot 2 + \mathbf{1} \\
2130 &= 1065 \cdot 2 + \mathbf{0} \\
1065 &= 532 \cdot 2 + \mathbf{1} \\
532 &= 266 \cdot 2 + \mathbf{0} \\
266 &= 133 \cdot 2 + \mathbf{0} \\
133 &= 66 \cdot 2 + \mathbf{1} \\
66 &= 33 \cdot 2 + \mathbf{0} \\
33 &= 16 \cdot 2 + \mathbf{1} \\
16 &= 8 \cdot 2 + \mathbf{0} \\
8 &= 4 \cdot 2 + \mathbf{0} \\
4 &= 2 \cdot 2 + \mathbf{0} \\
2 &= 1 \cdot 2 + \mathbf{0} \\
1 &= 0 \cdot 2 + \mathbf{1}
\end{aligned}
$$

So, reading from the bottom up, $34092_{10} = 1000010100101100_2$.

b.

$$
\begin{aligned}
4997 &= 2498 \cdot 2 + \mathbf{1} \\
2498 &= 1249 \cdot 2 + \mathbf{0} \\
1249 &= 624 \cdot 2 + \mathbf{1} \\
624 &= 312 \cdot 2 + \mathbf{0} \\
312 &= 156 \cdot 2 + \mathbf{0} \\
156 &= 78 \cdot 2 + \mathbf{0} \\
78 &= 39 \cdot 2 + \mathbf{0} \\
39 &= 19 \cdot 2 + \mathbf{1} \\
19 &= 9 \cdot 2 + \mathbf{1} \\
9 &= 4 \cdot 2 + \mathbf{1} \\
4 &= 2 \cdot 2 + \mathbf{0} \\
2 &= 1 \cdot 2 + \mathbf{0} \\
1 &= 0 \cdot 2 + \mathbf{1}
\end{aligned}
$$

So, reading from the bottom up, $4997_{10} = 1001110000101_2$.

c.

$$
\begin{aligned}
20507 &= 10253 \cdot 2 + \mathbf{1} \\
10253 &= 5126 \cdot 2 + \mathbf{1} \\
5126 &= 2563 \cdot 2 + \mathbf{0} \\
2563 &= 1281 \cdot 2 + \mathbf{1} \\
1281 &= 640 \cdot 2 + \mathbf{1} \\
640 &= 320 \cdot 2 + \mathbf{0} \\
320 &= 160 \cdot 2 + \mathbf{0} \\
160 &= 80 \cdot 2 + \mathbf{0} \\
80 &= 40 \cdot 2 + \mathbf{0} \\
40 &= 20 \cdot 2 + \mathbf{0} \\
20 &= 10 \cdot 2 + \mathbf{0} \\
10 &= 5 \cdot 2 + \mathbf{0} \\
5 &= 2 \cdot 2 + \mathbf{1} \\
2 &= 1 \cdot 2 + \mathbf{0} \\
1 &= 0 \cdot 2 + \mathbf{1}
\end{aligned}
$$

So, reading from the bottom up, $20507_{10} = 101000000011011_2$.

Exercise 1.4

a. To convert binary integers to octal integers, work from the right-hand side and convert each 3 bits to a single octal digit.

  a. $1\,010_2 = 12_8$ **b.** $10\,100_2 = 24_8$ **c.** $10\,101_2 = 25_8$ **d.** $10\,110_2 = 26_8$

  e. $11\,101\,110_2 = 356_8$ **f.** $10\,101\,011_2 = 253_8$ **g.** $11\,111_2 = 37_8$ **h.** $10\,000_2 = 20_8$

  i. $11\,100\,111_2 = 347_8$ **j.** $11\,111\,111_2 = 377_8$ **k.** $10\,000\,001_2 = 201_8$ **l.** $10\,111\,111_2 = 277_8$

b. To convert binary integers to hexadecimal integers, work from the right-hand side and convert each 4 bits to a single hex digit.

  a. $1010_2 = A_{16}$ **b.** $1\,0100_2 = 14_{16}$ **c.** $1\,0101_2 = 15_{16}$ **d.** $11\,0110_2 = 16_{16}$

  e. $1110\,1110_2 = EE_{16}$ **f.** $1010\,1011_2 = AB_{16}$ **g.** $1\,1111_2 = 1F_{16}$ **h.** $11\,0000_2 = 10_{16}$

  i. $1110\,0111_2 = E7_{16}$ **j.** $1111\,1111_2 = FF_{16}$ **k.** $1000\,0001_2 = 81_{16}$ **l.** $1101\,1111_2 = BF_{16}$

Exercise 1.5

Write the binary representation of the first hex digit followed by the 4-bit binary representation of the second hex digit. That is, you must include leading zeros for the second hex digit. There is a small space between the two pieces in the answers so you can see the conversion for each hex digit.

a. $17 = 1\,0111$ b. $19 = 1\,1001$ c. $24 = 10\,0100$ d. $29 = 10\,1001$

e. $3A = 11\,1010$ f. $B2 = 1011\,0010$ g. $CF = 1100\,1111$ h. $60 = 110\,0000$

i. $F3 = 1111\,0011$ j. $99 = 1001\,1001$ k. $DD = 1101\,1101$ c. $A3 = 1010\,0011$

Multiplication

Exercise 1.6

a. $27 \times 6 = 162$

$$
\begin{array}{r}
1\ 1\ 0\ 1\ 1 \\
\times \qquad\ 1\ 1\ 0 \\
\hline
1\ 1\ 0\ 1\ 1 \\
1\ 1\ 0\ 1\ 1 \quad \\
\hline
1\ 0\ 1\ 0\ 0\ 0\ 1\ 0
\end{array}
$$

b. $23 \times 11 = 253$

$$
\begin{array}{r}
1\ 0\ 1\ 1\ 1 \\
\times \qquad 1\ 0\ 1\ 1 \\
\hline
1\ 0\ 1\ 1\ 1 \\
1\ 0\ 1\ 1\ 1 \quad \\
1\ 0\ 1\ 1\ 1 \quad\quad \\
\hline
1\ 1\ 1\ 1\ 1\ 1\ 0\ 1
\end{array}
$$

c. $11 \times 23 = 253$

$$
\begin{array}{r}
1\ 0\ 1\ 1 \\
\times \quad 1\ 0\ 1\ 1\ 1 \\
\hline
1\ 0\ 1\ 1 \\
1\ 0\ 1\ 1 \quad \\
1\ 0\ 1\ 1 \quad\quad\quad \\
1\ 0\ 1\ 1 \quad\quad\quad\quad \\
\hline
1\ 1\ 1\ 1\ 1\ 1\ 0\ 1
\end{array}
$$

d. $46 \times 7 = 322$

```
              1  0  1  1  1  0
     ×                 1  1  1
     ─────────────────────────
              1  0  1  1  1  0
           1  0  1  1  1  0
        1  0  1  1  1  0
     ─────────────────────────
        1  0  1  0  0  0  0  1  0
```

Patterns

Exercise 1.7

a. The first pattern is represented in hex digits by: 03, 1B, D8, C0, 03, 1B, D8, C0.

The second pattern is represented in hex digits by: CC, CC, 33, 33, CC, CC, 33, 33.

The third pattern is represented in hex digits by: 01, 02, 04, 28, 70, D8, F0, 60.

The fourth pattern is represented in hex digits by: 90, 05, 50, 02, 88, 21, 08, 42.

b. Convert each hex digit to a 4-bit binary number and then use black for each 1 and white for each 0. The pattern given by 39, 7B, 42, 88, 88, 24, B7, 93 is shown below

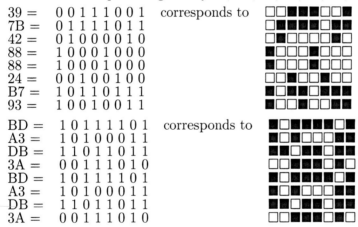

```
39 =   0 0 1 1 1 0 0 1   corresponds to
7B =   0 1 1 1 1 0 1 1
42 =   0 1 0 0 0 0 1 0
88 =   1 0 0 0 1 0 0 0
88 =   1 0 0 0 1 0 0 0
24 =   0 0 1 0 0 1 0 0
B7 =   1 0 1 1 0 1 1 1
93 =   1 0 0 1 0 0 1 1

BD =   1 0 1 1 1 1 0 1   corresponds to
A3 =   1 0 1 0 0 0 1 1
DB =   1 1 0 1 1 0 1 1
3A =   0 0 1 1 1 0 1 0
BD =   1 0 1 1 1 1 0 1
A3 =   1 0 1 0 0 0 1 1
DB =   1 1 0 1 1 0 1 1
3A =   0 0 1 1 1 0 1 0
```

Two's Complement

Exercise 1.8

a. For positive numbers, we transform them into binary form and pad with 0s on the left to obtain 8 total bits.

$$34 \implies 100010 \implies 00100010$$

$$66 \implies 1000010 \implies 01000010$$

For a negative number, we compute a binary representation of the magnitude of the number (appropriately padded with 0s), then flip all the bits, and finally add 1.

$$-71 \implies 1000111 \implies 01000111 \implies 10111000 \implies 10111001$$

$$-27 \implies 11011 \implies 00011011 \implies 11100100 \implies 11100101$$

b. If the first bit of the two's complement representation is 0, then the value is a positive number in standard binary form. In this case, we simply transform the binary representation to its equivalent decimal form. If the first bit of the two's complement representation is 1, then the value is a negative number. In this case, we flip all the bits, add 1, and interpret the resulting bits as the magnitude of the negative value.

$$01100110 \implies 2 + 4 + 32152 + 64 \implies 102$$
$$10011001 \implies 01100110 \implies 01100111 \implies 1 + 2 + 4 + 32 + 64 \implies -103$$
$$01010101 \implies 1 + 4 + 16 + 64 \implies 85$$
$$11011101 \implies 00100010 \implies 00100011 \implies 1 + 2 + 32 \implies -35$$

c. Here are the equivalent equations in decimal and two's complement forms:

$$66 + (-27) = 39$$
$$01000010 + 11100101 = 00100111$$

Note that binary 00100111 is equivalent to decimal 39, as required.

$$(-71) + (-27) = -98$$
$$10111001 + 11100101 = 10011110$$

$$10011110 \implies 01100001 \implies 01100010 \implies 2 + 32 + 64 \implies -98$$

Chapter 2 Solutions

Circuits

Exercise 2.1

Convert the circuit into a truth table.

a.

A	B	Out
0	0	0
0	1	1
1	0	1
1	1	1

b. This circuit is equivalent to an or gate.

Exercise 2.2

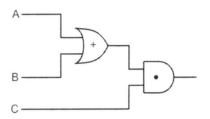

Chapter 3 Solutions

Logic

Exercise 3.1

a. Fill in the following truth table:

X	X NAND X
0	1
1	0

What logical operation does X NAND X correspond to? NOT

b. Fill in the following truth table:

X	Y	$\neg X$ NAND $\neg Y$
0	0	0
0	1	1
1	0	1
1	1	1

What logical operation does $\neg X$ NAND $\neg Y$ correspond to? OR

c. Using only NAND gates, draw circuit diagrams corresponding to the AND, OR, and NOT gates.

AND, OR, and NOT circuits, respectively:

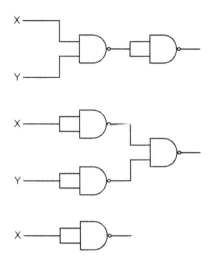

Exercise 3.2

Fill in the following table with the missing truth tables, Boolean formulae, and circuits.

Truth Table	Boolean Formula	Circuit
A B Out 0 0 0 0 1 1 1 0 0 1 1 0	$\neg A \land B$	
A B Out 0 0 1 0 1 0 1 0 1 1 1 1	$A \lor (\neg A \land \neg B)$	
A B Out 0 0 0 0 1 1 1 0 1 1 1 1	$B \lor (\neg B \land A)$	

Chapter 5 Solutions

Caesar Cipher and Encoding

Exercise 5.1

a. EXIT UNDER STAIRS $\Longrightarrow$ HALW XWGHU VWDLUV

c. EXIT UNDER STAIRS $\Longrightarrow$ 04230819 2013030417 181900081718

The mod Function

Exercise 5.2
a. $19 \bmod 7 = 5$ **b.** $7 \bmod 19 = 7$ **c.** $27 \bmod 7 = 6$

g. $14 \bmod 24 = 14$ **h.** $51 \bmod 11 = 7$ **i.** $212 \bmod 3 = 2$

Exercise 5.3
a. $-19 \bmod 7 = 2$ **b.** $-7 \bmod 19 = 12$ **c.** $-27 \bmod 7 = 1$

g. $-14 \bmod 24 = 10$ **h.** $-51 \bmod 11 = 4$ **i.** $-212 \bmod 3 = 1$

Exercise 5.4

a.
$$337 \bmod 3 = 1 \qquad\qquad 9962 \bmod 3 = 2$$
$$(9962 + 337) \bmod 3 = (1 + 2) \bmod 3 = 0 \quad (337 \times 9962) \bmod 3 = (1 \times 2) \bmod 3 = 2$$
$$-337 \bmod 3 = 3 - (337 \bmod 3) = 2 \quad (9962 - 337) \bmod 3 = (2 + 2) \bmod 3 = 1$$

Simple Substitution Ciphers

Exercise 5.5

a.

Plaintext	B	E	H	I	N	D	B	I	G	C	L	O	C	K
Coded	01	04	07	08	13	03	01	08	06	02	11	14	02	10
Shifted	12	15	18	19	24	14	12	19	17	13	22	25	13	21
Ciphertext	M	P	S	T	Y	O	M	T	R	N	W	Z	N	V

Encoded Message: MPSTYOMTRNWZNV

b.

Plaintext	L	N	I	N	E	R	S	E	V	E	N	L	F	O	U	R
Coded	11	13	08	13	04	17	18	04	21	04	13	11	05	14	20	17
Shifted	00	02	23	02	19	06	07	19	10	19	02	00	20	03	09	06
Ciphertext	A	C	X	C	T	G	H	T	K	T	C	A	U	D	J	G

Encoded Message: ACXCTGHTKTCAUDJG

Exercise 5.6

a. UBTFURNQGUERRCZBEQREOHGGREORRE, shift 13

Use $26 - 13 = 13$ to decipher. The result is

$$HOGSHEADTHREEPMORDERBUTTERBEER$$

or HOGS HEAD THREE PM ORDER BUTTERBEER with spaces added.

b. DRIBKNRZEYFLJVYRIKWFIUTKJLEURP, shift 17

Use $26 - 17 = 09$ to decipher. The result is

$$MARKTWAINHOUSEARTFORDCTSUNDAY$$

MARK TWAIN HOUSE ART FOR DCT SUNDAY with spaces added.

Linear Encryption

Exercise 5.7

a. r e b D ng w D q l D gh j D p

b. r $\rightarrow$ 17

e $\rightarrow$ 4

b $\rightarrow$ 1

D $\rightarrow$ 3

ng $\rightarrow$ 12

w $\rightarrow$ 23

D $\rightarrow$ 3

q $\rightarrow$ 15

l $\rightarrow$ 9

D $\rightarrow$ 3

gh $\rightarrow$ 5

j $\rightarrow$ 8

D $\rightarrow$ 3

p $\rightarrow$ 14

c. $26 = 15 * 1 + 11$

$15 = 11 * 1 + 4$

$11 = 4 * 2 + 3$

$4 = 3 * 1 + 1$

$3 = 1 * 3 + 0$

So, going back...

$1 = 4 - 3 * 1$

$1 = 4 - (11 - 4 * 2) * 1$

$1 = -11 + 4 * 3$

$1 = -11 + (15 - 11 * 1) * 3$

$1 = 15 * 3 - 11 * 4$

$1 = 15 * 3 - (26 - 15 * 1) * 4$

$1 = 15 * 7 - 26 * 4$

If we mod everything by 26 we get: $1 = 15 * 7$ (mod 26)

The multiplicative inverse of 15 is 7 in arithmetic mod 26.

d.

0	1	2	3	4	5	6	7	8	9	10	11	12
a	b	ch	D	e	gh	H	I	j	l	m	n	ng
23	24	25	0	1	2	3	4	5	6	7	8	9
5	12	19	0	7	14	21	2	9	16	23	4	11
gh	ng	t	a	I	p	u	ch	l	Q	w	e	n

13	14	15	16	17	18	19	20	21	22	23	24	25
o	p	q	Q	r	S	t	tlh	u	v	w	y	'
10	11	12	13	14	15	16	17	18	19	20	21	22
18	25	6	13	20	1	8	15	22	3	10	17	24
S	'	H	o	tlh	b	j	q	v	D	m	r	y

The first line is the corresponding decimal code for the symbols of the cipher.

On the second line are the symbols of the cipher text.

The third line represents the values after adding the additive inverse of 3.

The fourth line represents the values after multiplying with the multiplicative inverse of 15.

On the fifth line are the deciphered codes.

e. tlhIngan maH Qapla'

f. The spy speaks **Klingon**.

The translation is: **We are Klingons. Success!**

Modular Arithmetic

Exercise 5.8

+	0	1	2	3	4	5	6	7
0	0	1	2	3	4	5	6	7
1	1	2	3	4	5	6	7	0
2	2	3	4	5	6	7	0	1
3	3	4	5	6	7	0	1	2
4	4	5	6	7	0	1	2	3
5	5	6	7	0	1	2	3	4
6	6	7	0	1	2	3	4	5
7	7	0	1	2	3	4	5	6

*	0	1	2	3	4	5	6	7
0	0	0	0	0	0	0	0	0
1	0	1	2	3	4	5	6	7
2	0	2	4	6	0	2	4	6
3	0	3	6	1	4	7	2	5
4	0	4	0	4	0	4	0	4
5	0	5	2	7	4	1	6	3
6	0	6	4	2	0	6	4	2
7	0	7	6	5	4	3	2	1

Exercise 5.9

a. Give the additive inverse of each number mod8:

Additive inverse of 0 mod8 is **0**: $(0 + 0) \bmod 8 = 0$

Additive inverse of 1 mod8 is **7**: $(1 + 7) \bmod 8 = 0$

Additive inverse of 2 mod8 is **6**: $(2 + 6) \bmod 8 = 0$

Additive inverse of 3 mod8 is **5**: $(3 + 5) \bmod 8 = 0$

Additive inverse of 4 mod8 is **4**: $(4 + 4) \bmod 8 = 0$

Additive inverse of 5 mod8 is **3**: $(5 + 3) \bmod 8 = 0$

Additive inverse of 6 mod8 is **2**: $(6 + 2) \bmod 8 = 0$

Additive inverse of 7 mod8 is **1**: $(7 + 1) \bmod 8 = 0$

b. Give the multiplicative inverse of each number mod8:

0 doesn't have a multiplicative inverse mod8.

Multiplicative inverse of 1 mod8 is **1**: $(1 * 1) \bmod 8 = 1$

2 doesn't have a multiplicative inverse mod8.

Multiplicative inverse of 3 mod8 is **3**: $(3 * 3) \bmod 8 = 1$

4 doesn't have a multiplicative inverse mod8.

Multiplicative inverse of 5 mod8 is **5**: $(5 * 5) \bmod 8 = 1$

6 doesn't have a multiplicative inverse mod8.

Multiplicative inverse of 7 mod8 is **7**: $(7 * 7) \bmod 8 = 1$

c. Which numbers are zero divisors mod8?

0 is a zero-divisor mod8. $(0 * 1) \bmod 8 = 0$

1 is not a zero-divisor mod8.

2 is a zero-divisor mod8. $(2 * 4) \bmod 8 = 0$

3 is not a zero-divisor mod8.

4 is a zero-divisor mod8. $(4 * 2) \bmod 8 = 0$

5 is not a zero-divisor mod8.

6 is a zero-divisor mod8. $(6 * 4) \bmod 8 = 0$

7 is not a zero-divisor mod8.

Powers mod n

Exercise 5.10

a. $48 \bmod 5 = 3$

b. $48^2 \bmod 5 = 3^2 \bmod 5 = 4$

b. $48^4 \bmod 5 = 4^2 \bmod 5 = 1$

d. $48^8 \bmod 5 = 1^2 \bmod 5 = 1$

e. $48^{16} \bmod 5 = 1$

f. $48^{32} \bmod 5 = 1$

g. $48^{64} \bmod 5 = 1$

h. $48^{128} \bmod 5 = 1$

i. $48^{256} \bmod 5 = 1$

j. $48^{79} \bmod 5 = 48^{64+8+4+2+1} \bmod 5 = 48^{64} \cdot 48^{8} \cdot 48^{4} \cdot 48^{2} \cdot 48^{1} \bmod 5 = 1 \cdot 1 \cdot 1 \cdot 4 \cdot 3 \bmod 5 = 2$

Exercise 5.11

a. $48 \bmod 11 = 4$ **b.** $48^2 \bmod 11 = 4^2 \bmod 11 = 5$ **c.** $48^4 \bmod 11 = 5^2 \bmod 11 = 3$

d. $48^8 \bmod 11 = 3^2 \bmod 11 = 9$ **e.** $48^{16} \bmod 11 = 9^2 \bmod 11 = 4$ **f.** $48^{32} \bmod 11 = 4^2 \bmod 11 = 5$

g. $48^{64} \bmod 11 = 5^2 \bmod 11 = 3$ **h.** $48^{128} bmod 11 = 3^2 \bmod 11 = 9$ **i.** $48^{256} \bmod 11 = 9^2 \bmod 11 = 4$

j. $48^{79} \bmod 5 = 48^{64+8+4+2+1} \bmod 11 = 48^{64} \cdot 48^{8} \cdot 48^{4} \cdot 48^{2} \cdot 48^{1} \bmod 11 = 3 \cdot 9 \cdot 3 \cdot 5 \cdot 4 \bmod 11 = 3$

Chapter 6 Solutions

Prime Number Decomposition

Exercise 6.1

a. $162 = 2 \cdot 81 = 2 \cdot 3^4$ **c.** $363 = 3 \cdot 121 = 3 \cdot 11^2$

e. $1000 = 10^3 = 2^3 \cdot 5^3$ **g.** $102400 = 1024 \cdot 100 = 2^{10} \cdot 10^2 = 2^{10} \cdot 2^2 \cdot 5^2 = 102 \cdot 5^2$

i. $29 = 19$ **k.** $256 \cdot 81 = 2^8 \cdot 3^4$

Exercise 6.2

Give the prime number decomposition for each of the following. You should not need a calculator.

a. $8! = 8 \cdot 7 \cdot 6 \cdot 5 \cdot 4 \cdot 3 \cdot 2 = 2^3 \cdot 7 \cdot 2 \cdot 3 \cdot 5 \cdot 2^2 \cdot 3 \cdot 2 = 2^7 \cdot 3^2 \cdot 5 \cdot 7$

b. $9! = 9 \cdot 8 \cdot 7 \cdot 6 \cdot 5 \cdot 4 \cdot 3 \cdot 2 = 3^2 \cdot 2^3 \cdot 7 \cdot 2 \cdot 3 \cdot 5 \cdot 2^2 \cdot 3 \cdot 2 = 2^7 \cdot 3^4 \cdot 5 \cdot 7$

c. $10! = 10 \cdot 9 \cdot 8 \cdot 7 \cdot 6 \cdot 5 \cdot 4 \cdot 3 \cdot 2 = 2 \cdot 5 \cdot 3^2 \cdot 2^3 \cdot 7 \cdot 2 \cdot 3 \cdot 5 \cdot 2^2 \cdot 3 \cdot 2 = 2^8 \cdot 3^4 \cdot 5^2 \cdot 7$

d. $\frac{6!}{2^4} = \frac{2^4 \cdot 3^2 \cdot 5}{2^4} = 3^2 \cdot 5$

e. $\frac{10!}{2^4 \cdot 3^3} = \frac{2^8 \cdot 3^4 \cdot 5^2 \cdot 7}{2^4 \cdot 3^3} = 2^4 \cdot 3 \cdot 5^2 \cdot 7$

f. $(6!)^3 = (2^4 \cdot 3^2 \cdot 5)^3 = 2^12 \cdot 3^6 \cdot 5^3$

g. $\frac{8!}{4!} = \frac{8 \cdot 7 \cdot 6 \cdot 5 \cdot 4 \cdot 3 \cdot 2}{4 \cdot 3 \cdot 2} = 8 \cdot 7 \cdot 6 \cdot 5 = 2^3 \cdot 7 \cdot 2 \cdot 3 \cdot 5 = 2^4 \cdot 3 \cdot 5 \cdot 7$

h. $\frac{8!}{4!} = \frac{2^7 \cdot 3^2 \cdot 5 \cdot 7}{(2^3 \cdot 3)^2} = \frac{2^7 \cdot 3^2 \cdot 5 \cdot 7}{2^6 \cdot 3^2} = 2 \cdot 5 \cdot 7$

i. $\frac{10!}{3!} = \frac{10 \cdot 9 \cdot 8 \cdot 7 \cdot 6 \cdot 5 \cdot 4 \cdot 3 \cdot 2}{3 \cdot 2} = 10 \cdot 9 \cdot 8 \cdot 7 \cdot 6 \cdot 5 \cdot 4 = 2 \cdot 5 \cdot 3^2 \cdot 2^3 \cdot 7 \cdot 2 \cdot 3 \cdot 5 \cdot 2^2 = 2^7 \cdot 3^3 \cdot 5^2 \cdot 7$

j. $\frac{10!}{7!} = \frac{10 \cdot 9 \cdot 8 \cdot 7 \cdot 6 \cdot 5 \cdot 4 \cdot 3 \cdot 2}{7 \cdot 6 \cdot 5 \cdot 4 \cdot 3 \cdot 2} = 10 \cdot 9 \cdot 8 = 2^4 \cdot 3^2 \cdot 5$

k. $\frac{10!}{3!7!} = \frac{10 \cdot 9 \cdot 8 \cdot 7 \cdot 6 \cdot 5 \cdot 4 \cdot 3 \cdot 2}{3 \cdot 2 \cdot 7 \cdot 6 \cdot 5 \cdot 4 \cdot 3 \cdot 2} = \frac{10 \cdot 9 \cdot 8}{3 \cdot 2} = 10 \cdot 3 \cdot 4 = 120$

l. $\frac{2^5 \cdot 3^7 \cdot 5^9 \cdot 7^6}{2^2 \cdot 3^4 \cdot 7^6} = 2^3 \cdot 3^3 \cdot 5^9$

Greatest Common Divisor and Least Common Multiple

Exercise 6.3
Evaluate the following. You should not need a calculator.

a. $gcd(60, 80) = gcd(60, 20) = gcd(20, 0) = 20$

c. $gcd(256, 162) = gcd(2^8, 2 \cdot 131) = 2$

e. $lcm(512, 1024) = 1024$

g. $lcm(6!, 8!) = 8!$

i. $lcm(2^3 \cdot 3^5 \cdot 5^4, 2^2 \cdot 3^7 \cdot 5^2) = 2^3 \cdot 3^7 \cdot 5^4$

Exercise 6.4
Use the Euclidean Algorithm to find each of the following. Show your work.

a. $gcd(612, 584) = gcd(584, 28) = gcd(28, 24) = gcd(24, 2) = gcd(2, 0) = 2.$

b. $gcd(488, 183) = gcd(183, 122) = gcd(122, 61) = gcd(61, 0) = 61.$

c. $gcd(217, 124) = gcd(124, 93) = gcd(93, 31) = gcd(31, 0) = 31.$

Exercise 6.5
Use the Extended Euclidean Algorithm to solve ax + by = $gcd(a, b)$. If the gcd is 1, also give the multiplicative inverse of a mod b as a number from 1 to $b - 1$.

a. $gcd(24, 119)$

$$119 - 4 \cdot 24 = 23$$
$$24 - 1 \cdot 23 = 1$$
$$23 - 23 \cdot 1 = 0$$
$$gcd(119, 24) = 1$$

Now work backwards

$$24 - 1 \cdot (119 - 4 \cdot 24) = 1$$
$$5 \cdot 24 - 1 \cdot 119 = 1$$

So

$$a \cdot 5 - b \cdot 1 = 1$$

Or using table method

a	b	d	q
0	1	119	
1	0	24	4
-4	1	23	1
5	-1	1	

$$a \cdot 5 - b \cdot 1 = 1$$

Multiplicative inverse of 24 mod 119 is 5.

b. $gcd(20, 151)$

$$151 - 7 \cdot 20 = 11$$
$$20 - 1 \cdot 11 = 9$$
$$11 - 1 \cdot 9 = 2$$
$$9 - 4 \cdot 2 = 1$$
$$2 - 2 \cdot 1 = 0$$
$$gcd(20, 151) = 1$$

Working backwards

$$9 - 4 \cdot (11 - 1 \cdot 9) = 1$$
$$5 \cdot 9 - 4 \cdot 11 = 1$$
$$5 \cdot (20 - 1 \cdot 11) - 4 \cdot 11 = 1$$
$$5 \cdot 20 - 9 \cdot 11 = 1$$
$$5 \cdot 20 - 9 \cdot (151 - 7 \cdot 20) = 1$$
$$68 \cdot 20 - 9 \cdot 151 = 1$$

So

$$a \cdot 68 - b \cdot 9 = 1$$

Or using table method...

a	b	d	q
0	1	151	
1	0	20	7
-7	1	11	1
8	-1	9	1
-15	2	2	4
68	-9	1	

$$a \cdot 68 - b \cdot 9 = 1$$

Multiplicative inverse of 20 mod 151 is 68.

Chapter 7 Solutions

The RSA Cryptosystem

Exercise 7.1

a. $M^e \bmod 15 = 2^3 \bmod 15 = 8$

b. $(M^e)^d \bmod 15 = 8^3 \bmod 15 = (64 \bmod 15)(8 \bmod 15) = 4 \cdot 8 \bmod 15 = 32 \bmod 15 = 2 = M$

Exercise 7.2

a. 7, 11, 13, 17, 23, 29, 31, 37, 41, 43, 47, 49, 53, 57

b. We want $2^{17} \bmod 77 = 2 \cdot 2^{16} \bmod 77$ In 7.2, we computed $2^8 \bmod 77 = 25$ so $2^{16} \bmod 77 = 625 \bmod 77 = 9$ and $2^{17} \bmod 77 = 2 \cdot 9 \bmod 77 = 18$.

c. 53

Exercise 7.3

a. $n = p \cdot q = 23 \cdot 41 = 943$.

b. $(p-1)(q-1) = 22 \cdot 40 = 880$.

c. $d = 587$, the multiplicative inverse of 3 mod 880

Chapter 8 Solutions

Set Builder Notation

Exercise 8.1

a. $A = \{n \in \mathbb{Z} \mid 1 \leq |2 \times n| \leq 6\} = \{-3, -2, -1, 1, 2, 3\}$

c. $C = \{n \in \mathbb{Z} \mid n \leq 4\} = \{\cdots, -2, -1, 0, 1, 2, 3, 4\}$

e. $E = \{n^2 \in \mathbb{Z} \mid |n| \leq 4\} = \{0, 1, 4, 9, 16\}$

g. $G = \{n \in \mathbb{R} \mid n^2 \leq 4\} = [-2, 2]$

Venn Diagrams

Exercise 8.2

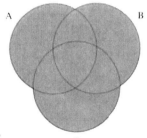

a. $A \cup B \cup C$

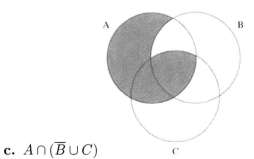

c. $A \cap (\overline{B} \cup C)$

Set Operations

Exercise 8.3
a. $\{0, 2, 3, 4, 6, 7, 9\}$ **b.** $\{7\}$ **c.** $\{2, 3, 4, 9\}$ **d.** $\{0, 6\}$ **e.** $\{0, 2, 3, 4, 6, 9\}$

f. $\{0, 4, 6, 7, 9\}$ **g.** $\{0\}$ **h.** $\{4, 9\}$ **i.** $\{6, 7\}$ **j.** $\{4, 6, 7, 9\}$

k. $\{0, 2, 3, 4, 7, 9\}$ **l.** $\{4, 9\}$ **m.** $\{2, 3, 7\}$ **n.** $\{0\}$ **o.** $\{0, 2, 3, 7\}$

Exercise 8.4

a. $\{0, 1, 2, 3, 4, 5, 6, 7, 8, 9\}$ **b.** $\{\}$ **c.** $\{0, 1, 2, 3, 4\}$ **d.** $\{5, 6, 7, 8, 9\}$ **e.** $\{0, 1, 2, 3, 4, 5, 6, 7, 8, 9\}$

f. $\{3, 4, 5, 6, 7, 8, 9\}$ **g.** $\{5, 6\}$ **h.** $\{3, 4\}$ **i.** $\{7, 8, 9\}$ **j.** $\{3, 4, 7, 8, 9\}$

k. $\{0, 1, 2, 3, 4, 5, 6\}$ **l.** $\{3, 4\}$ **m.** $\{0, 1, 2\}$ **n.** $\{5, 6\}$ **o.** $\{0, 1, 2, 5, 6\}$

Exercise 8.5

a. $\{0, 1, 2, 3, 4, 5, 6\}$ **b.** $\{\}$ **c.** $\{0, 1, 2\}$ **d.** $\{3, 4, 5, 6\}$ **e.** $\{0, 1, 2, 3, 4, 5, 6\}$

f. $\{3, 4, 5, 6, 7, 8, 9\}$ **g.** $\{\}$ **h.** $\{7, 8, 9\}$ **i.** $\{3, 4, 5, 6\}$ **j.** $\{3, 4, 5, 6, 7, 8, 9\}$

k. $\{0, 1, 2, 7, 8, 9\}$ **l.** $\{\}$ **m.** $\{0, 1, 2\}$ **n.** $\{7, 8, 9\}$ **o.** $\{0, 1, 2, 7, 8, 9\}$

Power Set

Exercise 8.6

a. $\{\emptyset, \{1\}\}$

b. $\{\emptyset, \{X\}\}$

c. $\{\emptyset, \{21\}\}$

d. $\{\emptyset, \{\alpha\}\}$

e. $\{\emptyset, \{1\}, \{2\}, \{1, 2\}\}$

f. $\{\emptyset, \{X\}, \{Y\}, \{X, Y\}\}$

g. $\{\emptyset, \{21\}, \{33\}, \{21, 33\}\}$

h. $\{\emptyset, \{\alpha\}, \{\beta\}, \{\alpha, \beta\}\}$

i. $\{\emptyset, \{1\}, \{2\}, \{3\}, \{1, 2\}, \{2, 3\}, \{1, 3\}, \{1, 2, 3\}\}$

j. $\{\emptyset, \{X\}, \{Y\}, \{Z\}, \{X, Y\}, \{X, Z\}, \{Y, Z\}, \{X, Y, Z\}\}$

k. $\{\emptyset, \{21\}, \{33\}, \{42\}, \{21, 33\}, \{21, 42\}, \{33, 42\}, \{21, 33, 42\}\}$

l. $\{\emptyset, \{\alpha\}, \{\beta\}, \{\gamma\}, \{\alpha, \beta\}, \{\alpha, \gamma\}, \{\beta, \gamma\}, \{\alpha, \beta, \gamma\}\}$

m. $\{\emptyset, \{1\}, \{2\}, \{3\}, \{4\}, \{1, 2\}, \{1, 3\}, \{1, 4\}, \{2, 3\}, \{2, 4\}, \{3, 4\},$
$\{1, 2, 3\}, \{1, 2, 4\}, \{1, 3, 4\}, \{2, 3, 4\}, \{1, 2, 3, 4\}\}$

n. $\{\emptyset, \{W\}, \{X\}, \{Y\}, \{Z\}, \{W, X\}, \{W, Y\}, \{W, Z\}, \{X, Y\}, \{X, Z\}, \{Y, Z\},$
$\{W, X, Y\}, \{W, X, Z\}, \{W, Y, Z\}, \{X, Y, Z\}, \{W, X, Y, Z\}\}$

o. $\{\emptyset, \{21\}, \{33\}, \{42\}, \{56\}, \{21, 33\}, \{21, 42\}, \{21, 56\}, \{33, 42\}, \{33, 56\}, \{42, 56\},$
$\{21, 33, 42\}, \{21, 33, 56\}, \{21, 42, 56\}, \{33, 42, 56\}, \{21, 33, 42, 56\}\}$

p. $\{\emptyset, \{\alpha\}, \{\beta\}, \{\gamma\}, \{\delta\}, \{\alpha, \beta\}, \{\alpha, \gamma\}, \{\alpha, \delta\}, \{\beta, \gamma\}, \{\beta, \delta\}, \{\gamma, \delta\}, \{\alpha, \beta, \gamma\},$
$\{\alpha, \beta, \delta\}, \{\alpha, \gamma, \delta\}, \{\beta, \gamma, \delta\}, \{\alpha, \beta, \gamma, \delta\}\}$

q. $\{\emptyset, \{\emptyset\}, \{\{1\}\}, \{\emptyset, \{1\}\}\}$

r. $\{\emptyset, \{\emptyset\}, \{\{X\}\}, \{\emptyset, \{X\}\}\}$

s. $\{\emptyset, \{\emptyset\}, \{\{21\}\}, \{\emptyset, \{21\}\}\}$

t. $\{\emptyset, \{\emptyset\}, \{\{\alpha\}\}, \{\emptyset, \{\alpha\}\}\}$

u. $\{\emptyset, \{\emptyset\}, \{\{X\}\}, \{\{Y\}\}, \{\{X, Y\}\}, \{\emptyset, \{X\}\}, \{\emptyset, \{Y\}\}, \{\emptyset, \{X, Y\}\},$
$\{\emptyset, \{1\}, \{2\}\}, \{\emptyset, \{1\}, \{1, 2\}\}, \{\emptyset, \{1, 2\}, \{2\}\}, \{\{1\}, \{2\}, \{1, 2\}\},$
$\{\emptyset, \{1\}, \{2\}, \{1, 2\}\}\}$

v. $\{\emptyset, \{\emptyset\}, \{\{X\}\}, \{\{Y\}\}, \{\{X, Y\}\}, \{\emptyset, \{X\}\}, \{\emptyset, \{Y\}\}, \{\emptyset, \{X, Y\}\},$
$\{\emptyset, \{X\}, \{Y\}\}, \{\emptyset, \{X\}, \{X, Y\}\}, \{\emptyset, \{X, Y\}, \{Y\}\}, \{\{X\}, \{Y\}, \{X, Y\}\},$
$\{\emptyset, \{X\}, \{Y\}, \{X, Y\}\}\}$

w. $\{\emptyset, \{\emptyset\}, \{\{X\}\}, \{\{Y\}\}, \{\{X, Y\}\}, \{\emptyset, \{X\}\}, \{\emptyset, \{Y\}\}, \{\emptyset, \{X, Y\}\},$
$\{\emptyset, \{21\}, \{33\}\}, \{\emptyset, \{21\}, \{21, 33\}\}, \{\emptyset, \{21, 33\}, \{33\}\}, \{\{21\}, \{33\}, \{21, 33\}\},$
$\{\emptyset, \{21\}, \{33\}, \{21, 33\}\}\}$

x. $\{\emptyset, \{\emptyset\}, \{\{\alpha\}\}, \{\{\beta\}\}, \{\{\alpha, \beta\}\}, \{\emptyset, \{\alpha\}\}, \{\emptyset, \{\beta\}\}, \{\emptyset, \{\alpha, \beta\}\},$
$\{\emptyset, \{\alpha\}, \{\beta\}\}, \{\emptyset, \{\alpha\}, \{\alpha, \beta\}\}, \{\emptyset, \{\alpha, \beta\}, \{\beta\}\}, \{\{\alpha\}, \{\beta\}, \{\alpha, \beta\}\},$
$\{\emptyset, \{\alpha\}, \{\beta\}, \{\alpha, \beta\}\}\}$

Cartesian Product

Exercise 8.7

a. $\{(1, X), (1, Y), (1, Z), (2, X), (2, Y), (2, Z)\}$

b. $\{(X, 1), (Y, 1), (Z, 1), (X, 2), (Y, 2), (Z, 2)\}$

c. $\{(X, \alpha), (X, \beta), (X, \gamma), (Y, \alpha), (Y, \beta), (Y, \gamma), (Z, \alpha), (Z, \beta), (Z, \gamma)\}$

d. $\{(\alpha, X), (\beta, X), (\gamma, X), (\alpha, Y), (\beta, Y), (\gamma, Y), (\alpha, Z), (\beta, Z), (\gamma, Z)\}$

e. $\{(1, \alpha), (1, \beta), (1, \gamma), (2, \alpha), (2, \beta), (2, \gamma)\}$

f. $\{(\alpha, 1), (\beta, 1), (\gamma, 1), (\alpha, 2), (\beta, 2), (\gamma, 2)\}$

g. $\{(1, 1), (1, 2), (2, 1), (2, 2)\}$

h. $\{(1, X, 1), (1, X, 2), (1, Y, 1), (1, Y, 2), (1, Z, 1), (1, Z, 2), (2, X, 1), (2, X, 2), (2, Y, 1), (2, Y, 2),$
$(2, Z, 1), (2, Z, 2)\}$

i. $\{(1, 1, 1), (1, 1, 2), (1, 2, 1), (1, 2, 2), (2, 1, 1), (2, 1, 2), (2, 2, 1), (2, 2, 2)\}$

j. $\{\emptyset\}$

k. $\{(X, \emptyset), (Y, \emptyset), (Z, \emptyset)\}$

l. $\{(\emptyset, X), (\emptyset, Y), (\emptyset, Z), (0, X), (0, Y), (0, Z)\}$

Cardinality

Exercise 8.8

a. $2 \times 3 = 6$	**b.** $2 \times 2 \times = 8$	**c.** $3 \times 3 \times 3 = 27$
d. $2 \times 2^2 = 8$	**e.** $2^2 \times 2^2 = 16$	**f.** $2^2 \times 2^3 = 32$
g. $2^{(2^2)} = 2^4 = 16$	**h.** $2^{(2^3)} = 2^5 = 32$	**i.** $2^{(2^{(2 \times 3)})} = 2^{(2^6)} = 2^{64}$
j. $2^{2^2 \times 2^3} = 2^{32}$	**k.** $2^{(2^0)} \times 3 = 2^1 \times 3 = 6$	**l.** $2^{2^2 \times 2^{2^3}} = 2^{10}$

Computer Representation of Sets

Exercise 8.9

Let the universal set $U = \{0, 1, 2, 3, 4, 5, 6, 7, 8, 9\}$. Let $A = \{1, 3, 5, 7, 8, 9\}$ and $B = \{0, 2, 4, 6, 8, 9\}$. Using the representation of sets shown in Section 8.6, give the representation for each of these sets.

    a. 0101010111 **b.** 1010101011 **c.** 1111111111

    d. 0000000011 **e.** 1010101000 **f.** 0101010100

    g. 1111111100 **h.** 0000000000 **i.** 0101010111

    j. 1111111111 **k.** 1010101011 **l.** 0000000000

Chapter 9 Solutions

Simple Counting

Exercise 9.1

  a. Both dice must show 1 for the total to be 2. There is only one way to do this.

  b. There are 3 ways to roll a 4.

red	1	2	3
black	3	2	1

  c. There are 6 ways to roll a 7.

red	1	2	3	4	5	6
black	6	5	4	3	2	1

  d. There are 3 ways to roll a 10.

red	4	5	6
black	6	5	4

  e. There are 4 ways to roll a 5, 5 ways to roll a 6, 6 ways to roll a 7, and 5 ways to roll an 8. That makes $4 + 5 + 6 + 5 = 20$ ways to roll a total between 5 and 8, 5 and 8 included.

  f. The total is always between 2 and 12, 2 and 12 included, so 36 possible rolls.

  g. The black die can have any value from 1 to 6 so 6 possible rolls.

  h. There is 1 way: The red die is 3 and the black die is 6.

  i. There are 0 ways to roll a 1, 1 way to roll a 2, 2 ways to roll a 3, 3 ways to roll a 4 so there are $1 + 2 + 3 = 6$ ways to roll a total less than 5.

  j. The only ways for the red die to be less than the black are 5

red	1	1,2	1,2,3	1,2,3,4	1,2,3,4,5
black	2	3	4	5	6

so $1 + 2 + 3 + 4 + 5 = 15$ possible ways.

k. There are exactly 6 ways for the two dice to be equal, both 1, both 2, ...

l. There are $36 - 6 = 30$ ways for the two dice to be different.

Exercise 9.2

a. Both dice must show 1 for the total to be 2. There is only one way to do this.

b. There are 3 ways to roll a 4.

red	1	2	3
black	3	2	1

c. There are 6 ways to roll a 7.

red	1	2	3	4	5	6
black	6	5	4	3	2	1

d. There are 5 ways to roll a 10.

red	4	5	6	7	8
black	6	5	4	3	2

e. There are 4 ways to roll a 5, 5 ways to roll a 6, 6 ways to roll a 7, and 7 ways to roll an 8. That makes $4 + 5 + 6 + 7 = 22$ ways to roll a total between 5 and 8, 5 and 8 included.

f. There is 1 way to roll a 2, 2 ways to roll a 3, 3 ways to roll a 4, 4 ways to roll a 5, 5 ways to roll a 6, 6 ways to roll a 7, 7 ways to roll an 8, 8 ways to roll a 9, 7 ways to roll a 10, 6 ways to roll an 11 and 5 ways to roll a 12. That makes $1+2+3+4+5+6+7+8+7+6+5 = 54$ ways to roll a total between 5 and 8, 5 and 8 included.

g. The black die can have any value from 1 to 8 so 8 possible rolls.

h. There is 1 way: The red die is 3 and the black die is 6.

i. There are 0 ways to roll a 1, 1 way to roll a 2, 2 ways to roll a 3, 3 ways to roll a 4 so there are $1 + 2 + 3 = 6$ ways to roll a total less than 5.

j. The only ways for the red die to be less than the black are

red	1	1,2	1,2,3	1,2,3,4	1,2,3,4,5	1,2,3,4,5,6	1,2,3,4,5,6,7
black	2	3	4	5	6	7	8

so $1 + 2 + 3 + 4 + 5 + 6 + 7 = 28$ possible ways.

k. There are exactly 8 ways for the two dice to be equal, both 1, both 2, ...

l. There are $64 - 8 = 30$ ways for the two dice to be different.

Exercise 9.3

If you draw a card from a standard deck of 52 cards, how many different ways are there to do each of the following?

   a. There are 52 ways to draw a card

   b. There are 4 jacks so 4 ways to draw a jack.

   c. 13

   d. The face cards are those that show a person, i.e jack, queen, or king. There are 4 suits so a total of 12 ways to draw a face card.

   e. 1

   f. 1

   g. $52 - 12 = 40$

   h. There are no jokers in a standard deck of 52 cards so the answer is 0.

   i. Half the cards are black so $52/2 = 26$

   j. There are 4 tens and 4 eights so 8 ways to draw a 10 or an 8.

Sum and Product Rules
Exercise 9.4

   a. By the sum rule, Eloise's daughter has $45 + 10 = 55$ choices for a gift.

   b. By the product rule, Eloise has $45 \times 10 = 450$ choices for her gift.

Exercise 9.5

   a. By the sum rule, students have $7 + 15 = 55$ choices for the assignment.

   b. By the product rule, students have $7 \times 15 = 105$ choices for the assignment.

Exercise 9.6

   a. By the product rule, there are $7 \times 3 \times 2 \times 11 \times 5 = 2310$ different 5-course meals.

   b. By the sum rule, there are $3 + 5 + 2 + 1 = 11$ different lunches.

Exercise 9.7

There are 52 letters (uppercase and lowercase) and 10 numbers for a total of 62 characters. Here is how you count the number of 6-character passwords.

   There are 62^2 6-character passwords with no restrictions.

   There are 52^6 6-character passwords that have 0 digits.

   There are $10 \times 52^5 \times 6$ 6-character passwords that have exactly 1 digit.

   There are 10^6 6-character passwords that have 0 letters.

   There are $52 \times 10^5 \times 6$ 6-character passwords that have exactly 1 letter.

   There are $62^2 - 52^6 - (10 \times 52^5 \times 6) - 10^6 - (52 \times 10^5 \times 6)$

   6-character passwords with at least 2 letters and at least 2 digits.

A similar approach will give you the counts for 7-, 8-, 9-, and 10-character passwords. Add up all these values to get the result.

Exercise 9.8

There are $10^3 26^3 = 17,576,000$ plates with three digits followed by three letters. There are $10^4 26^2 = 6,760,000$ plates with four digits followed by two letters. In all, there are $17,576,000 + 6,760,000 = 24,336,000$ possible license plates.

Exercise 9.9

Members of the Secret Superwoman Society each have a password composed of **different** letters from the word "SUPERWOMAN."

   a. There are 10 letters in "SUPERWOMAN" so any rearrangement (permutation) of them is a possible password for a total of $P(10, 10) = 10!$.

   b. There are 10 choices for the first letter, 9 for the second, 8 for the third, 7 for the fourth, and 6 for the fifth for a total of $10 \times 9 \times 8 \times 7 \times 6 = P(10, 5) = 10!/5!$.

   c. How many 5-letter passwords can they form if the middle letter must be a vowel?

   There are 4 choices (U, E, O, A) for the middle letter. Then there are 9 choices left for the first letter, 8 for the second, 7 for the fourth, and 6 for the fifth so there are $4 \times 9 \times 8 \times 7 \times 6 = 12096$ passwords satisfying these constraints.

   d. There are $9 \times 8 \times 7 \times 6 = 3024$ possible passwords if the first letter must be "W."

e. How many 5-letter passwords can they form if the first letter must be "W" and the middle letter must be a vowel?

There is 1 choice for the first letter and 4 choices for the third letter. The other three letters can be chosen from the 8, then 7, then 6 remaining letters for a total of $4 \times 8 \times 7 \times 6$.

Inclusion-exclusion Principle

Exercise 9.10

Still referring to the Secret Superwoman Society above 9.9, how many 5-letter passwords can they form if the first letter must be "W" or the middle letter must be a vowel?

Number with first letter W = 3024, number with middle letter vowel = 12096, number with first letter W **and** middle letter vowel $1 \times 4 \times 8 \times 7 \times 6 = 1344$ so the number first letter must be "W" or the middle letter must be a vowel is $3024 + 12096 - 1344 = 13776$.

Exercise 9.11

320	computer science	35	computer science and math
145	math	20	business and math
580	business	90	business and computer science
10	all three subjects		

a. computer science or math: $320 + 145 - 35 = 430$

b. computer science or business: $320 + 580 - 90 = 810$

c. business or math: $580 + 145 - 20 = 705$

d. computer science, business, or math: $320 + 580 + 145 - 35 - 20 - 90 + 10 = 910$

Pigeonhole Principle

Exercise 9.12

a. 75 students could each have their own room, filling all available rooms. Adding an additional student would require two students to share a room, so 76.

b. 150 students could each have only one roommate, filling all available rooms. Adding an additional student would require three students to share a room, so 151.

c. Assuming each room is filled with 2 students before any room has 3, we can be sure. However, the problem says the assignment is done by taking the student ID mod 75. We have no control over the student ID numbers. There might well be three or more students whose ID numbers mod 75 are the same.

d. If the assignment is done fairly and equally, no more than 2 people will have to occupy one room. However, as in the last part, the assignment is out of our control. It is even possible that all 150 students have ID numbers that are the same mod 75—not a very comfy arrangement.

Exercise 9.13

a. $N = \left\lceil \frac{1111}{6} \right\rceil = 186.$

b. $N = \left\lceil \frac{1111}{5} \right\rceil = 223.$

Permutations
Exercise 9.15

   a. $5 \cdot 4 = 20$ **b.** $5 \cdot 4 \cdot 3 = 60$ **c.** $5 \cdot 4 \cdot 3 \cdot 2 = 120$
   d. $6 \cdot 5 = 30$ **e.** $6 \cdot 5 \cdot 4 = 120$ **f.** $6 \cdot 5 \cdot 4 \cdot 3 = 360$
   g. $10 \cdot 9 = 90$ **h.** $10 \cdot 9 \cdot 8 = 720$ **i.** $11 \cdot 10 \cdot 9 = 990$
   j. 1 **k.** 1234 **l.** $10000 \cdot 9999 = 99990000$

Exercise 9.16

a. He has 6 choices for the first city, 5 for the second, and so on. He has $6! = 6 \cdot 5 \cdot 4 \cdot 3 \cdot 2 \cdot 1 = 720$ possible itineraries.

b. $1 \cdot 5 \cdot 4 \cdot 3 \cdot 2 \cdot 1 = 120$ possible itineraries.

c. $1 \cdot 4 \cdot 3 \cdot 2 \cdot 1 \cdot 1 = 24$ possible itineraries.

Exercise 9.17

a. You can choose one of 8 letters for the first position, 7 for the second, and so on. $8! = 40320.$

b. $P(8,5) = 8 \cdot 7 \cdot 6 \cdot 5 \cdot 4 = 6720.$

c. $P(8,3) = 8 \cdot 7 \cdot 6 = 336.$

Exercise 9.18

There are 4 different prizes. A student can win at most one prize. 130 students can win the first prize, 129 the second prize, and so on. There are $130 \cdot 129 \cdot 128 \cdot 127 = 272,613,120$ ways the prizes might be distributed.

Combinations

Exercise 9.19

a. $\frac{5!}{3! \cdot 2!} = \frac{5 \cdot 4 \cdot 3 \cdot 2}{3 \cdot 2 \cdot 2} = \frac{5 \cdot 4}{2} = 10$ b. $\frac{5!}{2! \cdot 3!} = \frac{5 \cdot 4 \cdot 3 \cdot 2}{2 \cdot 3 \cdot 2} = \frac{5 \cdot 4}{2} = 10$

c. $\frac{5!}{4! \cdot 1!} = \frac{5 \cdot 4 \cdot 3 \cdot 2}{4 \cdot 3 \cdot 2} = 5$ d. $\frac{6!}{4! \cdot 2!} = \frac{6 \cdot 5 \cdot 4 \cdot 3 \cdot 2}{4 \cdot 3 \cdot 2 \cdot 2} = \frac{6 \cdot 5}{2} = 15$

e. $\frac{6!}{3! \cdot 3!} = \frac{6 \cdot 5 \cdot 4 \cdot 3 \cdot 2}{3 \cdot 2 \cdot 3 \cdot 2} = \frac{6 \cdot 5 \cdot 4}{3 \cdot 2} = 20$ f. $\frac{6!}{2! \cdot 4!} = \frac{6 \cdot 5 \cdot 4 \cdot 3 \cdot 2}{2 \cdot 4 \cdot 3 \cdot 2} = \frac{6 \cdot 5}{2} = 15$

g. $\frac{10!}{8! \cdot 2!} = \frac{10 \cdot 9 \cdot 8 \cdot 7 \cdot 6 \cdot 5 \cdot 4 \cdot 3 \cdot 2}{8 \cdot 7 \cdot 6 \cdot 5 \cdot 4 \cdot 3 \cdot 2 \cdot 2} = \frac{10 \cdot 9}{2} = 45$ h. $\frac{10!}{7! \cdot 3!} = \frac{10 \cdot 9 \cdot 8 \cdot 7 \cdot 6 \cdot 5 \cdot 4 \cdot 3 \cdot 2}{7 \cdot 6 \cdot 5 \cdot 4 \cdot 3 \cdot 2 \cdot 3 \cdot 2} = \frac{10 \cdot 9 \cdot 8}{3 \cdot 2} = 120$

i. $\frac{11!}{8! \cdot 3!} = \frac{11 \cdot 10 \cdot 9 \cdot 8 \cdot 7 \cdot 6 \cdot 5 \cdot 4 \cdot 3 \cdot 2}{8 \cdot 7 \cdot 6 \cdot 5 \cdot 4 \cdot 3 \cdot 2 \cdot 3 \cdot 2} = \frac{11 \cdot 10 \cdot 9}{3 \cdot 2} = 165$ j. 1

k. 1234   l. $\frac{10000!}{9999! \cdot 2!} = \frac{10000}{2} = 5000$

Exercise 9.20

a. $C(60,6) = \frac{60 \cdot 59 \cdot 58 \cdot 57 \cdot 56 \cdot 55}{6 \cdot 5 \cdot 4 \cdot 3 \cdot 2} = 50,063,860$

b. $C(60,12) = \frac{60 \cdot 59 \cdot 58 \cdot 57 \cdot 56 \cdot 55 \cdot 54 \cdot 53 \cdot 52 \cdot 51 \cdot 50 \cdot 49}{12 \cdot 11 \cdot 10 \cdot 9 \cdot 8 \cdot 7 \cdot 6 \cdot 5 \cdot 4 \cdot 3 \cdot 2} = 1,399,358,844,975$

Exercise 9.21

a. $C(52,5) = \frac{52 \cdot 51 \cdot 50 \cdot 49 \cdot 48}{5 \cdot 4 \cdot 3 \cdot 2} = 2598960$

b. You must have the ace of spades, then choose 4 more cards. $C51,4 = \frac{51 \cdot 50 \cdot 49 \cdot 48}{4 \cdot 3 \cdot 2} = 249900$

c. You must have all 4 aces, and then choose 1 more card. $C(48,1) = 48$

d. There are 16 of these cards to choose from. $C(16,5) = \frac{16 \cdot 15 \cdot 14 \cdot 13 \cdot 12}{5 \cdot 4 \cdot 3 \cdot 2} = 4368$

e. There are 36 of these cards to choose from. $C(36,5) = \frac{36 \cdot 35 \cdot 34 \cdot 33 \cdot 32}{5 \cdot 4 \cdot 3 \cdot 2} = 376992$

Exercise 9.22

$C(130,4) = \frac{130 \cdot 129 \cdot 128 \cdot 127}{4 \cdot 3 \cdot 2} = 11358880$

Binomial Theorem

Exercise 9.23

a. $(x + y)^3 = x^3 + 3x^2y + 3xy^2 + y^3$

c. $(x + y)^6 = x^6 + 6x^5y + 15x^4y^2 + 20x^3y^3 + 15x^2y^4 + 6xy^5 + y^6$

e. $(x + 3y)^4 = x^4 + 12x^3y + 54x^2y^2 + 108xy^3 + 81y^4$

g. $(x - y)^5 = x^5 - 5x^4y + 10x^3y^2 - 10x^2y^3 + 5xy^4 - y^5$

i. $(x^2 + y^{-2})^5 = (x^2)^5 + 5(x^2)^4(y^{-2}) + 10(x^2)^3(y^{-2})^2 + 10(x^2)^2(y^{-2})^3 + 5(x^2)(y^{-2})^4 + (y^{-2})^5$

   $= x^{10} + 5x^8y^{-2} + 10x^6y^{-4} + 10x^4y^{-6} + 5x^2y^{-8} + y^{-10}$

Exercise 9.24

Use the Binomial Theorem to show the following.

a.

$$1 \cdot \binom{n}{0} + 2 \cdot \binom{n}{1} + 4 \cdot \binom{n}{2} + 8 \cdot \binom{n}{3} + \cdots + 2^n \cdot \binom{n}{n} = (1 + 2)^n = 3^n.$$

Pascal's Triangle

Exercise 9.25

We show just past the middle as the result is symmetric.

	1		15		105		455		1365		3003		5005		6435		6435
1		16		120		560		1820		4368		8008		11440		12870	
1	17		136		680		2380		6188		12376		19448		24310		24310

Balls-in-Bins

Exercise 9.27

I have a box with 50 Snickers candy bars. Eight kids come over on Halloween night to trick-or-treat.

a. How many ways can I distribute all 50 Snickers candy bars to the 8 kids?

   $\binom{n+m-1}{n} = \binom{50+7}{50} = \binom{57}{50}$

b. How many ways can I distribute all 50 Snickers candy bars to the 8 kids if every kid gets at least 2 candy bars?

   After each child gets 2 Snickers bars, there are 34 bars left to distribute and the number of ways to do this is $\binom{n+m-1}{n} = \binom{34+7}{34} = \binom{41}{34}$

Chapter 10 Solutions

Dice

Exercise 10.1

Recall that if two dice are rolled, the size of the sample space is 36.

a. There are exactly 3 ways that the two dice result in a total of 4

Black	1	2	3
Red	3	2	1

so the probability of rolling a 4 is $\frac{3}{36} = \frac{1}{12}$.

b. There are exactly 6 ways that the two dice result in a total of 7

Black	1	2	3	4	5	6
Red	6	5	4	3	2	1

The probability of rolling a 7 is $\frac{6}{36} = \frac{1}{6}$.

c. There are 5 ways to roll a 6, 4 ways to roll a 5, 3 ways to roll a 4, 2 ways to roll a 3, and 1 way to roll a 2. So there are 15 ways to roll a total that is less than 7 and the probability of rolling a total less than 7 is $\frac{15}{36} = \frac{5}{12}$.

d. The possible ways for the red die to be higher than the black die are shown in this table.

Red	1	2	3	4	5	6
Black	-	1	1, 2	1, 2, 3	1, 2, 3, 4	1, 2, 3, 4, 5
Total	0	1	2	3	4	5

The total number of possible rolls with the red die higher than the black die is 15 and the probability of such a roll is $\frac{15}{36} = \frac{5}{12}$.

e. The total is even only if both dice come up even or both dice come up odd. There are 9 ways for them both to come up even and 9 ways for them both to come up odd so the probability of an even roll is $\frac{18}{36} = \frac{1}{2}$.

Exercise 10.2

The size of the sample space is $8 \cdot 8 = 64$.

a. As in the last problem, there are exactly 3 ways that the two dice result in a total of 4 but the probability of rolling a 4 is now $\frac{3}{64}$.

b. As in the last problem, there are exactly 6 ways that the two dice result in a total of 7 but the probability of rolling a 7 is now $\frac{6}{64} = \frac{3}{32}$.

c. As in the last problem, there are 5 ways to roll a 6, 4 ways to roll a 5, 3 ways to roll a 4, 2 ways to roll a 3, and 1 way to roll a 2. So there are 15 ways to roll a total that is less than 7 but the probability of rolling a total less than 7 is now $\frac{15}{64}$.

d. The possible ways for the red die to be higher than the black die are shown in this table.

Red	1	2	3	4	5	6	7	8
Black	-	1	1, 2	1, 2, 3	1, 2, 3, 4	1, 2, 3, 4, 5	1, 2, 3, 4, 5, 6	1, 2, 3, 4, 5, 6, 7
Total	0	1	2	3	4	5	6	7

so the total number of possible rolls with the red die higher than the black die is 28 and the probability of such a roll is $\frac{28}{64} = \frac{7}{16}$.

e. The total is even only if both dice come up even or both dice come up odd. There are 16 ways for them both to come up even and 16 ways for them both to come up odd so the probability of an even roll is $\frac{32}{64} = \frac{1}{2}$.

Lottery
Exercise 10.7

a. There are 10 possible outcomes and only 1 successful outcome so the probability is $\frac{1}{10}$.

b. Here we are sampling with and without replacement, respectively.

  i. There are $10^3 = 1000$ possible outcomes. There are $9^3 = 729$ outcomes that do not have an 8 in any draw. That leaves 271 outcomes that do contain an 8 so the probability is 271/1000.

  ii. There are $10 \cdot 9 \cdot 8 = 720$ possible outcomes. There are $9 \cdot 8 \cdot 7 = 504$ possible outcomes that do not include an 8 in any of the three draws. That leaves $720 - 504 = 216$ outcomes that do include an 8 so the probability is $216/720 = 3/10$.

c. Again, we are sampling with and without replacement, respectively.

  i. There is one successful outcome out of 1000 possible outcomes; the probability is 1/1000.

  ii. There is one successful outcome out of $10 \cdot 9 \cdot 8 = 720$ possible outcomes; the probability is 1/720.

d. Again, we are sampling with and without replacement, respectively.

    i. There are six successful outcomes $(952, 925, 592, 529, 259, 295)$ out of 1000 possible outcomes; the probability is $6/1000 = 3/500$.

    ii. There are six successful outcomes out of 720 possible outcomes; the probability is $6/720 = 1/120$.

Chapter 11 Solutions

Search Algorithms

Exercise 11.1

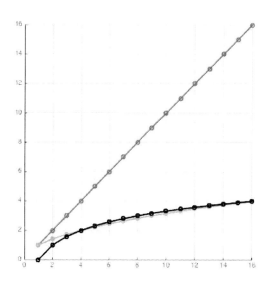

Figure D.1: ORDERED-LINEAR-SEARCH $T1(n) = n$ magenta; CHUNK-SEARCH $T2(n) = sqrt(n)$ green; BINARY-SEARCH $T3(n) = log_2(n)$ black.

Exercise 11.2

    i. For a budget of 20 element examinations, ORDERED-LINEAR-SEARCH can handle lists of size 20, CHUNK-SEARCH can handle lists of size 400, and BINARY-SEARCH can handle lists of size 1048576. Thus,

- BINARY-SEARCH can handle lists $33554432/156 \approx 215092$ times larger than CHUNK-SEARCH,

- BINARY-SEARCH can handle lists $33554432/25 \approx 1342177$ times larger than ORDERED-LINEAR-SEARCH, and

- CHUNK-SEARCH can handle lists $156/25 \approx 6$ times larger than ORDERED-LINEAR-SEARCH.

ii. In general, suppose we are given a budget of B units of "effort". The largest list size n that ORDERED-LINEAR-SEARCH can handle is given by the equation:

$$T_1(n) = n = B,$$

which implies that $n = B$. The largest list size n that CHUNK-SEARCH can handle is given by the equation:

$$T_2(n) = \sqrt{n} = B,$$

which implies that $n = (B)^2$. The largest list size n that BINARY-SEARCH can handle is given by the equation:

$$T_3(n) = \log_2(n) = B,$$

which implies that $n = 2^B$. Taking their ratios, we obtain the following.

- BINARY-SEARCH can handle lists $2^B/(B^2)$ times larger than CHUNK-SEARCH,

- BINARY-SEARCH can handle lists $2^B/B$ times larger than ORDERED-LINEAR-SEARCH, and

- CHUNK-SEARCH can handle lists $(B)^2/B = B$ times larger than ORDERED-LINEAR-SEARCH.

Exercise 11.3

i. Since Moe's computer running ORDERED-LINEAR-SEARCH is 50 times faster than Curly's computer running BINARY-SEARCH, we can write the following equation in n:

$$T_1(n) = 50 \times T_3(n),$$

where n is the length of the list when the search times of ORDERED-LINEAR-SEARCH and BINARY-SEARCH on the two computers are approximately equal. For lists of length smaller than n ORDERED-LINEAR-SEARCH performs better, while for lists of length larger than n BINARY-SEARCH performs better.

We substitute the formulas for $T_1(n)$ and $T_3(n)$, and the equation becomes:

$n = 50 \times \log_2(n)$.

Instead of doing a binary search, as suggested in the hint, we plot the 2 functions and find out that they meet at $n \approx 439$. For lists larger than 439, the computer running BINARY-SEARCH will outperform the one running ORDERED-LINEAR-SEARCH.

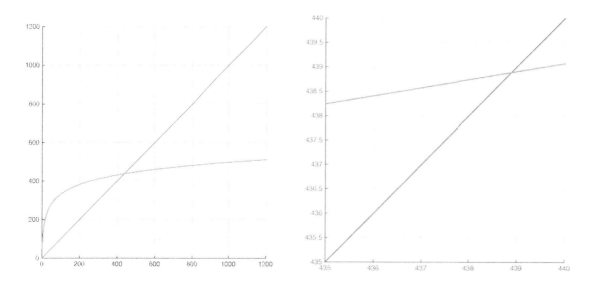

Figure D.2:   ORDERED-LINEAR-SEARCH $T1(n) = n$ blue; BINARY-SEARCH on 50-times slower machine $50 * T3(n) = 50 * log_2(n)$ red; For $n \geq 439$ BINARY-SEARCH is faster even though it is running on a 50-times slower machine.

   ii. Since Moe's computer running ORDERED-LINEAR-SEARCH is 10 times faster than Larry's computer running CHUNK-SEARCH, we can write the following equation in n:

$T_1(n) = 10 \times T_2(n)$,

where n is the length of the list when the search times of ORDERED-LINEAR-SEARCH and CHUNK-SEARCH on the two computers are approximately equal. For lists of length smaller than n ORDERED-LINEAR-SEARCH performs better, while for lists of length larger than n CHUNK-SEARCH performs better.

We substitute the formulas for $T_1(n)$ and $T_2(n)$, and the equation becomes:

$n = 10 \times sqrt(n)$.

The solution to this equation is $n = 100$ so CHUNK-SEARCH is faster on Larry's slower machine when $n > 100$.

iii. Since Larry's computer running CHUNK-LINEAR-SEARCH is 5 times faster than Cyrly's computer running BINARY-SEARCH, we can write the following equation in n:

$T_2(n) = 5 \times T_3(n),$

where n is the length of the list when the search times of CHUNK-SEARCH and BINARY-SEARCH on the two computers are approximately equal. For lists of length smaller than n CHUNK-SEARCH performs better, while for lists of length larger than n BINARY-SEARCH performs better.

We substitute the formulas for $T_2(n)$ and $T_3(n)$, and the equation becomes:

$sqrt(n) = 5 \times \log_2(n).$

This time, let's use the hint given with the problem. If $n = 1024$, $sqrt(n) = 32$ and $5 \times \log_2(n) = 50$ so CHUNK-SEARCH on the faster machine performs better. If $n = 4096$, $sqrt(n) = 64$ and $5 \times \log_2(n) = 60$ so BINARY-SEARCH performs better for a list this size even on the 5-times slower machine. The turing point is somewhere between $n = 1024$ and $n = 4096$. Let's check 2560 which is halfway between these values. $sqrt(2560) \approx 50.6$ and $5 \times \log_2(2560) \approx 107$ so CHUNK-SEARCH on the faster machine performs better when $n = 2560$. Now let's check 3328 which is halfway between $n = 2560$ and $n = 4096$. $sqrt(3328) \approx 57.7$ and $5 \times \log_2(3328) \approx 58.5$. CHUNK-SEARCH on the faster machine is still better (though we are getting close) so we check halfway between $n = 3328$ and $n = 4096$, i.e. $n = 3712$. $sqrt(3712) \approx 60.9$ and $5 \times \log_2(3712) \approx 59.3$ so BINARY-SEARCH wins out at $n = 3712$. The turning point is between $n = 3328$ and $n = 3712$. Continuing in this manner, we find the turning point at $n = 3454$; $sqrt(3454) \approx 58.77 \approx 5 \times \log_2(3454)$. If $n \geq 3454$, Binary search on the slower machine performs better.

Chapter 12 Solutions

Arithmetic Sequences

Exercise 12.1

a. next term $= 18$, $a_n = 2 \cdot n + 4$, $a_k = 2 \cdot k + 6$

c. next term $= -4$, $a_n = 2(n - 9)$, $a_k = 2(k - 8)$

e. next term $= 12$, $a_n = 3(n-3)$, $a_k = 3(k-2)$

g. next term $= 35$, $a_n = 5 \cdot n$, $a_k = 5(k+1)$

i. next term $= 7.7$, $a_n = 1.1 \cdot n$, $a_k = 1.1(k+1)$

Geometric Sequences

Exercise 12.2

a. next term $= 4096$, $a_n = 4^n$, $a_k = 4^{(k+1)}$

c. next term $= -4096$, $a_n = (-1)^{n-1}4^n$, $a_k = (-1)^k 4^{k+1}$

e. next term $= \frac{1}{3}$, $a_n = \left(\frac{1}{3}\right)^{n-5}$, $a_k = \left(\frac{1}{3}\right)^{k-4}$

g. next term $= -6$, $a_n = (-1)^{n-1}$, $a_k = (-1)^k$

i. next term $= 432$, $a_n = 2 \cdot 3^{n-1}$, $a_k = 2 \cdot 3^k$

Quadratic Sequences

Exercise 12.3

a. next term $= 31$, first differences: $2, 4, 6, 8, \ldots$, second difference $= 2$
$a_n = n^2 - n + 1$, $a_k = k^2 + k + 1$

c. next term $= 23$, first differences: $1, 3, 5, 7 \ldots$, second difference $= 2$
$a_n = n^2 - 2n - 1$, $a_k = k^2 - 2$

e. next term $= -5$, first differences: $-1, -2, -3, -4, \ldots$, second difference $= -1$
$a_n = -\frac{1}{2}n^2 + \frac{1}{2}n + 10$, $a_k = -\frac{1}{2}k^2 - \frac{1}{2}k + 10$

g. next term $= -3$, first differences: $3, 1, -1, -3 \ldots$, second difference $= -2$
$a_n = -n^2 + 6n - 3$, $a_k = -k^2 + 4k + 2$

i. $15, 6, 0, -3, -3, \ldots$ next term $= 0$, first differences: $-9, -6, -3, 0 \ldots$, second difference $= 3$
$a_n = \frac{3}{2}n^2 - \frac{27}{2}n + 27$, $a_k = \frac{3}{2}k^2 - \frac{21}{2}k + 15$

Miscellaneous Sequences

Exercise 12.4

a. arithmetic: difference $= -2$, next term $= $ -3, $a_k = 7 - 2 \cdot k$

c. geometric: ratio $= 2$, next term $= 160$, $a_k = 5 \cdot 2^k$

e. geometric + constant, next term $= 344$, $a_k = 3^k + 1$

g. $-6, 1, 22, 57, 106, \ldots$ quadratic: first differences $7, 21, 35, 49, \ldots$, second difference $= 14$, next term $= 169$, $a_k = 7k^2 - 6$

i. Fibonacci, each term is the sum of the last two terms, next term $= 11 + 18 = 29$

j. $4, 14, 23, 34, 42, \ldots$ - Don't get frustrated. This one is a joke. Ask someone from New York City or see http://www.nycsubway.org/lines/8thave.html

Summation Notation

Exercise 12.5

a. $\displaystyle\sum_{k=1}^{6} 3k = 3 \cdot 1 + 3 \cdot 2 + 3 \cdot 3 + 3 \cdot 4 + 3 \cdot 5 + 3 \cdot 6 = 3 + 6 + 9 + 12 + 15 + 18 = 63$

c. $\displaystyle\sum_{k=1}^{6} \frac{1}{k} = \frac{1}{1} + \frac{1}{2} + \frac{1}{3} + \frac{1}{4} + \frac{1}{5} + \frac{1}{6} = \frac{49}{20} = 2.45$

e. $\displaystyle\sum_{m=2}^{10} \frac{m}{2} = \frac{2}{10} + \frac{3}{10} + \frac{4}{10} + \frac{5}{10} + \frac{6}{10} + \frac{7}{10} + \frac{8}{10} + \frac{9}{10} + \frac{10}{10} = \frac{54}{10} = 5.4$

g. $\displaystyle\sum_{j=-3}^{3} j^2 = (-3)^2 + (-2)^2 + (-1)^2 + 0^2 + 1^2 + 2^2 + 3^2 = 9 + 4 + 1 + 0 + 1 + 4 + 9 = 28$

i. $\displaystyle\sum_{k=1}^{5} k^2 - k + 1 = (1^2 - 1 + 1) + (2^2 - 2 + 1) + (3^2 - 3 + 1) + (4^2 - 4 + 1) + (5^2 - 5 + 1) = 1 + 3 + 7 + 13 + 21 = 44$

Exercise 12.6

Write each of the following sums using summation notation. Try to make your answers as simple as possible.

a. $7 + 12 + 17 + 22 + \cdots + 177 = \displaystyle\sum_{k=1}^{35} (2 + 5k)$

c. $1 + 11 + 21 + 31 + \cdots + 251 = \displaystyle\sum_{m=0}^{25} (1 + 10m)$

e. $2 + 6 + 18 + 54 + \cdots + 2,324,522,934 = \sum\limits_{n=0}^{19} 2 \cdot 3^n$

Arithmetic Sums

Exercise 12.7

a. first + last $= 7 + 177 = 184$, there are $1 + 170/5 = 35$ terms, sum $= \frac{184 \cdot 35}{2} = 3,220$

c. first + last $= 1 + 251 = 252$, there are $1 + 250/10 = 26$ terms, sum $= \frac{252 \cdot 26}{2} = 3,276$

e. $1 + 3 + 5 + 7 + \cdots + 1001$ first + last $= 1 + 1001 = 1002$, there are $1 + 1000/2 = 501$ terms, sum $= \frac{1002 \cdot 501}{2} = 251,001$

Exercise 12.8

a. first + last $= 3 + 600 = 603$, there are 200 terms, sum $= \frac{603 \cdot 200}{2} = 60,300$

c. first + last $= 9 + 450 = 459$, there are 50 terms, sum $= \frac{459 \cdot 50}{2} = 11,475$

e. first + last $= 7 + 259 = 266$, there are 37 terms, sum $= \frac{266 \cdot 37}{2} = 4,921$

g. first + last $= 21 + 249 = 270$, there are $83 - 6 = 77$ terms, sum $= \frac{270 \cdot 77}{2} = 10,395$

i. $\sum\limits_{k=43}^{450} 9k$ first + last $= 387 + 4,050 = 4,437$, there are $452 - 42 = 408$ terms, sum $= \frac{4,437 \cdot 408}{2} = 905,148$

Exercise 12.9

a. The difference between two consecutive terms, $d = 3$, is our factor a, and we also have $n = 41$. We must now determine b. The first term in our series, 5, corresponds to $k = 1$. We must therefore have

$$
\begin{aligned}
a \cdot k + b &= 5 \\
\Leftrightarrow \quad 3 \cdot 1 + b &= 5 \\
\Leftrightarrow \quad b &= 5 - 3 \\
\Leftrightarrow \quad b &= 2.
\end{aligned}
$$

Thus, we can write this series as a summation in the following form:

$$\sum_{k=1}^{41}(3 \cdot k + 2).$$

b. Since b is a constant, the value of

$$\sum_{k=1}^{n} b$$

is just $n \cdot b$. For our values of $n = 41$ and $b = 2$, the value of the summation is $41 \cdot 2 = 82$.

Apply the standard arithmetic summation formula to evaluate the following summation:

$$\sum_{k=1}^{n} k = \frac{n \cdot (n + 1)}{2}.$$

For our value of $n = 41$, the value of the summation is

$$\frac{41 \cdot (41 + 1)}{2} = \frac{41 \cdot 42}{2} = 861.$$

Since we already have the value of $a = 3$, now we could evaluate the original expression by using the values of these summations.

$$a \cdot \sum_{k=1}^{n} k + \sum_{k=1}^{n} b = 3 \cdot 861 + 82 = 2665.$$

Thus, we obtain the same value as in part ii above.

Geometric Sums

Exercise 12.10

a. $S = 1+2+4+8+\cdots+1024,\ r = 2,\ 2S = 2+4+8+16+\cdots+1024+2048,\ 2S-S = 2048-1,$
$S = 2047$

c. $S = 1 + \frac{1}{2} + \frac{1}{4} + \frac{1}{8} + \cdots + \frac{1}{1024},\ r = \frac{1}{2},\ \frac{1}{2}S = \frac{1}{2} + \frac{1}{4} + \frac{1}{8} + \frac{1}{16} + \cdots + \frac{1}{1024} + \frac{1}{2048},$
$\frac{1}{2}S = S - \frac{1}{2}S = 1 - \frac{1}{2048},\ S = 2(1 - \frac{1}{2048}) = 2 - \frac{1}{1024} = \frac{2047}{1024}$

e. $S = 1 + \frac{1}{3} + \frac{1}{9} + \frac{1}{27} + \cdots + \frac{1}{59,049} = 1 + \frac{1}{3} + \frac{1}{9} + \frac{1}{27} + \cdots + \frac{1}{3^{10}},\ 3S = 3 + 1 + \frac{1}{3} + \frac{1}{9} + \frac{1}{27} + \cdots + \frac{1}{3^9},$
$2S = 3S - S = 3 - \frac{1}{3^{10}},\ S = \frac{3}{2} - \frac{1}{2 \cdot 3^{10}} = \frac{3^{11}-1}{2 \cdot 3^{10}} = 1.49999153246$

g. $S = 5^{10} + 5^9 + 5^8 + \cdots + 1 + \frac{1}{5} + \cdots + \frac{1}{5^{10}},\ 5S = 5^{11} + 5^{10} + 5^9 + \cdots + 1 + \frac{1}{5} + \cdots + \frac{1}{5^9},$
$4S = 5S - S = 5^{11} - \frac{1}{5^{10}},\ S = \frac{5^{11}}{4} - \frac{1}{4 \cdot 5^{10}} = 12,207,031.25$

Exercise 12.11

a. $S = \sum_{k=1}^{200} 3^k$, $3S = \sum_{k=2}^{201} 3^k$, $2S = 3S - S = 3^{201} - 3$, $S = \frac{3^{201}-3}{2}$

c. $S = \sum_{k=1}^{50} 2 \cdot 5^{-k}$, $5S = \sum_{k=0}^{49} 2 \cdot 5^{-k}$, $4S = 5S - S = 2 - 5^{50}$, $S = \frac{2-5^{50}}{4}$

e. $S = \sum_{k=1}^{37} 7^k$, $7S = \sum_{k=2}^{38} 7^k$, $6S = 7S - S = 7^{38} - 7$, $S = \frac{7^{38}-7}{6}$

g. $S = \sum_{k=1}^{N} 3^k$, $3S = \sum_{k=2}^{N+1} 3^k$, $2S = 3S - S = 3^{N+1} - 3$, $S = \frac{3^{N+1}-3}{2}$

i. $S = \sum_{k=1}^{2N} 10^k$, $10S = \sum_{k=2}^{2N+1} 10^k$, $9S = 10S - S = 10^{2N+1} - 10$, $\frac{10^{2N+1}-10}{9}$

Miscellaneous Sums

Exercise 12.12

a. Show that $\sum_{k=1}^{n} (a_k - a_{k+1}) = a_1 - a_{n+1}$.

One could informally argue that this statement is true by expanding the sum and canceling terms; we instead prove the statement true for all $n \geq 1$ by induction. For the base case $n = 1$, we have:

$$\sum_{k=1}^{1} (a_k - a_{k+1}) = a_1 - a_2$$

which is $a_1 - a_{n+1}$ for $n = 1$. Thus, our base case is correct. For the inductive step, assume that the statement is true for $n = i$, i.e.,

$$\sum_{k=1}^{i} (a_k - a_{k+1}) = a_1 - a_{i+1}.$$

Our task is then to show that the statement is true for $n = i + 1$, i.e.,

$$\sum_{k=1}^{i+1} (a_k - a_{k+1}) = a_1 - a_{i+2}.$$

Start with $\sum_{k=1}^{i+1}(a_k - a_{k+1})$ and break out the last term so that the inductive hypothesis can be applied:

$$
\begin{aligned}
\sum_{k=1}^{i+1}(a_k - a_{k+1}) &= \sum_{k=1}^{i}(a_k - a_{k+1}) + (a_{i+1} - a_{i+2}) \\
&= a_1 - a_{i+1} + (a_{i+1} - a_{i+2}) \\
&= a_1 - a_{i+2}
\end{aligned}
$$

Thus, our inductive step holds and the statement is proven.

b. Show that $\sum_{k=1}^{n} \frac{1}{k(k+1)}$ is a telescoping series. What is the form of a_k for any k?

$$
\begin{aligned}
\frac{1}{k(k+1)} &= \frac{(k+1) - k}{k(k+1)} \\
&= \frac{k+1}{k(k+1)} - \frac{k}{k(k+1)} \\
&= \frac{1}{k} - \frac{1}{k+1}
\end{aligned}
$$

Therefore,

$$
\sum_{k=1}^{n} \frac{1}{k(k+1)} = \sum_{k=1}^{n} \left(\frac{1}{k} - \frac{1}{k+1} \right).
$$

This is a telescoping series where $a_k = 1/k$.

c. Using parts i and ii above, show that

$$
\sum_{k=1}^{n} \frac{1}{k(k+1)} = 1 - \frac{1}{n+1}.
$$

Explain.

From parts i and ii above, we have:

$$
\sum_{k=1}^{n}(a_k - a_{k+1}) = a_1 - a_{n+1}
$$

and

$$\sum_{k=1}^{n} \frac{1}{k(k+1)} = \sum_{k=1}^{n} \left(\frac{1}{k} - \frac{1}{k+1} \right)$$

$$= \sum_{k=1}^{n} (a_k - a_{k+1})$$

where $a_k = 1/k$. Applying these facts, we obtain:

$$\sum_{k=1}^{n} \frac{1}{k(k+1)} = \sum_{k=1}^{n} \left(\frac{1}{k} - \frac{1}{k+1} \right)$$

$$= \frac{1}{1} - \frac{1}{n+1}$$

$$= 1 - \frac{1}{n+1}$$

Thus, the statement is proven.

Chapter 13 Solutions

Induction

Exercise 13.1

a. For the base case, we must show that $\sum_{k=1}^{n} k(k+1) = \frac{n(n+1)(n+2)}{3}$ for $n = 1$. When $n = 1$, the left-hand side $\sum_{k=1}^{n} k(k+1) = \sum_{k=1}^{1} k(k+1) = 1(1+1) = 2$ and the right-hand side $\frac{n(n+1)(n+2)}{3} = \frac{1(2)(3)}{3} = 2$ so the equation holds.

For the induction step, we show that whenever $\sum_{k=1}^{n} k(k+1) = \frac{n(n+1)(n+2)}{3}$ is true for $n = m$, it is also true for $n = m+1$. *assume* that $\sum_{k=1}^{n} k(k+1) = \frac{n(n+1)(n+2)}{3}$ is true for $n = m$.

If $n = m+1$,

$$\sum_{k=1}^{n} k(k+1) = \sum_{k=1}^{m+1} k(k+1) = \left(\sum_{k=1}^{m} k(k+1) \right) + (m+1)(m+2)$$

$$= \frac{m(m+1)(m+2)}{3} + (m+1)(m+2)$$

$$= \frac{m(m+1)(m+2)}{3} + \frac{3(m+1)(m+2)}{3}$$

$$= \frac{(m+3)(m+1)(m+2)}{3} = \frac{(m+1)(m+2)(m+3)}{3}$$

b. For the base case, we must show that $\sum_{k=1}^{n} \frac{1}{k(k+1)} = 1 - \frac{1}{n+1}$ for $n = 1$. When $n = 1$, the left-hand side $\sum_{k=1}^{n} \frac{1}{k(k+1)} = \sum_{k=1}^{1} \frac{1}{k(k+1)} = \frac{1}{1(2)} = \frac{1}{2}$ and the right-hand side $1 - \frac{1}{n+1} = 1 - \frac{1}{1+1} = \frac{1}{2}$ so the equation holds.

For the induction step, we show that whenever $\sum_{k=1}^{n} \frac{1}{k(k+1)} = 1 - \frac{1}{n+1}$ is true for $n = m$, it is also true for $n = m + 1$. *assume* that $\sum_{k=1}^{n} \frac{1}{k(k+1)} = 1 - \frac{1}{n+1}$ is true for $n = m$.

If $n = m + 1$,

$$
\begin{aligned}
\sum_{k=1}^{n} \frac{1}{k(k+1)} = \sum_{k=1}^{m+1} \frac{1}{k(k+1)} &= \left(\sum_{k=1}^{m} \frac{1}{k(k+1)} \right) + \frac{1}{(m+1)(m+2)} \\
&= 1 - \frac{1}{m+1} + \frac{1}{(m+1)(m+2)} \\
&= 1 - \frac{(m+2)}{(m+1)(m+2)} + \frac{1}{(m+1)(m+2)} \\
&= 1 - \frac{(m+2-1)}{(m+1)(m+2)} = 1 - \frac{(m+1)}{(m+1)(m+2)} = 1 - \frac{1}{m+2}
\end{aligned}
$$

Chapter 14 Solutions

Exercise 14.1

a. Consider the recurrence $T(n) = 4T(n/2) + n$. In order to solve the recurrence, we will first rewrite the recurrence with the recursive component *last* and using a generic parameter not to be confused with n. We may think of the following equation as our general pattern, which holds for any value of $\Box$.

$$
T(\Box) = \Box + 4T(\Box/2) \tag{D.1}
$$

Since our pattern (Equation D.1) is valid for any value of $\Box$, we may use it to "iterate" the recurrence as follows.

$$
\begin{aligned}
T(n) &= n + 4T(n/2) \\
&= n + 4\left((n/2) + 4T(n/2^2) \right) \\
&= n + 2n + 4^2 T(n/2^2) \tag{D.2}
\end{aligned}
$$

Always simplify the expression, eliminating parentheses as in Equation D.2, before expanding further. Continuing...

$$
\begin{aligned}
T(n) &= n + 2n + 4^2\left((n/2^2) + 4T(n/2^3)\right) \\
&= n + 2n + 2^2 n + 4^3 T(n/2^3) \\
&\vdots \\
&= n + 2n + 2^2 n + \ldots + 2^{k-1}n + 4^k T(n/2^k) \\
&= \sum_{j=0}^{k-1} 2^j n + 4^k T(n/2^k)
\end{aligned}
$$

One can then prove this pattern correct, via induction.

We thus have that $T(n) = \sum_{j=0}^{k-1} 2^j n + 4^k T(n/2^k)$ for all $k \geq 1$. We next choose a value of k which causes our recurrence to reach a known base case. Since $n/2^k = 1$ when $k = \lg n$, and $T(1) = \Theta(1)$, we have

$$
\begin{aligned}
T(n) &= \sum_{j=0}^{\lg n - 1} 2^j n + 4^{\lg n} T(1) \\
&= n \sum_{j=0}^{\lg n - 1} 2^j + n^{\lg 4}\Theta(1) \\
&= n(2^{\lg n} - 1) + \Theta(n^2) \\
&= n(n-1) + \Theta(n^2) \\
&= \Theta(n^2).
\end{aligned}
$$

Chapter 17 Solutions

Simple Graph Basics

Exercise 17.1

a. $\langle F, B, C\rangle$, $\langle F, D, A, C\rangle$, $\langle F, E, D, A, C\rangle$

b. $deg(A) = 2$, $deg(B) = 2$, $deg(C) = 2$, $deg(D) = 3$, $deg(E) = 2$, $deg(F) = 3$,

c. 6

d. 1: There is a trivial cycle of length 0 from each vertex to itself, e.g. $\langle A \rangle$. The shortest non-trivial cycle has length 3, $\langle D, E, F, D \rangle$.

Weighted Graphs

Exercise 17.3

a. $5 + 2 + 4 + 5 = 16$

c. $\langle H, N \rangle$ weight $= 3$
$\langle H, J, N \rangle$ weight $= 6 + 5 = 11$
$\langle H, G, J, N \rangle$ weight $= 5 + 3 + 5 = 13$
$\langle H, G, J, M, N \rangle$ weight $= 5 + 3 + 2 + 7 = 17$
$\langle H, D, A, G, J, N \rangle$ weight $= 2 + 5 + 3 + 3 + 5 = 18$

e. $\langle F, I \rangle$ has weight $= 7$.
$\langle F, L, I \rangle$ has weight $= 4 + 1 = 5$.

Adjacency Lists

Exercise 17.4

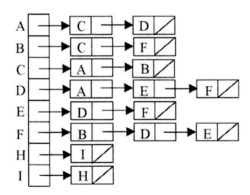

Exercise 17.5

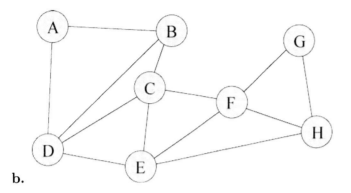

b.

Adjacency Matrices

Exercise 17.6

b.

$$
\begin{array}{cccccccc}
0 & 1 & 1 & 0 & 1 & 0 & 1 & 1 \\
1 & 0 & 1 & 0 & 0 & 0 & 0 & 0 \\
1 & 1 & 0 & 1 & 1 & 0 & 0 & 0 \\
0 & 0 & 1 & 0 & 1 & 0 & 0 & 0 \\
1 & 0 & 1 & 1 & 0 & 1 & 1 & 0 \\
0 & 0 & 0 & 0 & 1 & 0 & 1 & 0 \\
1 & 0 & 0 & 0 & 1 & 1 & 0 & 1 \\
1 & 0 & 0 & 0 & 0 & 0 & 1 & 0
\end{array}
$$

Depth-first Search

Exercise 17.7

a. $\langle I, D, A, B, H, F, C, E \rangle$

c. $\langle A, B, C, D, E, F, G, H \rangle$

Breadth-first Search

Exercise 17.8

a. $\langle I, D, F, A, C, E, H, B \rangle$

c. $\langle A, B, C, E, G, H, D, F \rangle$

Any Path
Exercise 17.9

    a. $\langle I, D, A \rangle$

    c. $\langle I, D, F, A \rangle$

    e. You traverse the connected component of vertex A, following the path $\langle A, C, B, F, D, E \rangle$. The search then ends without ever visiting the vertex H.

Shortest Path
Exercise 17.10

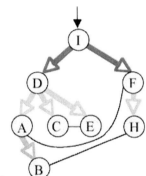

    a.

    b. $\langle I, D, A \rangle$
        $\langle I, D, A, B \rangle$
        $\langle I, D, C \rangle$
        $\langle I, D \rangle$
        $\langle I, D, E \rangle$
        $\langle I, F \rangle$
        $\langle I, F, H \rangle$

Cheapest Path
Exercise 17.11

    a. weight($\langle M, J, H, I, C \rangle$) $= 2 + 6 + 8 + 1 = 17$.

b. weight($\langle I, F \rangle$) = 7 but weight($\langle I, L, F \rangle$) = $1 + 4 = 5$

weight($\langle C, F \rangle$) = 9 but weight($\langle C, I, L, F \rangle$) = $1 + 1 + 4 = 6$

Spanning Tree

Exercise 17.12

a. The fat edges in this image show a spanning tree.

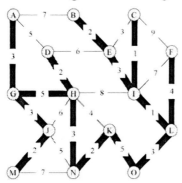

b. weight = 39.

Graph Theory

Exercise 17.14

The longest possible simple path goes through each vertex exactly once and has length $n - 1$. There may not be such a path.

Exercise 17.15

b. Make one component with 3 vertices at the corners of a triangle, one component with 4 vertices at the corners of a square, and one component with the remaining vertex.

Chapter A Solutions

Variables and Expressions

Exercise 1.1

a. $3x^2 - 5x + 7 = 3(5^2) - 5 \cdot 5 + 7 = 3 \cdot 25 - 25 + 7 = 57$ when $x = 5$

c. $x^3 - x^2 + x + 1 = 2^3 - 2^2 + 2 + 1 = 8 - 4 + 2 + 1 = 7$ when $x = 2$

e. $\left(\frac{4x^4y^3}{12x^{-5}y^6}\right)^2 = \frac{4}{12}\frac{x^{4+5}}{y^{6-3}} = \frac{x^9}{3y^3}$

g. $(a^7b^3c^{-2})(a^{-5}b^6c^{-1})(a^2bc^3) = a^{7-5+2}b^{3+6+1}c^{-2-1+3} = a^4b^{10}c^0 = a^4b^{10}$

Chapter B Solutions

Composite Expressions

Exercise 2.1

a. $3x^2 - 5x + 7 = 3(2t-1)^2 - 5(2t-1) + 7 = 3(4t^2 - 4t + 1) - 5t + 5 + 7 = 12t^2 - 12t + 3 - 5t + 12 = 12t^2 - 17t + 15$ when $x = 2t - 1$. $12t^2 - 17t + 15 = 12(3^2) - 12 \cdot 3 + 3 = 72 - 36 + 3 = 39$ when $t = 3$.

c. $z = \frac{3u^2}{1+v^2} = \frac{3(3^2)}{1+2^2} = \frac{3 \cdot 9}{5} = \frac{27}{5}$ when $u = 3$ and $v = 2$

e. $z = \frac{3u^2}{1+v^2} = \frac{3(r^5)^2}{1+(s^3)^2} = \frac{3r^{10}}{1+s^6}$ when $u = r^5$ and $v = s^3$ $\frac{3(3^{10})}{1+2^6} = \frac{177{,}147}{65}$ when $r = 3$, and $s = 2$.

g. $z = \frac{3u^2}{1+v^2} = \frac{3(t-1)^2}{1+(1/t)^2}$ when $u = t - 1$ and $v = 1/t$ $\frac{3(t-1)^2}{1+(1/t)^2} = \frac{3(3-1)^2}{1+(1/3)^2} = \frac{3(2)^2}{1+(1/9)} = \frac{12}{10/9} = \frac{2}{15}$ when $t = 3$

Chapter C Solutions

Exponents and Exponential Functions

Exercise 3.1

a. $b^0 = 1$

By the definition C.1, $b^1 = b$.

The *Quotient of two powers with the same base* property of exponentiation says $\frac{b^x}{b^y} = b^{x-y}$.

So by substitution, $1 = \frac{b}{b} = \frac{b^1}{b^1} = b^{1-1} = b^0$.

c. $b^{\frac{1}{n}} = \sqrt[n]{b}$

By definition, $\sqrt[n]{b}$ is the unique real number x such that $x^n = b$.

The *Power of a Power* property of exponentiation says $(b^x)^y = b^{xy}$.

So $(b^{\frac{1}{n}})^n = b^{\frac{n}{n}} = b^1 = b$.

Logarithms and Logarithmic Functions

Exercise 3.2

    a. 0 **c.** 4 **e.** 8 **g.** -1 **i.** 10240

Bibliography

[1] R. Kent Dybvig. *The Scheme Programming Language*. Prentice Hall, second edition, 1996. Available online at `http://www.scheme.com/tspl2d/`.

[2] Matthew Flatt. *The Racket Reference*. PLT Design Inc., 2014. Available online at `http://docs.racket-lang.org/reference/index.html`.

[3] Paul A. Foerster. *Algebra and Trigonometry: Functions and Applications*. Addison Wesley, 1980.

[4] Paul A. Foerster. *Precalculus with Trigonometry: Concepts and Applications*. Key Curriculum Press, 2002.

[5] James L. Hein. *Discrete Mathematics*. Jones and Bartlett Mathematics, second edition, 2003.

[6] R. J. Lipton. *Amplifying on the PCR Amplifier*. http://rjlipton.wordpress.com/, August 2009. Available online at `http://rjlipton.wordpress.com/2009/08/13/amplifying-on-the-pcr-amplifier/`.

[7] Wikipedia.org. *Conjunctive normal form*. Wikipedia.org, March 2014. Available online at `http://en.wikipedia.org/wiki/Conjunctive_normal_form`.

[8] Wikipedia.org. *P versus NP problem*. Wikipedia.org, August 2014. Available online at `http://en.wikipedia.org/wiki/P_versus_NP_problem#NP-complete`.

[9] Wikipedia.org. *Polymerase chain reaction*. Wikipedia.org, November 2014. Available online at `http://en.wikipedia.org/wiki/Polymerase_chain_reaction`.

[10] Wikipedia.org. *Étienne Bézout.* Wikipedia.org, April 2015. Available online at `http://en.wikipedia.org/wiki/Etienne_Bezout`.

[11] Wikipedia.org. *Extended Euclidean Algorithm - Table Method.* Wikipedia.org, April 2015. Available online at `http://en.wikipedia.org/wiki/Extended_Euclidean_algorithm#Example`.

Index

additive identity, 64

additive inverse, 64

adjacency list, 221

adjacency matrix, 223

algorithms, 161

analysis, 161, 164

AND gate, 22

arithmetic sequence, 176

ASCII, 9, 59

associative law, 34

associativity, 63

balls-in-bins, 126

base

    2, 3

    8, 11

    10, 3

    of expansion, 4

binary, 3

    representation, 5

binary arithmetic, 5, 26

binary numbers

    arithmetic, 5

    bytes, 9

binary search, 163

    analysis, 168

binomial coefficient, 122, 124

binomial theorem, 123

bit strings, 112

bits, 3

Boolean algebra, 31

Boolean formula, 33

breadth-first search, 227

Bridges of Königsberg, 231

byte, 9, 142

Caesar cipher, 58

cardinality, 96

cards, 139

Cartesian product, 102

    tuple, n-tuple, 103

central processing unit, 21

cheapest path, 229

chunk search, 163

    analysis, 166

cipher

    Caesar, 58

    linear, 62, 77

    rot13, 58

    shift, 57, 61

CPSIA information can be obtained
at www.ICGtesting.com
Printed in the USA
LVOW09s2112130917
548633LV00009B/50/P

9 781634 876469